Edgar M. Williams
Feb., 1993

THE PHYSICS
AND TECHNOLOGY
OF XEROGRAPHIC
PROCESSES

THE PHYSICS AND TECHNOLOGY OF XEROGRAPHIC PROCESSES

EDGAR M. WILLIAMS

Gemini Magnetics Incorporated
Formerly Advisory Physicist
International Business Machines Corporation

KRIEGER PUBLISHING COMPANY
MALABAR, FLORIDA
1993

Original Edition 1984
Reprint Edition 1993 with corrections

Printed and Published by
KRIEGER PUBLISHING COMPANY
KRIEGER DRIVE
MALABAR, FLORIDA 32950

FROM A DECLARATION OF PRINCIPLES JOINTLY ADOPTED BY A COMMITTEE OF THE AMERICAN BAR ASSOCIATION AND A COMMITTEE OF PUBLISHERS:

This publication is designed to provide accurate and authoritative information in regard to the subject matter covered. It is sold with the understanding that the publisher is not engaged in rendering legal, accounting, or other professional service. If legal advice or other expert assistance is required, the services of a competent professional person should be sought.

Library of Congress Cataloging-In-Publication Data
  Williams, Edgar M.
    The physics and technology of xerographic processes / Edgar M. Williams.
        p.   cm.
    Originally published: New York : Wiley, 1984.
    Includes bibliographical references and index.
    ISBN 0-89464-772-5 (alk. paper)
    1. Xerography.   I. Title.
  [TR1045.W55 1992]
  686.4'4--dc20   92-20095
                                             CIP

10   9   8   7   6   5   4   3   2

To

OTTO KORNEI

for his pioneering contributions
to xerographic technology

PREFACE

The purpose of this book is to explain some of the processes used today in high-speed xerographic document copiers and laser printers. The general subject of electrophotography is treated in several good references, but there remains a need for a book that discusses the associated processes from a phenomenological viewpoint and brings those discussions to the point of specific numerical expression, so that the reader can obtain a practical grasp of the technology. This book was written to fill some of that need, and its title, *The Physics and Technology of Xerographic Processes*, was chosen to reflect the scope of its contents. Each step of the process of converting light intensity patterns into visible permanent images on plain paper is discussed.

Many readers may find this book relevant to their interests. Professional scientists and engineers just entering the field and desiring a helpful entry point to xerographic technology will find this book particularly helpful. University professors and their students will discover areas worthy of academic investigation and will find useful suggestions for thesis topics. Industrial and government researchers with various backgrounds and fields of expertise may use this book to assist in relating their knowledge to aspects of xerographic science.

The subject matter is organized around the sequential process steps normally found in high-speed xerographic machines. The first chapter presents a broad overview of electrophotography, and the remaining eleven chapters treat the underlying physics and some engineering realizations of associated processes. Chapter 2 discusses photogenerators and photoconductors and the characteristics of materials that are electrophotographically useful. Chapters 3 and 4 address the physics of electrical corona and the engineering aspects of corona devices employed for charging and discharging the surfaces of materials used in the xerographic process. In Chapter 5, image exposure by raster scanned laser beam or by flash tube, and the resultant alteration of photoconductor surface potential, is treated in considerable depth. The variations in photoconductor voltage created by exposure to light are manifested as electrostatic field variations above the photoconductor surface; this important subject is analyzed in Chapter 6. The electrostatic field is a latent "image" which must be rendered visible. This process step, called image development, is interesting in its own right and involves the physics of small particle adhesion and deposition, as well as contact (i.e., frictional) electrification. The subjects of particle charging, the measurement of charge-to-mass, aerodynamic drag forces on small particles, and particle adhesion arising from electrostatic charge and electrodynamic (van der Waals or London dispersion) forces are given broad treatment in Chapter 7. In Chapter 8, one finds analyses of image development based on the electrostatic considerations and particle adhesion studies given in Chapter 7. Taken together, Chapters 7 and 8 present material relevant to the science of electrically charged aerosols. Indeed, some of the work on the behavior of charged aerosols in an electric field challenges the conventional understanding of aerodynamic drag forces on small particles.

Most high-speed printers and copiers use "magnetic brush" developer technology. These devices exploit magnetic forces to overcome the electrostatic force of attraction between "carrier" beads and the photoconductor. Carrier beads are used in two-component developers as the vehicle for transporting and charging the much smaller "toner" particles which develop the latent image. The magnetic brush device is common to almost all high-speed xerographic machines, and an analysis of its behavior is given in Chapter 9. Here one discovers a thorough treatment of magnetic forces between permanent magnets and magnetic carrier beads. Carrier–carrier interactions and competition between electric and magnetic forces are also treated here.

Chapters 10, 11, and 12 offer discussions of image transfer to plain paper, photoconductor cleaning and restoration, and the final process step that permanently fuses or fixes the toned (developed) image to the paper. The discussion of image transfer (Chapter 10) includes information and questions on the electrical behavior of ordinary xerographic quality paper, the electric field of corona devices used to assist in image transfer, and a brief analysis of toner particle charging by corona ions.

Mathematical expression is used throughout the book to bring crispness and precision to the discussions. Essential ideas and results can be appreciated without reading the mathematical notations, since approximately 150 figures, drawings, and plots are included in these pages. The general level of presentation is aimed toward those individuals having a background in a physical science, engineering, or mathematics at the Bachelor of Science level, with perhaps some additional independent study. Important mathematical derivations and an extensive list of references are found at the end of the book.

It is with pleasure that I acknowledge the following individuals for their contributions: Larry Williams, Reinhard Wolter, and Ro Surty for their administrative support and encouragement; Len Witcher, Bill Escobedo, and Jim Patrick for their assistance with experiments; Elwyn Erickson, Bill Hausle, and Ulo Vahtra for discussions on image development; Will Banks and Wally Larson for information and discussions on corona devices; Keith Larson, Dick Debrunce, and Bill Bernardelli for assistance with toner and carrier materials and experiments; Vince DePalma, Dave Randolph, and Karl Gong for assistance with toner charge statistics and measurement; Mel Rabedeau, Milt Latta, and Ray Froess for information and discussions on acousto-optical modulation; Peter Melz, Haj Seki, Kay Kanazawa, and Karl Loeffler for discussions on photogeneration and photoconductors; David Tabor for discussions on van der Waals and London dispersion forces; Truman Williams for discussions on aerosol science and aerodynamic drag; Bruce Prime and Karl Loeffler for information on image fusing; and Joseph Crowley, Neal Bertram, Dave Heim, and David Hannon for reading the manuscript and offering many helpful criticisms. Haik Marcar deserves special thanks and acknowledgment for his assistance in all phases of preparing the original manuscript for publication. Each of these individuals shared in the task of producing this book. Over the years, many others have helped me learn about electrophotography. I am very grateful to all, named and unnamed, for their contributions to this work.

EDGAR M. WILLIAMS

Palo Alto, California
May 1984

CONTENTS

ONE

ELECTROPHOTOGRAPHY
AN OVERVIEW

1.1   The Electrophotographic Process

Producing a permanent image on plain paper requires numerous sequential operations. In the electrophotographic process, the interaction of light with an electrically charged photogenerator–photoconductor material creates an electrostatic field pattern that varies in a one-to-one manner with the intensity of the exposing light beam. The electric field penetrates into the space above the surface of the photoconductor, and electrically charged particles are attracted or repelled, depending on the polarity ($\pm$) of their charge. If the photoconductor (hereafter abbreviated by the initials PC) is charged negatively, the exposing light beam will discharge the PC toward zero potential (ground) and the electric field will be positive in the region exposed to light. Negatively charged particles will be attracted toward the positive field region, whereas positively charged particles will be repelled. These experimental observations form much of the basis for the electrophotographic processes found today in document copying machines and laser printers. This book explains the six process steps required to produce an archival quality permanent image on a page of plain paper. These steps are: PC charging, image exposure, image development, image transfer from the PC to the paper, fusing or fixing the visible image to the paper, and cleaning or restoring the PC for additional use.

For the individual who has little or no experience or acquaintance with electrophotography, it seems appropriate to discuss the process by referring to specific examples of successful realizations of the six process steps, as illustrated by the laser printer sketched in Figure 1.1. The process elements arranged

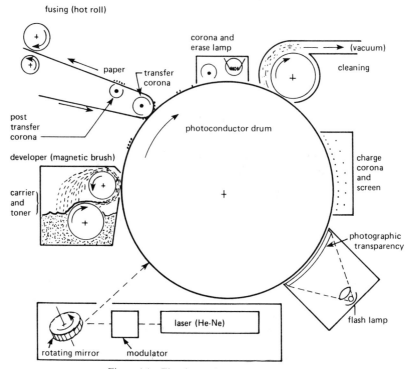

Figure 1.1   The electrophotographic process.

around the photoconductor drum represent devices found in a variety of commercially produced xerographic printers. With appropriate mirrors, lenses, and scanning devices, this same process would (by eliminating the laser, modulator, and rotating mirror) become a fair representation of many high-speed office document copiers. Articles concerning specific products and devices are also available. Vahtra and Wolter (1978) review the IBM 3800 Printing Subsystem (laser printer electrophotographic process); Jewett (1977) discusses the process organization of the KODAK EKTAPRINT Copier–Duplicator; and Hewlett-Packard (1982) surveys its 2680 laser printer.

The processes and concerns falling within the scope of electrophotography are quite diverse, thus creating a challenge in locating important references. Dessauer and Clark (1965) and Schaffert (1975) must be regarded as fundamental sources; Schaffert cites nearly 400 references in his original text and includes about 400 additional uncited references in the second edition. Dessauer and Clark incorporate as their first chapter the history of electrostatic recording, written by Chester F. Carlson, the inventor of xerography. Here, Carlson gives more than 100 citations to the patent and technical literature, up to about 1962. Since 1975, reviews have been written by Schmidlin (1976), Keiss (1978), Schaffert (1978), Weigl (1977), and Winkelmann (1978).

High-speed xerographic printing, copying, and duplicating involve cyclic repetition of PC charging, exposing, developing, image transferring and fixing, and PC cleaning and restoring. For this reason, the process devices are arranged appropriately around either a PC drum (as depicted in Figure 1.1) or a continuous web of PC material supported on a flexible transparent substrate. Thus, the PC is transported past the various fixed elements and the high accelerations and decelerations normally associated with the reciprocal motion of elements past a fixed PC are avoided. Engineering designs based on this philosophy tend to be quieter, less wasteful of energy, and more reliable than machines based on reciprocal motion. This chapter briefly describes each step of the overall process; in subsequent chapters, the main ideas are extended and treated in more depth.

1.2 Photoconductors

Central to any electrophotographic process is a photogenerator–photoconductor, that is a PC. This is a material that generates and transports electron–hole pairs in response to absorbed photons. A PC is usually thin (about 10–50 micrometers) and is coated onto a ground plane. Some of the early office copiers used a layer of selenium coated onto a metallic drum; when the PC became damaged or worn out, the entire drum would be replaced with a new one. Organic polymers were developed later, and the technology produced many materials that could be mixed in flexible binders and coated onto webs of aluminized Mylar substrate. Organic photoconductors were thus made into long narrow sheets. These were rolled up and placed inside a PC drum around which the PC sheet was wrapped; hence, the PC could be replenished from the supply role as needed. Another approach uses a PC web that has been joined to make a seamless belt; when the belt is worn or otherwise damaged, it can be replaced easily with a new one.

Photoconductors useful in xerography are chosen, among other reasons, for their insulator-like behavior when kept in the dark. If one charges the PC surface with gaseous ions from a corona device, the surface potential (most often called the "dark voltage") is directly proportional to the surface charge density and is inversely proportional to the capacitance per unit area of the PC. The dark voltage is usually limited by the dielectric breakdown strength of the PC film. Useful values of dark voltage range from ± 500 to ± 1000 volts. When exposed to a pulse of light from a xenon flash tube or a scanning laser beam, for example, some of the photons absorbed by the PC will create electron–hole pairs. These charge carriers experience an electric field caused by the gas ions adsorbed to the PC surface. If these ions are negative, the electrical force on the holes is toward the film surface, whereas the electrons are directed toward the ground plane.

If the charge carriers can move within the PC material (i.e., if they have mobility), they will drift along the field direction such that holes travel up to negative surface ions, combine with them, and ultimately liberate neutral gas molecules. Electrons will drift down to the ground plane and be swept away through the external electrical circuitry. Neutralization of surface ions reduces the surface charge density; accordingly, the surface potential changes to a value called the "light voltage" or "image potential." The difference in PC surface voltage between regions that have and have not absorbed any photons from the light beam is often called the "contrast voltage." The useful range of contrast voltage is roughly 300–600 V.

Variations in voltage along the PC surface determine the electric field within the PC and above it; thus, one can generate an electrostatic "image" that varies in a one-to-one fashion with the pattern of light absorbed in the photogenerating medium. The subject matter of photoconductivity, sensitivity to light, voltage decay time, charge mobility, and other related topics are discussed in Chapter 2. Perhaps more has been written on photoconductivity and related phenomena than any other subject relevant to xerography. The interested reader can gain entry into the vast literature through any of the following selected references: Schaffert (1975), Bube (1960), Fridkin (1972), Meier (1974), Patsis and Seanor (1976), Mort and Pai (1976), or Berg and Hauffe (1972), to name only a few.

1.3 Corona Charging of Dielectric Surfaces

Electrostatic fields play a fundamental role in electrophotography. Initially, a PC is completely uncharged, so if light is absorbed within the photogenerating medium, the electron–hole pairs experience no net electric field which would force them to drift in opposite directions. This being the case, photogenerated electron–hole pairs would recombine to restore charge neutrality. Electrophotography depends upon the intentional separation of the electron–hole pairs; thus, it is necessary to establish an electric field within the PC film. A uniform charge distribution at the PC surface is generated by adsorbing ionized gas molecules that arise from an electrical corona device. In their most simple configurations, these devices employ thin wires (about 50 μm diameter) set to very high potentials (5–10 kV). The electric field within the vicinity of the wire is so high that any free electrons are accelerated to velocities sufficiently high to impact ionize an intervening gas molecule. The corona wires are thus sources of gas ions whose polarity is the same as that of the wires. Electrical corona is discussed in Loeb (1965), Cobine (1958), von Engel (1965), Alston (1968), Thompson and Thompson (1969), Townsend (1915), and White (1963).

Electrical corona is impossible to initiate without the presence of triggering electrons. These electrons are normally supplied by background radiations (alpha particles and cosmic rays) at a rate of perhaps 20 ion pairs per cubic centimeter per second (see Loeb, 1958, p. 201). A corona wire can be illuminated with UV light to generate photoelectrons from the wire surface; these liberated electrons become trigger electrons which accelerate in the high electric field and collide with neutral gas molecules. At or above a certain threshold field, trigger electrons gain sufficient kinetic energy to ionize upon impact with a molecule. The "daughter" electrons and the parent ion so generated then move in opposite directions, under the influence of the applied electric field. These new electrons also gain kinetic energy from the field and subsequently impact ionize other gas molecules; thus, the process quickly multiplies exponentially with distance travelled in the high field region around the corona wire. This basic process leads either to a spark or to corona discharge, depending upon the geometry of the field electrodes.

If the electrodes are smooth, have fairly large radii of curvature, and are well-removed from each other, the electric field in the space between will be fairly uniform. This geometry usually leads to spark-over between the electrodes. If the accelerating field is highly nonuniform, such as that produced by a thin wire or a sharp edge, the ion multiplication process is limited to a region surrounding the wire or edge where the field exceeds the threshold value. This geometry leads to a gaseous conduction process that will be a steady corona discharge, not a sudden spark. In normal air at standard temperature and pressure, the critical or threshold field for spark discharge is about 30 kV/cm in a 1.0 cm gap, reducing to around 24 kV/cm for very large gaps between electrodes (see Alston, 1968, p. 48). The critical field for corona discharge is somewhat higher, falling at about 40 kV/cm for coaxial cylinders, with the inner radius of curvature equal to 1.0 cm (see Cobine, 1958, p. 354).

The corona devices used for charging PCs have between 3 and 8 individual corona wires, usually made of tungsten drawn to a diameter of nearly 50 μm, which are set to a potential between 5 and 10 kV (positive or negative, depending on the choice of PC, its dielectric strength at positive or negative voltages, and the polarity of the charged "toner" particles used to develop the electrostatic image). The wires are placed about 0.5 cm or more above the PC surface and the flow of gaseous ions from the wires to the PC is controlled by an interposed screen of larger (250 μm) wires set at a much lower potential (500–1000 V, positive or negative). The screen voltage determines the approximate maximum potential to which the PC will be charged by the corona ions. This type of screen-controlled corona device is called a "Scorotron" (see Schaffert, 1975, p. 242 and Dessauer and Clark, 1965, p. 205), and these are discussed in Chapter 4. As the moving PC web or drum travels under each corona wire, additional ions are adsorbed to the PC and the surface potential increases in magnitude. When a given section of the PC emerges from the charge corona unit, its surface potential is at the "dark voltage" mentioned earlier, and the photoconductor is ready for exposure to light energy that is shaped into the desired image pattern.

1.4 Exposure

Office copying and duplicating machines expose the charged PC by reflecting light from the original document and then process this radiant energy by lenses and mirrors to form an image on the PC. Some copiers scan the document in synchronization with the moving PC, others use high energy flash lamps in conjunction with optics that focus the image onto the curved PC surface. Compared with laser beam printers, it is much more difficult to control the exposure energy at the PC in copiers, since the original documents have a wide range of reflectance values. Different papers and inks have unique spectral reflectance characteristics, so the light falling on the document must have broad spectral bandwidth. Gallo and Hammond (1976) discuss gas discharge lamps for electrophotographic exposure.

Laser exposure is a very precise operation with rather tight control on all optical elements within the exposure subsystem. This system contains a multi-faceted mirror rotating at very high RPM which sweeps the beam at high velocity across the width of the PC. The beam intensity is modulated (usually "On" or "Off") by an acoustooptical modulator electrically driven at an ultrasonic frequency. This is indicated schematically in Figure 1.1. The modulator is basically a light-diffraction grating controlled by the sonic wavelength of the input signal and is often made of special glass having a piezoelectric transducer bonded to one end. The laser beam enters the modulator almost perpendicular to the axis of propagation of the sonic wave in the glass. The beam exits at the same angle if there is no sonic wave present, and is diffracted into first- and higher-order directions if the sonic wave is present. The first order angle is small, being only a few milliradians. The theory of light diffraction by ultrasonic waves is found in Born and Wolf (1975). Since laser beam exposure is precisely controlled, it is amenable to straightforward analysis. A mathematical model of this process is given in Chapter 5; computation of the exposure energy per unit area is relatively simple, because the laser beam is monochromatic and the beam intensity cross section is fairly well-defined (usually following a Gaussian-profile).

The sources of radiant energy used in copiers are seldom monochromatic. Tungsten and tungsten–halogen incandescent lamps and xenon flash tubes are commonly found in copiers. Some laser printers also utilize an auxiliary flash lamp exposure station to generate repeating images, such as might be found in business forms. When this approach is employed, the flash energy is transmitted through a negative transparency such that those PC regions destined for subsequent laser exposure are protected from the flash exposure. The flash lamp deposits the radiant energy in the regions where the visible, developed image will appear. This is in contrast with the copier philosophy, where radiant energy is deposited in the regions where the final copy is to be free of image development, that is, light is put into the background region and toner particles are deposited into the unexposed (relatively unexposed, that is, since the dark image of the original will reflect some light) regions of the PC.

The electric fields resulting from various exposure patterns are treated in Chapter 6. It is in Chapters 5 and 6 that the reader discovers the difference between electrophotography and conventional photography. Many writers and workers in electrophotography use terminology borrowed directly from photographic science, technology, and literature. In more than a few cases, the analogy has been stressed and overused, to the detriment of a clearer understanding of electrophotographic phenomena. Mark Twain said, "The difference between the right word and the almost right word is the difference between lightning and the lightning bug." I agree with him, so photographic terminology does not appear in this book if more appropriate terms exist.

The exposure step generates charge carriers which drift under the influence of the internal electric field arising from the initially uniform PC surface charge. Since the drift velocity may be quite low (perhaps 0.05 cm/sec), it would require about 100 milliseconds for the charge carriers to travel the thickness of the PC. The surface voltage, being a direct function of the volume and surface charge densities, changes in a one-to-one manner depending on concentration of the photogenerated carriers and their location relative to the ground plane. Therefore, the surface potential does not change abruptly when the carriers are created, but gradually as the carriers drift up to the PC surface. The decay time can be approximately identified with the "transit time" necessary for carriers to move through the PC film thickness. The asymptotic value of the surface voltage is called the "light voltage" or "image potential."

Any variation in surface voltage creates an electric field whose magnitude and direction depend on the potential gradient. For a negatively charged PC, the vertical field at and above the surface will be positive in the regions where light is absorbed and the potential is subsequently less negative. An electric field is, by convention, the negative gradient of the potential, so a positive field is directed from a more positive potential toward regions of less positive potential. The electric field associated with exposure to light forms a "latent electrostatic image" that cannot be seen unless decorated with small charged particles or uncharged but polarizable particles. The action of particle deposition, using charged particles containing carbon black pigment, is called "image development."

1.5 Image Development

Several techniques exist for depositing toner onto the exposed PC, and all but one share the basic phenomenon of the motion of charged bodies in electric fields. This is known as Coulomb's Law, where the force on the body is equal to the product of the charge and the electric field. Uncharged polarizable bodies experience a force in a nonuniform electric field; the force is proportional to the electric dipole moment times the gradient of the electric field. Under most circumstances, these dipole forces are several orders of magnitude smaller than Coulomb forces. For this reason, modern high-speed development processes use particles that are rather highly charged, and the Coulomb force is exploited to attach the charged toner particles to the desired regions of the PC surface. Chen (1982) analyzes image development with dipole forces, but since this process is not found in high performance machines, it is not treated in this book.

Electrophoresis is the phenomenon of motion of charged particles through liquids, and *electrophoretic developers* pass the exposed PC through a liquid dielectric containing small charged toner particles. Many low-speed office copiers make good use of this technique. The particles suffer viscous drag forces within the liquid, and the liquid dielectric adheres to the PC as well, so these devices are not found in high-speed applications. The word *xerography* means "dry-writing" in the original Greek, and *xerographic developers* use dry toner particles transported through a gas, normally standard office quality air. High processing speeds require the rapid transport of toner particles to the exposed PC; thus, one finds xerographic devices in modern laser printers and copier–duplicators. Since xerographic technology dominates other approaches to image development, this book treats xerography in depth. Readers who desire information on electrophoretic development should consult Schaffert (1975).

Many xerographic toners are made from copolymers of styrene and acrylic, with a small amount of carbon black pigment added. The material is milled down to small fragments ranging in size between 5 and 30 μm. Toner particles are conventionally charged by contact electrification, often called frictional or triboelectrification. In modern xerographic developer units, one predominently finds "two-component" developers, where toner particles are charged and transported on the surfaces of larger carrier particles. These carriers (not to be confused with the earlier usage of the term in PC discussions) are about 70–300 μm in diameter, are magnetic, and have a thin dielectric skin chosen to impart the appropriate polarity of charge to the toner particles. Additionally, the surface coating on the carrier beads usually has relatively low surface energy, thereby discouraging permanent adhesion of toner to the carrier. If toner does bond (either chemically or mechanically) to the carrier, the contact electrification properties are altered, thus degrading the desired charging behavior. The sign and amount of charge donated from one surface to another depends on the difference between their respective work functions. Loeb (1958) and Harper (1967) discuss contact electricity and also Coehn's experimental "law," which states that substances of higher dielectric constant donate negative charge when in contact with substances of lower dielectric constant.

The magnetic core of the carrier bead is attracted toward a permanent magnet; thus, the carrier and toner particle mixture is easily transported against gravitational and electrical forces by a suitably designed array of magnets. Older technology in xerography used gravity only to cascade carrier and toner over an electrostatic image, but these devices did not function reliably at high processing speeds. The reason can be traced to the electrostatic force attracting a charged carrier bead toward the PC surface; if this force equals or exceeds that of gravity, then carrier flow is reduced. Carriers also become attached to the PC and interfere with faithful transfer of the toned image onto a sheet of paper. The rotating magnetic brush device solves this problem, and this technology has opened the path to high-speed processing in copiers and printers. The magnetic force associated with magnetic brush developers is analyzed in depth in Chapter 9. Magnetic interactions between carriers, such as sphere–sphere chaining and bead "carry-out" (a loss of carriers from the magnetic brush), are discussed in this chapter, and important information on competition between electrostatic and magnetic forces is also given.

A comprehensive theory of image development would take into account electrostatic, electrodynamic, and mechanical forces acting on toner particles adhering to the surface of carrier beads, but the resulting, complicated theory would not provide any clear insights. The literature on image development includes several theories, each built on certain simplifying assumptions. Thourson (1972) reviews xerographic development theory and practice, giving 63 references up to 1972. Additional references, in chronological order, are Cassiers and van Engeland (1965), Schein (1975), Harvapat (1975), Williams (1978), and Benda and Wnek (1981). Physical models of image development must account for the forces acting on toner particles; electrostatic, inertial, aerodynamic, and electrodynamic forces (van der Waals or London dispersion forces) play significant roles in the development process. Whether a toner particle will be deposited onto the latent electrostatic image or remain attached to its carrier host depends on the toner–carrier adhesive forces. An impressive amount of research has been done in adhesion theory and it is relevant to understanding toner–carrier and toner–photoconductor adhesion. Krupp (1967) and Zimon (1969) specifically address the adhesion of particles, powder, and dust. Some of the problems associated with toner–carrier adhesion (such as carrier wear and degradation of contact charging behavior) are eliminated with the use of magnetic *monocomponent* developers; this new technology obviates the requirement for magnetic carrier beads by using toner that contains magnetic pigment, usually Fe_3O_4 (magnetite). Minor (1975) and Takahashi et al. (1982) discuss the mechanism of monocomponent development with magnetic toners.

Two-component developers (i.e., toner and carrier) transport the toner–carrier mix up to the PC surface where the charged toner is rubbed over the electrostatic image. Regions of positive electric field attract negatively charged toner and, conversely, negative fields repel negative toner. If toner is attached to the carrier by electrostatic and electrodynamic forces (dispersion forces), it is essential to the development process that the toner–carrier adhesive bond be disrupted, usually by mechanical shear forces, such that toner particles are liberated to move under the influence of the PC image field. Electric fields acting alone will not detach toner from a carrier, as the dispersion force component acting between these bodies can be relatively large if the separation between is less than about 100 Angstroms. Mahanty and Ninham (1976) and Israelachvili (1974) offer much useful insight concerning the nature of van der Waals–London dispersion forces, the theory of these forces, and how to compute them for a variety of material types and shapes. One discovers a variety of electrodyanamic forces in the literature; they are called Keeson, Debye,

London, van der Waals, dispersion, intermolecular, electrodynamic, and all possible permutations of these appellations. Mahanty and Ninham (1976) simplify the terminology by referring to all as "dispersion forces," since each finds its origin in electrodynamic fluctuations.

If there is sufficient electrical and mechanical force to disrupt the adhesive bond between carrier and toner, toner will deposit on the PC surface in the regions where the PC field directs particle motion. Image development occurs in a zone where the toner–carrier mix and the PC are in intimate contact. Magnetic brush developer units transport the mix at velocities on the order of 100 cm/sec, so it is possible to create clouds of toner dust within the developer unit. The aerosol of charged toner particles is subject to electrical, aerodynamic, and gravitational forces, but the dispersion forces have relatively little influence. Aerosol development is discussed in Dessauer and Clark (1965), but this technique generates unwanted background toner and does not scale readily to the high process speeds required in laser printing and high production copier–duplicators.

One simple way to view the image development process is to imagine filling up a potential well with charged particles. The well was created by the photo-generated charges in the PC and charged toner tends to fill the well back up. The well depth can be measured in volts, charge per unit area, or V/cm (the electric field). The quantity of toner required to fill the well depends on the charge of each toner particle; that is, many low-charge particles, or a few high-charge ones, yield the same filling of the potential well. In normal practice, the PC exposure is controlled to yield a well-defined contrast potential difference and toner charge is controlled, along with the developer mix flow rate, to produce images with acceptable contrast and uniformity on the finished page. The control of print quality is an important concern in xerography and attention is given to many factors that degrade the image. Carrier beads, for example, are recirculated within the developer unit and fresh toner is added to the mix to maintain a reasonably constant level of toner concentration. Continued reuse of the carrier beads causes damage to their surfaces. Toner particles then fuse onto the damaged carrier surface due to pressure arising from vigorous mixing. When fresh toner receives charge from a carrier partially covered with fused-on toner, the net charge is reduced in proportion to the surface coverage of old fused-on toner. The latent electrostatic image attracts many low-charge particles or a few high-charge particles; thus, the developed image from old carrier-fresh toner mix may produce dense, thick lines, loss of fine details, and background toner may be present as well. Exactly the same behavior in image quality can be produced by increasing the toner concentration to high values.

Toner particles are statistically distributed in charge and in size. Size distributions are routinely controlled in the way toner is manufactured or by taking a broad size distribution and selecting out the desired size range. Since toner charge is distributed independently of the size distribution, it is important to learn how to control toner charge distributions. Depending on carrier type and age and the toner concentration, a toner species with low average charge can exhibit a broad distribution, including particles of zero charge and opposite polarity charge. Such distributions naturally lead to problems in print quality and machine contamination with toner and to cleaning failure.

1.6   Toner Transfer

The developed image is transported to a device that places a sheet of paper in intimate contact with the toned image and the PC. With a field of correct sign and magnitude, toner is attracted to the paper and, upon separating the paper from the PC surface, the toner image is transferred faithfully to the paper. In many copiers and printers, this step of the process is accomplished with an electrical corona device called the *transfer corona* unit (see Figure 1.1). Machines using positive toner have a negative transfer corona unit. Corona per se is not required to achieve toner motion from the PC to the paper; transfer by corona is only one means to an end. A conductor at high voltage can produce electric fields of sufficient amplitude to transfer toner, although such devices often generate corona breakdown, or worse, sparking. About half of the energy in a spark is dissipated acoustically; thus, the sound wave generates pressures sufficient to dislodge charged toner and impair the quality of the transferred image.

The amount of literature on image transfer is not large. Schaffert (1975) and Dessauer and Clark (1965) mention the subject but do not give any details on physical mechanisms. The paper by Yang and Hartman (1976) is the only reference giving a quantitative model of charged particle transfer from one surface to another. Toner transfer is similar to image development, but with different geometry involved. As in development, there must be intimate contact between paper and toner for transfer to occur. Without an attractive electric field present, toner remains on the PC. This is similar to the particle adhesion phenomenon involved in the development step; thus, dispersion forces and electrostatic forces play central roles in the transfer of toner.

Chapter 10 contains a discussion of the transfer process that leans heavily on the Yang–Hartman model cited above. The geometry of their model is appropriately simple (parallel plates at different potentials) and one can readily grasp the essential ideas. Since most copiers and printers use corona transfer devices, the geometry is somewhat more complicated. Therefore, Chapter 10 also contains an analysis of the electrostatic field caused by corona devices. Toner transfers readily to metal sheets, insulating films, and paper. There are many complicated aspects to paper transfer not found with metals or insulating sheets, and the discussion on transfer contains material on the electrical properties of paper and the behavior of the flow of ionized gases through paper fibers. Static electricity accumulates on and in paper; it comes from the transfer corona itself, as well as from contact electrification from all surfaces the paper touches. If the paper is well-dried, charge can remain trapped in the matrix of cellulose fibers for many seconds. Trapped charge causes problems in paper handling; hence, many xerographic machines exploit corona discharge devices to neutralize the paper charge. Well-designed machines must accept a wide variety of plain papers from numerous manufacturers, both domestic and abroad. This requirement opens the door to many problems that affect image quality, machine contamination, and variations in the efficiency with which toner transfers to the paper. The subject of paper, its production, chemistry, properties, and testing is covered in Hunter (1978) and in numerous reports and studies issued by the American Paper Institute (1974) and the Institute of Paper Chemistry (1975).

1.7 Image Fusing

After transferring the toned image to a sheet of paper, the charged particles stick to the paper fibers and fillers owing to the action of electrostatic and dispersion forces, but the image is very easily disturbed by inertial forces and it can be rubbed away by the fingers. Long-term fidelity of the print therefore requires some manner of fixing the image to the paper. Fusing a thermoplastic toner by heat and pressure into the paper fibers has proven to be one reliable method for permanently fixing an image. Other techniques such as pressure (only) and solvent fixing have also been used; pressure fixing does not work well with a large variety of papers and it tends to calender the paper, whereas solvent fixing requires equipment to trap and condense the solvent vapors for reuse. These observations may partially explain why most high-speed fusing is done with hot roll pressure fusers. Thermal fixing without pressure rolls has been done with radiant energy, usually high energy xenon flash lamps. This approach is highly inefficient because most paper reflects perhaps 70–80% of the incident radiant energy.

Lee (1975) shows that toner fusing involves three separate phenomena to yield images of reasonable permanence. First, toner particles must coalesce or sinter together, then the coalesced toner must spread, and finally it must penetrate into the paper fibers. Surface energy (surface tension), viscosity, and temperature greatly influence the kinetics of these phenomena; that is, toner rheology and the wettability of paper by molten toner each play fundamental roles in the fusing process. Huntsberger (1964) discusses the relationship between wetting and adhesion. The quality of toner fusing can be measured according to the standards adopted by the ASTM (Procedure #D3458-75); this procedure is apparently repeatable and the results correlate well with the performance of fused print in OCR readers. Prime (1983) showed that fuse quality for a given hot roll temperature depends on Pt^2, where P is the nip pressure between the hot roll and its backup roll and t is the time at P. The temperature dependence of fusing is related almost entirely to the toner properties, a subject discussed by O'Reilly and Erhardt (1974). Paper properties such as sizing, fiber diameter, and distance between fibers largely control how well toner can penetrate into the paper to form intimate contact. Paper is thus seen to form a capillary system into which molten toner can flow because of capillary pressure assisted by pressure from the paper rollers. Chapter 11 presents a physical model of pressure–temperature fusing based on unpublished work by K. H. Loeffler and R. B. Prime, both of IBM Corporation. Brooms (1978) discusses the fusing system used in the IBM 3800 laser printing system. As in all aspects of electrophotography, Schaffert (1975) and Dessauer and Clark (1965) should be consulted for additional information on image fixing.

1.8   Photoconductor Cleaning and Restoring

When toner particles are transferred to paper, some particles are invariably left behind on the PC surface. These particles are, on the average, noticeably smaller than the average size of the toner that successfully transferred. This size selection process occurs in image development as well, and it is one of the many clues that particle adhesion is broken only (usually) with mechanical contact with another (third) body. Indeed, the larger particles in a distribution of sizes can "protect" the smaller ones from contact with a third body. This phenomenon can be easily demonstrated by lifting up sand from a flat surface by using some adhesive tape; the smallest particles will be left on the flat surface. In xerographic machines, residual toner must be removed from the PC before another process cycle is started. Otherwise, residual toner can become permanently attached to the PC surface, thereby altering the electrical nature of the PC. Most toners used in two-component developers are fairly good insulators, so they can interfere with the normal conduction process expected at the surface of a PC when exposed to light energy.

As the studies of Mastrangelo (1982) show, electrostatic and dispersion forces are responsible for toner–photoconductor adhesion. A cleaning system must shear the adhesive bond; scraping blades or rotating brushes work successfully, aerodynamic forces acting alone do not. Once the toner particle is dislodged, then it is conventionally removed by appropriate air flow. The world of aerosols and aerosol science provides much guidance in understanding the aerodynamics of small particles. Fuchs (1964), Hidy and Brock (1970), and Davies (1966) are seminal references in aerosol science.

Photoconductor cleaning is often assisted by an erase lamp and a corona unit whose polarity opposes that of the the main charge corona. The erase lamp helps remove the latent electrostatic image and the preclean corona neutralizes surface charges. Cleaning failure occurs in several interesting ways; the syndromes are often called "cleaner offset," "streaking," and "fused-on toner." When failure does occur, the evidence clearly suggests that toner can be removed and redeposited by a rotating brush. If scraper blades are worn, toner is merely pressed more firmly onto the PC surface as it passes under the blade. In cases of excessive toner charge, the particles can adhere so strongly that they are not appreciably disturbed by a rotating brush, so the particles travel on the PC past the cleaner, the charge corona, the exposure unit, and the developer station and are subsequently transferred to paper as an "old" image. DePalma (1982) discusses toner removal from the IBM 3800 printer and Harvapat (1977) analyzes the mechanics of the cleaning blade used in many Xerox copiers.

After reading this overview of electrophotography, the newcomer should appreciate that it is a story of competition between opposing forces. The ubiquitous Coulomb and dispersion forces are evident from the moment corona ions are adsorbed to the PC surface to the instant an untransferred toner particle is detached by a cleaning brush and entrained by aerodynamic forces. A successful electrophotographic process depends upon the making and breaking of adhesive bonds between toner and other surfaces; hence, the extent to which adhesion is controlled is a measure of process reliability.

In the chapters that follow, much of the information relates to electrostatic phenomena, so if one is to appreciate the physics of electrophotographic processes, a good understanding of electrostatics is essential. Michael Faraday's *Experimental Researches in Electricity* and James Clerk Maxwell's *Treatise on Electricity and Magnetism* are particularly readable.

In the 1930s, the pace slowed in experimental and theoretical work in electrostatic phenomena. A revival of interest has occurred since the 1970s, partly owing to the commercial importance of electrophotography, electrostatic precipitation of industrial pollutants, electrostatic paint spraying, and other technologies as well as to renewed interest in weather, lightning, air pollution, biological membranes, and so forth, each of which has some fundamental dependence on electrostatics.

Many who are new to electrophotography will have to discover for themselves the many wonderful intricacies of electrostatics that were probably taken for granted by scientists and engineers a few generations ago. It is difficult at times to find important references to the literature. The *IEEE Transactions of Industry Applications* publishes many papers on corona discharge, electrostatics, and xerographic studies and gives some practical, device-oriented papers as well. The *Journal of Electrostatics* also publishes papers on scientific and engineering aspects of the subject. The *Journal of Colloid and Interface Science* publishes papers on interface phenomena such as adhesion and dispersion forces; there is a *Journal of Adhesion*, which covers practical aspects of adhesion along with scientific studies. The *Journal of Applied Physics* includes papers that fill the gap between pure theory and pure applications on a broad range of subjects. *Photographic Science and Engineering* publishes papers on electrophotography, and the Society (SPSE) sponsors an international conference on electrophotography, issuing an advanced printing of paper summaries at the conferences. Much has been written on contact (tribo) electrification, but the information may not be particularly easy to find because it hides behind a generic title such as "Electricity and Polymers" or "Progress in Dielectrics." Some important references are out of print and are available only on a roll of microfilm. Harper (1967) is out of print, but he wrote a review paper, Harper (1957), earlier. Much of the information appearing in Loeb (1958) can be found in Loeb (1962). A later review of contact electrification in polymers has been written by Seanor (1972) and his effort can be contrasted with much earlier ones by Richards (1923) and Sanford (1919). The latest review is by Lowell and Rose-Innes (1980).

TWO

PHOTOCONDUCTORS

Photoconductivity and photoconductors have probably received more investigation and documentation than any other aspect of electrophotography. This chapter emphasizes the phenomenon of photogeneration and its application to xerographic processes; photoconductor theory is not treated in any detail, since many readily available references on the subject exist. A few sources are Bube (1960), D. M. Pai's chapter, "Introduction to Photoconductivity in Solids," in Patsis and Seanor (1976), the collection of papers edited by Berg and Hauffe (1972), Fridkin (1972), Meier (1974), and Schaffert (1975). Schaffert should be consulted for his extensive bibliography and discussion of PCs used in xerography.

For xerographic printing and copying, an appropriate (PC) should have rather good insulating behavior when kept in the dark and should conduct charge of at least one polarity when exposed to light. Charging the surface of the PC, discharging by light energy, and recharging in the dark should be repeatable many thousands of cycles without objectionable changes in the dark or light voltages of the PC surface charge density. These requirements are met by a variety of materials; one workhorse of the industry has been amorphous selenium. More recently, some laser printers and office copiers use a PC composed of a 1:1 molar mixture of polyvinylcarbazole and trinitrofluorenone, otherwise known as "organic photoconductor" or OPC. This has been replaced by even more sensitive layered photoconductors (LPC) in which the photosensitive material (pyrazoline based material, such as chlorodianeblue) is coated in a very thin layer (about 0.1 μm).

Good dielectric strength and mechanical properties are given to the structure by covering the thin charge generation layer (CGL) with a thick (about 10–15 μm) film chosen to provide high dielectric strength, good wear characteristics, and the ability to transport charge carriers (holes or electrons) generated in the thin CGL. The thick top layer, called the charge transport layer (CTL) is transparent to visible light, allowing the exposing radiation to pass through, essentially unattenuated, to the CGL where the radiation is absorbed. Layered LPC is much more sensitive to visible light than OPC, so its use allows higher xerographic processing speeds. Layered PC systems are discussed by Melz et al. (1977). Organic and layered PCs are coated onto aluminized Mylar substrates; the aluminum ground plane is connected to the system reference ground potential. Kodak introduced PCs coated onto polyester base films with a clear conductive layer instead of aluminum (Laukaitis, 1978 and Jewett, 1977). The transparent conductor allowed image erasure with back-lighting. In all cases, the photogenerating–photoconducting medium is packaged to be tough, flexible, and reasonably forgiving to mechanical abuse.

2.1 Absorption Spectra

All polymeric insulators become photoconductors if the radiation wavelength is very short (Hughes, 1976). High-energy radiations, such as X-rays and gamma rays, are absorbed and ion pairs are formed; if an electric field is present, a photocurrent will flow. Except for *xeroradiography*, which uses X-rays, PCs are usually chosen for their photosensitivity at visible wavelengths. When photons are absorbed, some convert their energy to the creation of charged pairs, and the rest convert their energy into heat. Photon energy is related to wavelength by the well-known equation

$$E = \frac{hc}{\lambda} \quad \text{(ergs)} \qquad (2.1)$$

where h = Planck's constant = 6.626×10^{-27} erg-sec, c = speed of light in vacuum = 2.998×10^{10} cm/sec, and λ = wavelength of the radiation in centimeters.

Sensitivity spectra for several PCs and the absorption coefficient for OPC are shown in Figure 2.1a and b. Schaffert (1975) gives an extensive discussion on a variety of materials studied in relation to their suitability for use in xerography. Schaffert (1971) reviews OPC history and its chemical, electrical, and optical properties. Except for LPC, the data of Figure 2.1b are from Schaffert's book. The thickness of each PC film is as follows: OPC = 20 μm; Se = 50 μm; ZnS:CdS (70% CdS) = 25 μm; LPC = 15 μms. The symbols $(-)$ and $(+)$ refer to the polarity of the voltages used in the photosensitometric studies. The absorption peak at 3600 Å for LPC is shown as a dotted line because the data are uncalibrated in this region. The *sensitivity* ordinate is calibrated in units of coulombs/erg and follows Schaffert's usage. The maximum sensitivity for OPC is about 3.2×10^{-9} coulomb/erg, occurring at roughly 5800 Å (580 nanometers) wavelength. Schaffert states that the units "are given in terms of the amount of surface charge dissipated per unit of incident light energy

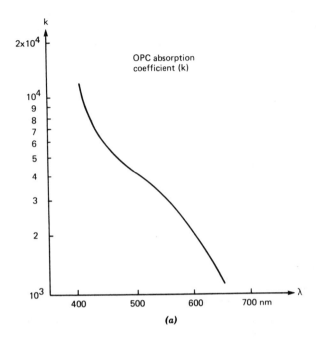

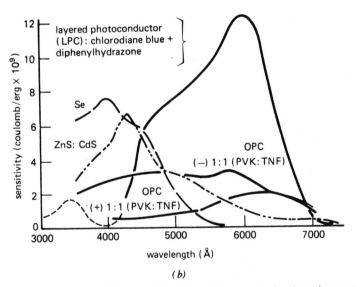

Figure 2.1   (a) Absorption coefficient of OPC. (b) Sensitivity spectra of various photoconductors. Data from Schaffert (1971), excluding LPC. Copyright 1971 by International Business Machines Corporation; reprinted with permission.

(C/erg) for a *surface charge contrast* of 3.5×10^{-8} C/cm^2." The energy/cm^2 necessary to achieve this contrast is found by dividing the charge contrast by the sensitivity, or about 11.0 ergs/cm^2 (1.10 microjoules/cm^2). The energy per photon at 580 nm is found with (2.1).

$$\text{Energy/photon} = \frac{1.98 \times 10^{-16} \text{ erg-cm}}{5.8 \times 10^{-5} \text{ cm}} = 3.4 \times 10^{-12} \text{ erg}$$

$$= 2.14 \text{ eV}$$

An energy of 11 ergs/cm^2 at 580 nm is then equivalent to absorbing 3.22×10^{12} photons/cm^2.

The charge transport layer of one type of LPC is composed of a 40 % (weight) mixture of diphenylhydrazone in polycarbonate. Polycarbonate is transparent at wavelengths above 275 nm; Burkinshaw and Caird (1975) give much useful information on films of polycarbonate. The extinction coefficient of diphenyl-hydrazone is plotted in Figure 2.2; the peak at 365 nm is evidence of photo-chemical processes in addition to photogeneration of charge carriers. Hydrazone is known to transport holes but not electrons, so this LPC system would be used at negative surface potentials such that photogenerated holes would transport through the CTL up to the negative surface charge. For positive potentials, electrons could not transit through the CTL, so the surface charge would not be discharged.

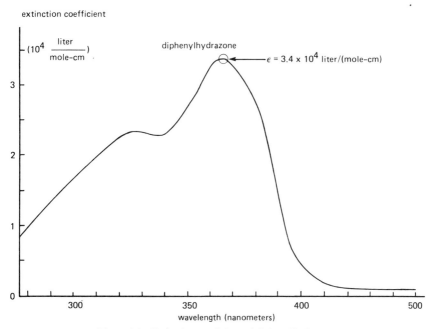

Figure 2.2 Extinction coefficient of diphenylhydrazone.

Light intensity at any distance (z) beneath the surface of the PC system can be computed using the Beer–Lambert Law, often called Beer's Law. (See, for example, Castellan, 1971, p. 808.) From a chemist's viewpoint, the intensity at any depth is

$$I = I_0 10^{-\varepsilon c z} \tag{2.2}$$

where I = the intensity at a depth (z) in cm,
  I_0 = the intensity at $z = 0$,
  ε = the molar extinction coefficient (liter/mole-cm), and
  c = the molar concentration (moles/liter).

A book on optics would say the same thing in a slightly different way. Born and Wolf (1975), for example, give the intensity as

$$I = I_0 e^{-kz} \tag{2.3}$$

where k = the absorption coefficient in $(cm)^{-1} = \varepsilon c \log_e 10 = 2.30\varepsilon c$.

At 365 nm (Figure 2.2), $\varepsilon = 3.4 \times 10^4$ liter/mole-cm; the *penetration depth*, that depth where $I/I_0 = e^{-1}$, is at $z = k^{-1}$. Since the molar concentration (c) is about 1.0 moles/liter in this example of a hydrazone CTL, the penetration depth is about 1.3×10^{-5} cm or 0.13 μm. That is, UV radiation is rapidly attenuated by this CTL and charge carriers generated by UV are created effectively in the top 0.13 μm.

Visible light conventionally falls in the wavelength range of 400–700 nm. Curves of relative visibility of the average human eye are shown in Figure 2.3. The "photopic eye" is bright-adapted, and the "scotopic eye" is dark-adapted. Ruch and Patton (1965) discuss the physiology of the human eye. Wavelengths of various radiations are given, among other places, in the *Handbook of Chemistry*

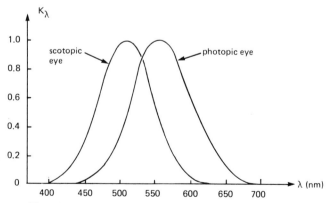

Figure 2.3   Relative visibility curves of the average human eye.

and *Physics*, 59th ed. Chemical Rubber Company, p. E-213. Table 2.1 is a
a partial list of radiation wavelengths.

Table 2.1 Radiation Wavelengths

Conventional Name	Wavelength (nm)
Cosmic rays	5×10^{-5}
Gamma rays	5×10^{-4}–0.14
X-rays	10^{-2}–10
Ultraviolet, below	400
Visible spectrum	400–700
Violet	400–424
Blue	424–491.2
Green	491.2–575
Yellow	575–585
Orange	585–647
Red	647–700
Infrared, more than	700

In a system designed for good xerographic efficiency, the absorption spectrum of the PC should have good absorption and sensitivity over the range of wavelengths present in the illumination source. Gallo and Hammond (1976) review the characteristics of gas discharge lamps used in electrophotography. Laser printers primarily use the popular helium–neon laser which emits a monochromatic beam at 632.8 nm, although helium–cadmium lasers (in the blue part of the spectrum) are also used. Selenium, for example, absorbs mostly in the blue part of the spectrum, so it would be a good choice for an He–Cd laser. Layered PC has an absorption peak around 600 nm, and would be a good choice for use with an He–Ne laser; OPC absorbs over the entire visible spectrum, but most absorption occurs at wavelengths below 600 nm (see Figure 2.1b). For this reason, OPC has a reddish appearance, and a beam of light at 632.8 nm is only partially absorbed as it travels through the approximately 10 μm thick film. Multiple reflections from the aluminum ground-plane and the OPC-air interface lead to interference effects with the monochromatic beam of laser light. Modulation in absorbed energy manifests itself in the final developed and transferred image as a contour map of absorption maxima and minima; it appears much like the wood grain of curly maple. Figure 2.4 shows a facsimile of the "wood grain" effect in OPC with 632.8 nm exposure. Unwanted modulation in exposure energy is discussed in Chapter 5. Machines that use spectrally broad illumination lamps do not exhibit the problems of light interference. The LPC absorption curve shown in Figure 2.1b reveals that this system with 632.8 nm exposure would not suffer much from exposure modulation caused by light interference.

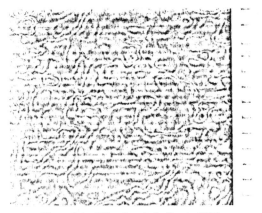

Figure 2.4 "Wood-grain" effect in OPC.

2.2 Electrophotographic Characteristics

After charging a PC by adsorbing gaseous ions to its surface, there is a leakage current which flows even when the PC is shielded from any source of light. This *dark current* flows as a result of thermally activated electron–hole pairs in the photogenerating medium. In xerographically useful PCs, the dark decay rate of the surface potential is held beneath certain limits; if the decay rate is too high, the surface voltage would drop to levels such that the developed image would lack adequate contrast and toner would appear in the background. When the exposing light beam is switched on, the surface potential decays rapidly toward a value that depends on the exposure energy per unit area. Surface voltage vs. time is sketched in Figure 2.5, along with a plot of dark decay for a layered PC.

It is helpful to think of the PC as a parallel-plate capacitor with the top electrode removed. When a gaseous ion is deposited at the top surface, the material must block injection of the surface ion. The bottom electrode is attached to system ground, so when corona ions flow to the top surface, counter charges flow into the ground plane, thus establishing an electric field within the PC. The cross section of a LPC is depicted in Figure 2.6. As measured at the top surface, the capacitance per unit area is

$$C = \frac{C'}{A} = \frac{\varepsilon}{d} \quad (\text{farad/cm}^2) \tag{2.4}$$

where ε = permittivity of the CTL (F/cm),

  $C' = \varepsilon(A/d)$ = total capacitance (F), and

  d = thickness of the CTL (the CGL is very thin and can be ignored for estimating the film capacitance/cm^2)

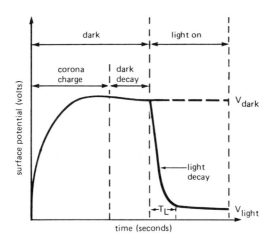

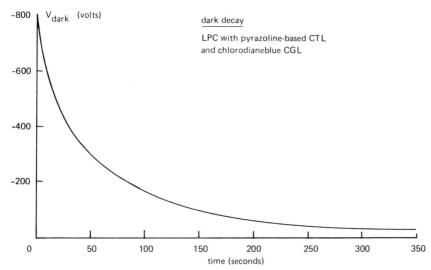

Figure 2.5   Photoconductor potential vs. time.

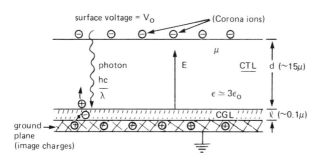

Figure 2.6   Layered PC.

Voltage and charge are related by the film capacitance, or the charge/cm^2 and the capacitance/cm^2; that is,

$$V = \frac{(Q/A)}{(C'/A)} = \frac{\sigma d}{\varepsilon} \quad \text{(V)} \tag{2.5}$$

Therefore, the PC surface potential (V) is directly proportional to the surface charge density (σ, in coulombs/cm^2) and inversely proportional to the capacitance/cm^2 of the PC film. The electric field (**E**) inside the CTL is a vector quantity pointing from the more positive to the less positive potential. Figure 2.6 shows negative surface ions, so the field direction is from the ground plane up to the film surface. The field magnitude is

$$E = \frac{V}{d} = \frac{\sigma}{\varepsilon} \quad \text{(V/cm)} \tag{2.6}$$

Capacitance is a geometrical quantity depending only on the shape and location of conductors and on the permittivity (dielectric polarizability or dielectric constant) of the intervening medium. Equation (2.4) is valid for infinite sheets. In (2.5), charges are assumed to be distributed uniformly over the top surface of the CTL film. Since the sheet is infinite and has a ground plane, there will be no external field, unless there are variations in surface potential; for the present discussion, σ is constant, so **E** is zero outside (i.e., above the sheet) and is equal in magnitude to V/d (V/cm) inside.

2.3   Decay Time of Surface Potential

If the PC is charged and a short burst of light is absorbed in the CGL, the hole–electron pairs generated in the thin CGL will experience a coulomb force $\mathbf{F} = q\mathbf{E}$. With negative surface charge, holes travel upward into the hole-transporting layer (CTL) and electrons within the thin CGL go quickly to the ground plane and are swept out to earth or system ground. The time required for a package of holes to transit the CTL is an important consideration when the architecture of a xerographic process is established. The distance between the exposure beam and the image developing unit must be great enough to allow time for the latent xerographic image to be formed. The distance should be approximately equal to the product of the linear velocity of the PC and the photogenerated carrier *transit time*. Pai (1976) and Hughes (1976) discuss some of the deeper aspects of charge transport.

The transit time depends on the *drift velocity* (**v**) and the film thickness (d); this time is called T_L in Figure 2.5.

$$T_L = \frac{d}{\mathbf{v}} \quad \text{(sec)} \tag{2.7}$$

where $\mathbf{v} = \mu\mathbf{E}$ = charge carrier drift velocity (cm/sec),
   μ = drift mobility (cm^2/V-sec), and
   $\mathbf{E}$ = electric field within the PC (V/cm).

As a simple first approximation, one can assume the field magnitude remains fairly constant at $E = V_0/d$ (where V_0 is the dark potential), so the drift velocity becomes

$$v = \frac{\mu V_0}{d} \qquad (2.8)$$

and the transit time can be roughly approximated by the simple relation

$$T_L \cong \frac{d^2}{\mu V_0} \quad \text{(sec)} \qquad (2.9)$$

To get a feeling for the magnitudes of the relevant quantities, let $d = 15 \ \mu m = 1.5 \times 10^{-3}$ cm, $\mu = 5 \times 10^{-8}$ cm^2/V-sec, and $V_0 = -800$ V. In this case, $T_L = 0.056$ sec. This is a best case estimate, since it assumes that all of the holes travel in one tight package and that the electric field remains constant as the holes traverse the CTL. The actual process is more complicated; Figure 2.7a, b, and c depicts an adaptation of the process as given by Pai (1976). In Figure 2.7a, photons are absorbed in the very thin CGL where holes and electrons are generated. The electrons leave quickly through the ground plane. The remaining holes form a charge sheet which, under constant illumination, would be just sufficient to neutralize the negative surface charges. The surface voltage is V_0, so the charge/cm^2 is CV_0, where C is given by (2.4). In Figure 2.7b, the sheet of holes has drifted a distance $d/4$ away from the ground plane, thereby reducing the surface voltage to $\frac{3}{4}V_0$. Within the CTL, but above the moving charge sheet, the electric field is

$$E = \frac{\frac{3}{4}V_0}{\frac{3}{4}d} = \frac{V_0}{d}$$

but below the moving sheet, the field is zero. If more light is absorbed in the CGL, the photogenerated charge carriers are in a zero field environment, so there is no coulomb force to cause charge separation, thus the excess holes and electrons recombine. This is called *geminate recombination*.

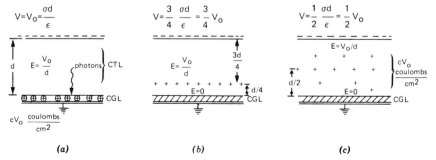

(a)   (b)   (c)

Figure 2.7   Surface potential (V) depends on position of photogenerated charges. C = capacitance/cm^2. Figures adapted from Patsis and Seaner (1976), with permission.

The initial charge package containing CV_0 C/cm^2 continues drifting upward. Since the charge sheet has a finite, nonzero thickness, carriers closest to the top experience a larger field than those near the bottom of the sheet, and the drift velocity is larger in the high field region than in the low; that is, the charge carriers spread out or disperse with time. Trailing edge carriers do not experience much drifting, because the electric field approaches zero in the trailing region. This situation is sketched in Figure 2.7c, where the centroid of the carrier space distribution has drifted just halfway through the CTL. The field is $V_0/(2d)$ at the charge centroid, increasing to V_0/d at the PC surface, and decreasing toward zero at the ground plane. The package of carriers is a *space charge* and its distribution and density are a source of additional electric field not considered earlier in this analysis. A. von Engel (1965, p. 148) discusses mutual repulsion of charges in vacuum. Zhigarev (1975) devotes a chapter to the problem of electron beams at high current densities and analyzes space charge effects.

A narrow line of photogenerated charges, formed by a scanning laser beam, for example, can spread as a result of coulombic interaction with other charges. *Lateral spreading*, and its relation to ultimate limits of image resolution, are discussed in more depth in this chapter. The genesis of a latent electrostatic image can be determined experimentally. The plot of voltage vs. time in Figure 2.8 shows significant curvature; this is evidence for time dispersion or spreading of the carrier package which, in this case, was created by a burst of light energy

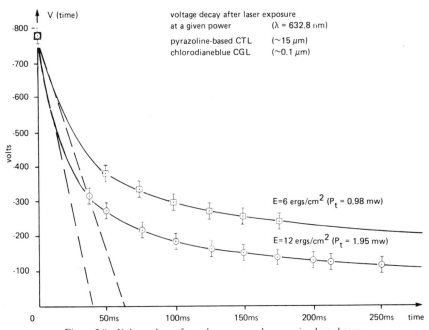

Figure 2.8   Voltage decay for pulse exposure by scanning laser beam.

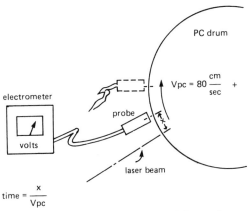

Figure 2.9   Experimental arrangement for determining carrier transit time.

from a laser beam. The data were obtained with an experimental printer using a LPC much like that described by Melz (1977). A vibrating shutter electrometer was mounted just above the scan line of the laser beam. Since the PC moved at a linear velocity of 80 cm/sec, a distance of 1.0 cm above the scan line was equivalent to an elapsed time of 12.5 msec between laser exposure and measurement of the surface potential. The setup is shown in Figure 2.9.

Referring again to Figure 2.8, the initial slopes of the voltage vs. time curves are extrapolated down to the abscissa, where the intercepts are at about 40–60 msec. If the charge packets, shown here for exposures at 6 and 12 ergs/cm² at 632.8 nm wavelength, did not spread and if every carrier experienced a constant field, the voltage decay would be linear with time, because the drift velocity would be constant. The departure from linearity gives a hint that carrier drift velocities are spread over a distribution, and that there are many stragglers bringing up the rear. At either level of exposure, the surface potential has not reached a final value after 250 msec; thus, some of the carriers are moving rather slowly. In (2.8), drift velocity is constant and equal to the product of electric field and drift mobility. In many materials, the drift mobility itself is field dependent and vanishes at low fields. A drift mobility of perhaps 10^{-13} cm²/V-sec at a field of 10^4 V/cm would be most difficult to measure and one might rightly claim that the carriers were immobile or trapped.

Hughes (1976) discusses mobility in disordered solids. He defines mobility as

$$\mu = \frac{\lambda f}{E} \quad (\text{cm}^2/\text{v-sec}) \tag{2.10}$$

where λ is the average distance (cm) a charge carrier moves when hopping over energy barriers in the CTL, f is the hopping frequency (number/sec) of the carriers [f is a function of the hopping distance, electric field, barrier height (erg), and temperature], and E is the electric field magnitude driving the carrier.

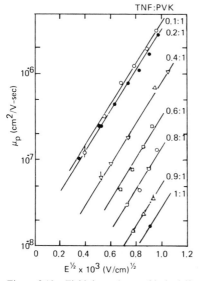

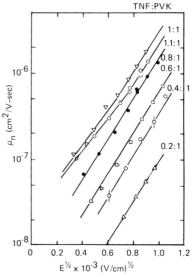

Figure 2.10   Field dependence of hole drift mobilities for a range of TNF: PVK molar ratios. Data taken at $T = 24°C$. From W. D. Gill, *J. Appl. Phys.* **43**, 5035 (1972), with permission.

Figure 2.11   Field dependence of electron drift mobilities for a range of TNF: PVK molar ratios. Data taken at $T = 24°C$. From W. D. Gill, *J. Appl. Phys.* **43**, 5035 (1972), with permission.

The mobility of an electron in copper is about 30 cm²/V-sec, an O_2^- ion in air is about 2.3 cm²/V-sec, and an electron in 1:1 PVK:TNF has a mobility of about 5×10^{-7} at a field of 5×10^5 V/cm. Gill (1972) studied the drift mobility of PVK–TNF complexes; the mobility of holes and electrons as a function of applied field are shown in Figures 2.10 and 2.11. Data on hole and electron mobilities in diphenylhydrazone are apparently unpublished. Transit time data, like that shown in Figure 2.8, suggest that the hole mobility is about 5×10^{-8} at field of 5×10^{-5} V/cm. Although studies have not been published on this material, electrons seem to be essentially immobile in LPC. Experimentally, it is known that LPC with a hydrazone transport layer shows no measurable photodischarge when the surface is positively charged.

2.4   Light Voltage and Exposure Energy

Each type of PC can be described according to its wavelength sensitivity and response time. As mentioned earlier, some of the absorbed photons generate carriers, whereas others merely give up their energy as heat. The ratio of photo-generated carriers to the number of absorbed photons is often called the *photo-injection efficiency* or the *quantum efficiency*. Layered PC systems like those studied by Melz (1977) show efficiencies ranging from 1 to 25%, with very strong field dependence of that efficiency. PVK-TNF (1:1) quantum efficiency is discussed by Schaffert (1971); his data show dependence upon wavelength,

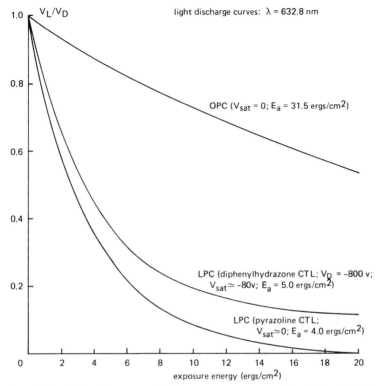

Figure 2.12   Light voltage (normalized) vs. exposure energy/cm² for OPC and LPCs.

electric field, and light intensity. At 632.8 nm and a field of 4×10^5 V/cm, the efficiency is about 20% for OPC. In a high-speed printing process, the PC must respond quickly and give a reasonable contrast or difference between dark and light voltages. A contrast of 400 V or more can yield adequate electric field strength for the image development step.

Light voltage vs. exposure energy per unit area for an OPC and two different LPCs are shown in Figure 2.12. Similar curves for the Kodak Ektavolt SO-102 PC were published by Buettner and May (1982). The data have been normalized by the dark voltage value, usually between -700 and -900 V. Empirically, the decay behavior with exposure energy is well-described by a negative exponential function, along with an asymptotic voltage V_{sat} (i.e., the saturation voltage or residual potential). The slope of the discharge curve is a measure of sensitivity. Analytically, the light voltage V_L can be written as

$$V_L = V_{\text{sat}} + (V_D - V_{\text{sat}})\exp\left(\frac{-E}{E_a}\right) \quad \text{(V)} \qquad (2.11)$$

where $V_{\text{sat}} = $ the voltage obtained for very high exposure energy/cm², $V_D = $ the dark voltage, E = the exposure energy/cm² (ergs/cm² or J/cm²), and $E_a = $ the "energy constant" (ergs/cm² or J/cm²) that describes the sensitivity of the

PC. Many writers and workers in electrophotography use photographic terminology when discussing the xerographic behavior of PCs. For example, the act of charging the PC to a dark potential is called "sensitizing" the PC; the voltage vs. exposure energy is usually plotted as a V-log E curve, in analogy with the Hurter–Driffield (H-D) curves which quantify silver grain image density and exposure. This method of plotting the relation between voltage and exposure unnecessarily obscures the remarkably simple exponential discharge characteristic seen in most xerographic grade PCs. If workers plotted their data as log V vs. E, they would in most cases obtain a nearly straight line; however, data are conventionally plotted as V vs. log E, so the line becomes an ogive and one speaks of the head, knee, and toe regions of this unnecessarily clumsy curve.

Over the useful ranges of dark voltages and exposure energies, the discharge behavior of PCs can be described by the simple exponential curve of (2.11). At a wavelength of 632.8 nm, the approximate values of V_{sat} for OPC and LPC are 0 and -80 V, respectively, and the energy constants are 31.5 and 4.3 ergs/cm^2, respectively. In other words, LPC is more than seven times as sensitive as OPC at 632.8 nm. A nonzero saturation voltage is very likely due to a strong field dependence of the carrier drift mobility, such that holes become trapped and cannot move at very low applied fields. Some workers call V_{sat} the "residual potential." Schaffert (1975), for example, discusses the dependence of residual potential on impurity doping of the xerographic material.

Photoconductor sensitivity can be defined several ways. In Schaffert's definition, he speaks of the energy required to create a specified contrast in charge per unit area; in this case, sensitivity is in units of C/erg. With exponentially decaying voltage vs. energy/cm^2, as given in (2.11), it is natural and convenient to define sensitivity by the initial slope of the V vs. E curve or by the V/V_d vs. E curve.

$$\text{Absolute sensitivity} = \frac{V_d}{E_a} \qquad (2.12)$$

$$\text{Normalized sensitivity} = (E_a)^{-1} \qquad (2.13)$$

Equation (2.13) is quite useful as a measure of sensitivity, since those PCs with large E_a, such as an OPC, have by that definition a relatively lower sensitivity. In this manner, terminology corresponds with normal usage and understanding of the word "sensitivity."

2.5   Lateral Spreading of Lines:
Intrinsic Limits to Image Resolution

The discussion thus far has been concerned with infinitely wide charge sheets drifting up to the surface of a PC. This section presents an approximate treatment of line broadening caused by mutual repulsion and diffusion of charge

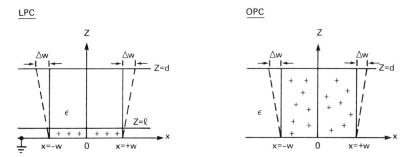

Figure 2.13   Charge carriers in LPC and OPC. In LPC, carriers are generated in a very thin layer; in OPC charge carriers are generated throughout the full thickness. ΔW is edge broadening from lateral drift of carriers.

carriers, and gives speculations on the intrinsic limits to image resolution imposed by the structure of the PC itself. These ideas are apparently not discussed in the literature and there are no known or published experimental results to support them. The subject of lateral spreading of lines is broached to stimulate continued inquiry into the subject.

Assume that a package of charges drifts to the PC surface with the normal drift velocity

$$v_z = \mu E_z \quad \text{(cm/sec)} \tag{2.14}$$

where μ is the mobility, as before, and E_z is the vertical or normal component of the electric field. Immediately after pulse exposure, the charge distribution would depend on the PC structure. As sketched in Figure 2.13, OPC is a so-called "bulk" PC and carriers are photogenerated throughout its volume, whereas LPC confines charge generation to a very thin volume in the CGL. In both cases, the exposure pattern has a width $2W$ along the x-direction and is very long in the y-direction (which is normal to the plane of the picture). A little broadening (ΔW) in linewidth is shown at the edges of the initial charge pattern. This broadening anticipates the argument and conclusion of this analysis; that is, the drifting charges have mobility sideways as well as upward, therefore, some motion should arise from the horizontal component of the electric field, caused by the space charge density of the drifting charge pattern.

The influence of the ground plane is accounted for by placing mirror "image" charges in the geometry. The "method of images" is a standard technique for solving field problems; here, the double usage of the term "image" is unfortunate, but the context should clarify whether the "image" is due to the conducting plane or to a pattern of exposure energy. Figure 2.14 shows a two-dimensional cross section for LPC. Equation (2.15) is the distance between a field point and the charge distribution existing in the CTL, and (2.16) is the

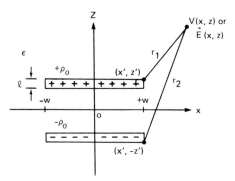

Figure 2.14   Charge distribution and its own image in a ground plane.

distance between a field point and the "image" charge distribution caused by the ground plane.

$$r_1 = [(x - x')^2 + (y - y')^2 + (z - z')^2]^{1/2} \tag{2.15}$$

$$r_2 = [(x - x')^2 + (y - y')^2 + (z + z')^2]^{1/2} \tag{2.16}$$

Source coordinates are the points x', y', and z', and field coordinates are the points x, y, and z. The potential arising from the photogenerated charges is found by integrating over the volume distribution, including the ground plane image charges. Here, the volume charge density is taken as constant. Since the charge strip is very long in the y-direction, the problem becomes two-dimensional. The potential resulting from the surface ions (unshown) is accounted for later in the discussion. Let $V(x, z)$ be the potential caused by the photogenerated charges. The potential can be found in general by integrating over the charge distribution, as shown in (2.17). Weber (1965, p. 8) is one of many useful texts on electromagnetic field theory.

$$V(x, z) = \frac{1}{4\pi\varepsilon} \iiint\limits_{\text{vol}} \frac{\rho_0 \, d\text{vol}}{r_1} - \frac{1}{4\pi\varepsilon} \iiint\limits_{\text{vol}} \frac{\rho_0 \, d\text{vol}}{r_2} \tag{2.17}$$

where $d\text{vol} = dx' \, dy' \, dz'$ and $\rho_0 =$ the space charge density (C/cm^3). Since a LPC has a very thin CGL, it is easy to approximate the space charge density with a constant value

$$\rho_{\text{LPC}} \cong \frac{\sigma_0}{l} \tag{2.18}$$

where $\sigma_0 = \Delta V \varepsilon / d =$ the surface charge/cm^2, which yields a contrast in surface voltage equal to ΔV.

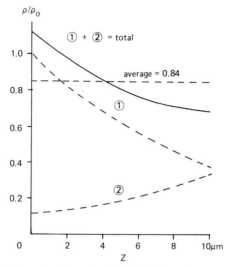

Figure 2.15   Computed charge density vs. depth for OPC (1 = primary wave; 2 = reflected wave).

Since OPC absorbs throughout its full thickness, the charge density will in general be a function of depth. Schaffert's curve, shown in Figure 2.1, indicates that the absorption coefficient at 632.8 nm is about 1200 cm^{-1}. Using (2.3) with $kz = 1.0$, the beam intensity at the ground plane is

$$I = I_0 e^{-1} = 0.37 I_0 \tag{2.19}$$

Schechtmann (1980) gives the reflectance coefficient at the interface between OPC and aluminum as

$$R = 0.847 \tag{2.20}$$

so the reflected wave starts upward with an intensity $I = 0.847 \times 0.37 I_0$. Ignoring interference effects and any reflections at the OPC-air interface, the charge density at any depth z becomes

$$\rho = \rho_0(e^{-1000z} + 0.847e^{1000z-2}) \tag{2.21}$$

This expression is plotted in Figure 2.15; the primary and reflected beam contributions are shown with their sum. The average charge density, which varies in a one-to-one manner with the total intensity, is about $0.84\rho_0$ for the full thickness, and the deviations are $+0.27$ and -0.18 around this average. Therefore, it is safe to assume that the space charge density is constant for OPC also. With $l = d$, the space charge density for OPC is defined in the same manner as for LPC.

$$\rho_{OPC} \cong \frac{\Delta V \varepsilon}{d^2} \quad (C/cm^3) \tag{2.22}$$

Equation (2.22) gives the volume charge density that, if uniform, would be required to produce a reduction in surface voltage by an amount of ΔV volts, provided the volume charges all move to the top surface of the PC.

It is interesting at this point to compare the charge densities found for OPC and LPC, given the same contrast voltage. Table 2.2 gives some useful values of properties for OPC and LPC which allow evaluation of (2.18), (2.22), and (2.23).

$$\frac{\rho_{LPC}}{\rho_{OPC}} = \frac{(\Delta V \varepsilon / l d)_{LPC}}{(\Delta V \varepsilon / d^2)_{OPC}} \cong 77 \tag{2.23}$$

Table 2.2   LPC and OPC Properties

OPC	LPC
$l = 0$	$l = 0.1 \ \mu m$
$d = 10 \ \mu m$	$d = 15 \ \mu m$
$\varepsilon = 2.6\varepsilon_0$	$\varepsilon = 3.0\varepsilon_0$

The space charge density within LPC is nearly two orders of magnitude greater than that in OPC, so the mutual repulsion of space charge within LPC ought to be significantly greater as well. Field computations within LPC are simplified by the very thin charge sheet, because the volume charge distribution can easily be approximated by a two-dimensional distribution, as given by (2.18). The potential $V(x, z)$ defined by (2.17) is evaluated by integrating along x' and y'. Potential computations for OPC involve all three dimensions because the charge distribution is quite thick. Derivations for the potential and field for LPC are found in the Appendix; the result for the horizontal field component is stated here.

$$E_x = -\frac{\partial V}{\partial x} = \frac{\Delta V}{4\pi d} \log_e \left\{ \frac{[(x + W)^2 + (z - z')^2][(x - W)^2 + (z + z')^2]}{[(x - W)^2 + (z - z')^2][(x + W)^2 + (z + z')^2]} \right\} \tag{2.24}$$

The simplicity of (2.24) is due to the assumptions that the charge distribution is very thin and has very sharp edges. The logarithmic singularities at $x = \pm W$ and $z = \pm z'$ are nonphysical. In reality, the edges would never be perfectly sharp.

The transit time for motion of the charges in the $+z$ − direction was given in (2.9). During this period of time, charge carriers would drift along the x-direction with velocity v_x, where

$$v_x = \mu E_x \quad (\text{cm/sec}) \tag{2.25}$$

During the transit time upward, charges at the edges of the exposed line travel a distance $x = \Delta W$ at each edge. Twice this distance is the line broadening caused by mutual repulsion of mobile charges.

$$\Delta W = v_x T_L = \mu E_x \frac{d}{\mu E_z} = \frac{E_x}{E_z} d \quad (\text{cm}) \tag{2.26}$$

The amount of broadening can be estimated using (2.24) for E_x, and recalling that $E_z = V_0/d$. Because there are nonphysical singularities in (2.24), calculations of the electric field at the edges must be avoided by arbitrarily choosing values of x and z some small distance removed from those edges. Figure 2.16 gives a calculated plot of E_x for $z' = 7.5$ μm and $z = 7.6$ μm, with $V = 600$ V

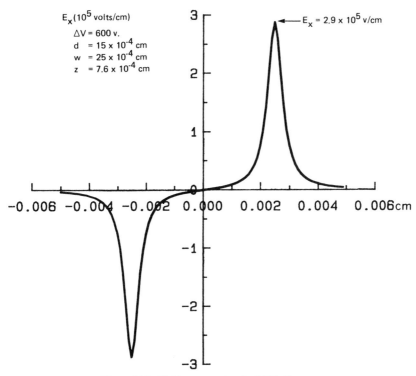

Figure 2.16   Field computation for LPC; E_x vs. x.

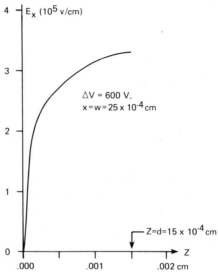

Figure 2.17   Field computation for LPC; E_x vs. Z.

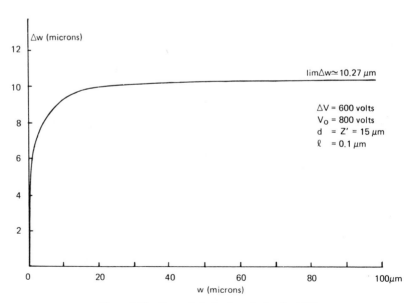

Figure 2.18   Computed edge broadening for LPC.

and $W = 25$ μm. Using these values in (2.24), the maximum field is 2.9×10^5 V/cm. Figure 2.17 depicts E_x as a function of distance above the ground (image) plane. An expression for edge broadening is found by evaluating (2.26) at $x = W$ and $z = z'$.

$$\Delta W = \left(\frac{\Delta V d}{4\pi V_0}\right) \log_e \left[\frac{(2W/l)^2 + 1}{[(2W)^2/(2z' + l)^2] + 1}\right] \qquad (2.27)$$

Edge broadening is a function of linewidth (W) for narrow lines, but quickly reaches a limit for large W.

$$\lim_{W \to \infty} \Delta W = \left(\frac{\Delta V d}{2\pi V_0}\right) \log_e \left(\frac{2z'}{l} + 1\right) \qquad (2.28)$$

For a reasonable choice of operating values, the limiting value of edge broadening is about 10 μm for LPC; this is shown in Figure 2.18. Total broadening of an isolated line (two edges) is about 20 μm, according to this much simplified line of reasoning. Total broadening for OPC is less than 2 μm.

Diffusion broadening should not be very important. From kinetic theory, the root-mean-square (rms) displacement of a charge carrier would be

$$\bar{x} = \sqrt{2Dt} \quad \text{(cm)}, \qquad (2.29)$$

where D = the diffusion coefficient (cm^2/sec) and t = time (sec). The Einstein Relation (see, for example, Kittel, 1956, p. 368) connects diffusion with charge mobility.

$$D = \frac{kT}{e} \mu \qquad (2.30)$$

where k = Boltzmann's Constant = 1.381×10^{-16} erg/$^\circ$K, T = temperature (kelvin), $e = 1.6 \times 10^{-19}$ coulomb, and $kT/e = 0.026$ V at $T = 300^\circ$K.

Measurements of light decay time (about 0.125 sec) indicate that LPC mobility for holes is about 5×10^{-8} cm^2/V-sec at $V = -800$ V (which implies that $E_z = 5.3 \times 10^5$ V/cm). Organic PC mobility for electrons is on the order of 10^{-7}, and for holes is about 10^{-8} cm^2/(V-sec). See Gill (1972) and Figures 2.10 and 2.11. Letting $\mu = 10^{-7}$, the most optimistic value for the rms diffusion distance x is roughly 0.7 μm for a diffusion time of 1 sec. With this semiquantitative argument, it seems diffusion broadening can be ignored.

Lewis (1978) discusses charge transport along polymer surfaces. Surface conduction on contaminated PCs results in degraded image resolution and quality; contaminants can be deposited by corona discharge.

THREE
CORONA
CHARGE GENERATION BY GAS BREAKDOWN

Generation and control of electrostatic charge is fundamentally important in the overall xerographic process. Corona devices are used for charging the PC, transferring toner to paper, neutralizing paper charges, and restoring the PC prior to recharging it for another process cycle. In this chapter, a brief review of corona physics and electrical conduction in gases is given. Corona devices typical of those found in printers and copiers are discussed in Chapter 4.

3.1 Electrical Conduction in Gases: Primary Ionization

Unlike metals and semiconductors, gases contain almost no free electrons or ions for transporting charge, so under reasonable electrical stresses, gases behave as nearly perfect electrical insulators. The extremely weak current densities supported by normal gases are due to drifting ion pairs generated by the ubiquitous background radiations of alpha particles and cosmic rays. A. von Engel (1965, p. 9) tabulates ion concentration and rates of production in the atmosphere. At ground level there are about 500–1100 positive ions/cm^3 and 400–850 electrons and negative ions/cm^3. The rate of production is somewhere between 4 and 20 ion-pairs/cm^3/sec, and this increases with increasing altitude because of reduced absorption of the less energetic components of cosmic radiation.

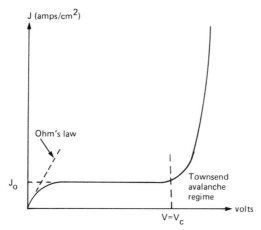

Figure 3.1 Current-voltage characteristic for air; J_0 = saturation current density caused by background ions, V_c = critical potential for field ionization.

At low electric fields, electrons and positive ions drift in opposite directions, elastically collide with neutral gas molecules, and continue in a zig-zag manner on the trip to the respective field electrodes. At increased fields, some electrons gain sufficient kinetic energy between collisions to *impact ionize* gas molecules. The *ionization potential* (energy) of the elements ranges from 4 eV (electron volts) for Fr to 24.5 eV for He; the gases O_2 and N_2 are 12.06 and 15.58 eV, respectively. Electrons released by *impact ionization* will travel some distance, on the average, before colliding with other molecules, and if the accelerating field is sufficiently large, additional ionization will ensue. In a reasonably *uniform electric field*, this field-ionization process grows exponentially with distance travelled by the original free electrons, and a spark discharge occurs. J. S. Townsend (1915) studied this gas ionization phenomenon in the 1890s, and the process is appropriately called the "Townsend avalanche" or the "Townsend discharge." A curve of current density vs. applied potential across a pair of parallel plate electrodes would behave much as that shown in Figure 3.1. For small potentials (fields), conduction is Ohmic (linear in voltage); but with increasing field, the current quickly saturates to a value that is limited by the number of ions generated by background radiations. At still higher fields, the Townsend avalanche region is entered and the current rapidly increases. Conduction is not *self-sustaining* in this region; if the background radiation is suddenly turned off, all of the available ions would quickly be swept away by the field and the current would stop. Townsend avalanche depends upon the presence of *trigger electrons* (see Loeb, 1965, p. 65). Without these trigger electrons, which are naturally generated by radiation, the applied field would have to strip electrons away from neutral gas molecules, and such a process for generating free electrons

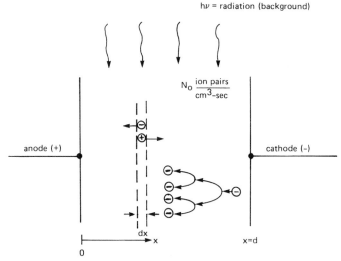

Figure 3.2 Electron multiplication in an electric field. Background radiation (hv) generates N_0(ion pairs/cm^3-sec) in the gas.

and ions would require an unrealistically high field. A rough estimate of the necessary field to steal a valence electron is

$$E = \frac{Q}{4\pi\varepsilon_0 R^2} = 1.4 \times 10^9 \quad (\text{V/cm})$$

where $R = 1 \times 10^{-8}$ cm.

The quantitative theory of field ionization receives a good treatment in von Engel (1965, Chapter 7). White (1963) applies gas ionization theory to explain the design and operation of electrostatic precipitators. Gallo (1975) reviews gas discharge devices used in electrophotography. The discussion of gas conduction in this chapter follows von Engel closely.

Figure 3.2 shows two plane parallel electrodes separated a distance $x = d$ (cm). The gas in the volume between the electrodes is irradiated to yield ionization at a rate $dN/dt = N_0$ ion-pairs/cm^3/sec. The parallel plate electrode geometry provides a reasonably uniform electric field over a substantial volume of the gas. A trigger electron has about 1000 times the mobility or mean free path of a much larger gaseous ion, so free electrons accelerate to much higher kinetic energies than do ions. The incremental increase in the number of liberated electrons arising from impact ionization will be

$$dn = \alpha n \, dx \qquad (3.1)$$

where α is the *first Townsend ionization coefficient* (a probability factor), which varies with gas species, pressure, and field strength; n is the number of free electrons at position x, and dx is an increment in path length. For an electron starting at a distance x from the anode, the number arriving at the anode (i.e., the current) will be

$$\frac{n}{n_0} = \frac{i}{i_0} = \exp(\alpha x) \tag{3.2}$$

by straightforward integration of (3.1).

There are trigger electrons throughout the volume between $x = 0$ and $x = d$, so the number of electrons/cm^2 $-$ sec in any element dx is $N_0 \, dx$. Equation (3.2) gives the amount of multiplication for an electron starting at some distance x from the anode; therefore, the total arriving per cm^2 per sec is found by integrating (3.2) over the interval $x = 0$ to $x = d$. That is,

$$N_t = \int_0^d N_0 \exp(\alpha x)dx = \left(\frac{N_0}{\alpha}\right)(e^{\alpha d} - 1) \quad \text{(electrons/cm}^2\text{-sec)} \tag{3.3}$$

The saturation current density is $J_0 = qN_0 d$ ($q =$ the charge per electron), so the multiplication factor is

$$\frac{J}{J_0} = \frac{N_t}{N_0 d} = \frac{e^{\alpha d} - 1}{\alpha d} \tag{3.4}$$

This relation assumes the background generation rate N_0 is uniform within the volume of gas in the electric field, and that electrons, once detached by impact ionization, do not attach to neutral molecules. Some gases are notorious for *attaching electrons*, so the electron multiplication phenomenon is significantly altered in these gases. Figure 3.3 is a plot of α/p vs. E/p ($E =$ field) for various gases. The gas pressure p is in torr of mm Hg; recall that 1.0 atmosphere of pressure is 760 torr = 760 mm Hg. Note that H_2 ionizes relatively easily, whereas SF_6 (sulfur hexafluoride) essentially *quenches avalanching*, by electron attachment, for E/p less than about 80 V/cm-torr. Sulfur hexafluoride is a gas used for spark suppression in high voltage switching devices; CCl_2F_2 (Freon) is also a spark suppressant. The halogens are effective in attaching electrons, since they need but one electron to complete their outer shell, that is, they are highly electronegative. Alston (1968) and Loeb (1965) discuss this very interesting subject. The information in Figure 3.3 is from White (1963, p. 79).

A classical argument gives a useful approximate relation for α/p. To ionize a molecule, an electron must gain by field acceleration an energy

$$qEx \geq qV_i \tag{3.5}$$

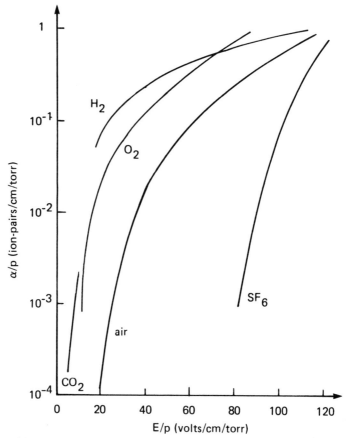

Figure 3.3 First Townsend ionization coefficients for several gases. From White (1963).

where q is the electronic charge, E is the field, x is the distance between collisions, and V_i is the first ionization potential of the molecule. The statistical distribution of free paths between collisions is

$$\frac{z_x}{z_0} = e^{-x/\lambda} \tag{3.6}$$

where z_x/z_0 is the relative number of collisions having paths x greater than the mean free path λ. One cm of pathlength contains $1/\lambda$ mean free ionizing paths, and the probability P (per cm of pathlength) for having an ionizing collision is

$$P = \left(\frac{1}{\lambda}\right)e^{(-x/\lambda)} = \alpha \quad \text{(ion pairs/cm)} \tag{3.7}$$

For a given gas, the pressure (p) and the mean free path (λ) are inversely related. Letting $\lambda = \lambda_0/p$, $A = 1/\lambda_0$, and $B = V_i/\lambda_0$, von Engel obtains, by combining (3.5) and (3.7), the following semiempirical relation for the Townsend ionization coefficient

$$\frac{\alpha}{p} = A \exp \frac{-Bp}{E} \quad \text{(cm-torr)}^{-1} \qquad (3.8)$$

Table 3.1 lists the coefficients A and B for some common gases. The data are from von Engel (1965, p. 181).

Table 3.1 Values of A and B in (3.8) for Some Common Gases

Gas	A (cm-torr)$^{-1}$	B (V/cm-torr)	Useful Range for E/p [(V/cm-torr)]
N_2	12	342	100–600
H_2	5.4	139	20–1000
Air	15	365	100–800
CO_2	20	466	500–1000
H_2O	13	290	150–1000
A	12	180	100–600
He	3	34	20–150
Hg	20	370	200–600

3.2 Secondary Ionization Effects

The discharge process described by (3.3) or (3.4) depends entirely upon trigger electrons, so it cannot be self-sustaining because there is no positive feedback mechanism to replace the trigger electrons. At least four secondary ionization mechanisms have been found experimentally, and each generates additional trigger electrons: (1) positive ion bombardment of the cathode, (2) photoelectric emission of electrons from the cathode caused by UV radiation from the excited gas, (3) photoionization of the gas by UV from excited gas molecules, and (4) ionization by metastable gas atoms or molecules. White (1963) points out that it is customary to group all secondary ionization mechanisms under the heading γ-*ionization processes*, where γ is often called the "second Townsend ionization coefficient." If a positive ion, for example, bombards the cathode and an electron is emitted from the cathode, the discharge process becomes self-sustaining and it is called *electrical breakdown*.

A primary or trigger electron at the cathode creates an avalanche of $\exp(\alpha d) - 1$ electrons and an equal quantity of positive ions drift to the cathode, bombard it, and generate $\gamma[\exp(\alpha d) - 1]$ secondary electrons. In Figure 3.2, let n_0 primary electrons per sec start at $x = d$ (the cathode) and ionize the gas. The current density (A/cm^2) at $x = d$, including secondary ionization processes, is

$$\frac{j}{j_0} = \frac{n}{n_0} = \frac{\exp(\alpha d)}{1 - \gamma[\exp(\alpha d) - 1]} \tag{3.9}$$

Electrical breakdown is said to occur when, without external circuit limitations, the current density approaches infinity. That is, breakdown occurs when

$$\gamma[\exp(\alpha d) - 1] = 1 \tag{3.10}$$

Figure 3.3 and Table 3.1 both give information about the dependence of α (primary ionization) upon gas species, field, and pressure. It increases with increasing field; so with constant γ, one can estimate the breakdown voltage for a given gap length d and gas at pressure p. The coefficient γ depends on the cathode material, its surface properties, and the microgeometry of the surface, as well as the type and energy of an impinging molecule; it is the least well-understood coefficient regarding breakdown predictions for a particular electrode. A. von Engel gives data on various substances (1965, p. 95). Except for the rare gases, γ increases with E/p.

3.3 Electron Attachment

Free electrons accelerate to high kinetic energies because they collide elastically with gas molecules in weak to moderate applied electric fields. Ions, however, in moderate fields have the same average energy as unionized gas molecules, that is, ions suffer inelastic collisions with molecules. Hence, the mobility of electrons is very high and the mobility of ions is low. Some gases are highly electronegative, so they readily attach electrons and become negative ions. The treatment of gas ionization so far has ignored this important point, but to understand spark suppression, say by Freon or sulphur hexafluoride, (3.9) and (3.10) must be modified to include the *coefficient of attachment*, η. *Free* electrons can ionize, *attached* electrons cannot.

In an electron-attaching gas, the number of free electrons at any distance x is the difference between the quantity generated by ionization and those that have attached to gas molecules. Attachment is a statistical event governed by the exponential survival equation given, for example, by White (1963, p. 81) in the form

$$n = n_0 \exp(-\eta x) \tag{3.11}$$

By combining (3.11) and (3.2), the number of free electrons is uniform fields becomes

$$\frac{n}{n_0} = \exp(\alpha - \eta)x \tag{3.12}$$

and (3.9) is modified to read

$$\frac{j}{j_0} = \frac{e^{(\alpha - \eta)d}}{1 - \gamma(e^{(\alpha - \eta)d} - 1)} \tag{3.13}$$

The defining condition for electrical breakdown in electron-attaching gases then becomes

$$\gamma(e^{(\alpha - \eta)d} - 1) = 1 \tag{3.14}$$

Figure 3.4 shows data from von Engel (1965, p. 187) for attachment in several gases. Pure N_2 does not attach electrons, which is an attribute that prevents

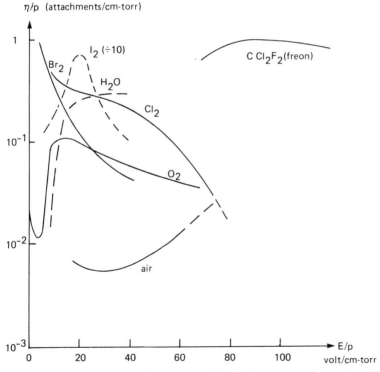

Figure 3.4   Electron attachment coefficient (η/p) vs. E/p. The halogens are for $p = 1$, and I_2 has been divided by 10 to bring it onto the ordinate shown. From von Engel (1965).

negative corona from developing but allows sudden spark-over. Alston (1968, p. 49) lists the relative electric breakdown strengths of various gases. His list is reproduced in Table 3.2.

Table 3.2   Relative Breakdown Strengths

Gas	Relative Strength
Air	1.0
N_2	1.0
SF_6	2.5
$30\%\ SF_6\ +\ 70\%$ Air (volume)	2.0
C_5F_8	5.5
H_2	0.5

3.4   Critical Field or Potential for Breakdown

Basic mechanisms for field ionization in gases were reviewed in the preceding pages. The application of these ideas to corona discharge is now given. From (3.8) and (3.4), one finds there is a critical value of E/p beyond which electron multiplication occurs without limit, except as imposed by the external circuitry. For uniform fields, the critical value E_c/p is estimated without difficulty. Using (3.8) and (3.14) with a little algebra, one obtains the final relation for E_c, the critical field for electrical breakdown.

$$E_c = \frac{Bp}{\log_e\{Apd/[\eta d + \log_e(1 + 1/\gamma)]\}} \qquad (3.15)$$

For air at $p = 760$ torr and a uniform field gap $d = 1.0$ cm, (3.15) predicts about 38 kV/cm for an assumed value $\gamma = 0.5$ for the cathode and $\eta = 7$ (see Table 3.1 and Figure 3.4 for electron attachment values and von Engel, 1965, p. 99 for secondary ionization coefficients). The experimental result for uniform fields is about 30 kV/cm, so the theory can be regarded as essentially correct. Exact quantitative agreement would require exact knowledge about the nature of the cathode surface and its geometry at a microscopic level.

F. Paschen (1889) published a paper showing that spark discharge across a gap was a function of pd, and his work has become known as "Paschen's Law." The experiments showed that sparking potential was a function of pressure and gap distance only. This fact is found in (3.15) by noting that $E_c = V_c/d$, where V_c is Paschen's sparking potential for parallel plate geometry. Therefore, $V_c = E_c d$ (V) and Townsend's theory of gas ionization accounts for Paschen's results. Paschen curves for several gases are given in Cobine (1958, p. 164) and in Schaffert (1975, p. 515). The data of Figure 3.5 are from Schaffert.

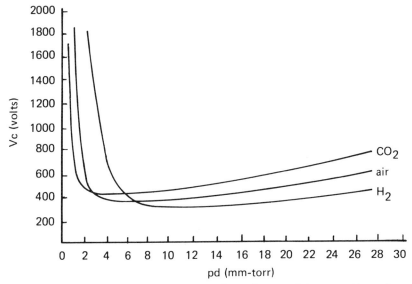

Figure 3.5   Paschen curves for common gases. Each gas shows a minimum sparking voltage at some value of *pd*. The curves are not generally valid for high pressures. From Schaffert (1975).

As he points out, the breakdown behavior of gases follows the Paschen curve reasonably well for the right-hand portion beyond the minimum in V_c. The region to the left of this minimum, where V_c is a very steep function of *pd*, is probably valid only at low pressures and large gap lengths. At atmospheric pressure (760 torr), there is no steep portion like that shown in Figure 3.5, and *field emission* current from the cathode dominates the Townsend avalanche current, which would flow at high *p* and small *d* (perhaps as small as 10 μm or less). Schaffert (1975, p. 517) presents a modified Paschen curve at $p = 760$ torr that shows V_c vs. gap length. Figure 3.6 shows adaptations of his curves for CO_2, air, and H_2. Note how the critical voltage behaves for small gaps, and compare with the curves of Figure 3.5. The behavior is entirely different, so uncritical use of Paschen curves can be misleading, since they imply that very large voltages are needed to cause current flow across small gaps. This is not true at pressures of 1 atm or greater, as other mechanisms, such as field emission and Schottky emission, take place at the cathode. For more information on the failure of Paschen's Law, see Alston (1968).

3.5   Nonuniform Electric Field Geometry: The Electrical Corona

The basic physics of electron avalanching and gaseous conduction has been given for the situation where the electric field does not change much from place to place. *Uniform fields*, therefore, lead to very rapid (microseconds) exponential

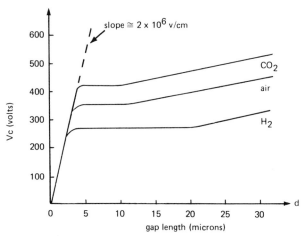

Figure 3.6   Critical voltage for small gaps at $p = 760$ torr. The electrodes are Pt. The spark potential is independent of the gas for a very small gap length (d). From Schaffert (1975).

growth of impact ionization throughout the volume from cathode to anode. This is called a "spark." The spark occurs because ion production is strongly field dependent, and in uniform fields, ionization spreads throughout the gas volume. If the field electrodes are highly asymmetrical, such as a thin wire or a point over a flat plane, the field is much larger at the wire or point than at the plane. In this highly *nonuniform field*, ionization is limited to the gas volume over

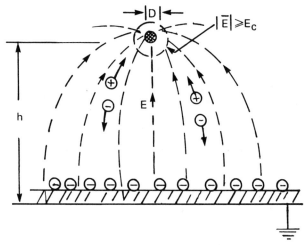

Figure 3.7   Example of highly nonuniform electric field. If $h \gg D$, an electric corona discharge occurs (before sparking). For $h \sim D$, or less, spark discharge occurs (before sustained corona can occur).

which the field exceeds the critical value E_c, as shown pictorially in Figure 3.7, and *corona discharge* is produced around the high field electrode. The physics of corona and spark do not differ substantially; each has the same basic requirements for primary or trigger electrons and secondary ionization mechanisms that lead to self-sustaining discharges. In corona discharge, the volume of ionization increases and penetrates further into the gap between electrodes as the potential increases. The ionization volume continues to increase until the gap is filled, at which point a spark occurs.

3.6   The Negative Corona

With negative potential at the high field electrode, corona starts in isolated spots scattered at random over the wire or point surface; the corona current at any given spot comes in short bursts called Trichel pulses. Loeb (1965), who named this pulse after his student G. W. Trichel, discusses it in detail. The negative electrode repels trigger electrons, which rapidly accelerate to velocities sufficient to ionize the gas in a limited region. As the trigger electrons proceed into the low field region, they can attach to any electronegative gas molecules present. After attachment occurs, the negative ions drift and are collected at the anode. A positive space charge of large, relatively slow moving ions surrounds the negative point or wire after the highly mobile electrons have moved toward the anode. The positive space charge shields the negative electrode, thereby reducing the net electric field beneath the critical value for corona. As the positive ions bombard the cathode, more trigger electrons are created to repeat the ionization burst or Trichel pulse. The pulse lasts about 20 nsec and has a maximum repetition rate of roughly 10^6 pulses per sec at a pressure of 760 torr. In very pure H_2, A, and N_2 Trichel pulses do not occur. The presence of very small quantities of O_2 or other electronegative gas (about 0.1 % by volume), changes the behavior radically and Trichel pulses develop. Also, small quantities of electronegative gases increase the magnitude of the critical field (E_c) and significantly reduce the current flow at fields exceeding E_c. Qualitatively, the pulse behavior can be understood by comparing the mobility of free electrons with that of positive ions. Electrons travel at about 2×10^7 cm/sec before they attach to electronegative gases, whereas positive ions travel at roughly 5×10^4 cm/sec (which is approximately equal to the average thermal velocity of neutral molecules). As the positive ion space charge is absorbed by the cathode, and the cloud of attached electrons recedes toward the anode, the space charge fields dissipate and the pulse repeats.

The negative corona is in general less uniform along a wire than the positive corona. With increasing negative potential, the number of isolated spots increases in proportion to the amount of current flowing. These spots are visible, as the ionization process creates radiation in the blue to UV wavelengths. Negative corona spots repel each other electrostatically, so at high currents the spacing between spots becomes stable and uniform. High electron emission is associated with the negative corona spot; this may be due to small differences in the secondary ionization coefficient (γ) along the wire. Positive ion bombardment and UV photoelectron mechanisms are dominant in the negative γ-ionization process. White (1963, p. 85) discusses negative corona stability and the implications for operation of electrostatic precipitators. Total corona current is quite sensitive to gas composition, and stable negative emission is possible only with gases or mixtures of gases that attach electrons (e.g., O_2, CO_2, H_2O, SO_2, CCl_2F_2, SF_6). Pure nitrogen, hydrogen, and argon tend to go directly to a power arc, instead of forming a stable negative corona. Loeb (1965) emphasizes the importance of gas purity; many studies have been done with impure gases and the results claimed for nitrogen, for example, were in actuality due to the presence of O_2 or CO_2.

When energetic positive ions bombard the cathode, some of the cathode material sputters away, in proportion to the current density. Sputtering is therefore confined to the corona spot and the process naturally changes the cathode surface chemistry, especially if the surface is initially contaminated, oxidized, or is reactive to the impinging gas. With new corona wires or points, the spots move around somewhat at first use; however, with continued use, the sputtering process enhances secondary emission. At 760 torr, the average energy of ions arriving at the high field cathode is about 10 eV (Loeb 1965, p. 309). The negative ions arriving at the anode have been studied by Shahin (1969) and by Gardiner and Craggs (1978). In air at 760 torr, about 90% of the charge carriers are CO_3^- ions, with the remainder composed of $CO_3^-(H_2O)$, $O^-(H_2O)$, and $O_3^-(H_2O)$ ions.

Davidson (1978) and Frank et al. (1974) discuss the generation of ozone in negative coronas. Some of the electrical energy is converted into acoustic energy, as an audible hissing accompanies the onset of current flow. Uman et al. (1968) studied the energy dissipated in large sparks and concluded that a major fraction of the input energy is converted into an acoustic shock wave.

3.7 The Positive Corona

A thin wire at positive voltages attracts trigger electrons from the surrounding gas, and the avalanche of electrons is collected at the wire. A uniform glow is characteristic of the positive corona, and the UV portion of this glow replenishes the primary electrons by photoionization of the gas. The wire anode does not participate in the secondary ionization process, so the current density is much more uniform along the length of the wire when compared with the negative corona case. Therefore, the positive corona depends on the gas only, and the electrode (anode) serves merely as a collector of charge. Positive ions drift from high to low field and are collected at the cathode. Shahin (1966) studied the ion species for N_2, O_2 and air, with controls placed on the water content of these gases. He found that $(H_2O)_n H^+$ ion clusters dominated the positive corona, with n ranging from 8 to 4 as the water content varied from 0.6

to about 0.1 mole % (20% relative humidity at room temperature is equivalent to about 0.65 mole %). The hydrated proton dominates in air corona until the water content is less than 0.1 mole %; at this point, $(H_2O)_nNO^+$ and $(H_2O)_nNO_2^+$ ions begin to appear. Small amounts of ozone are also present in the positive corona, although the quantity is about a factor of 10 less than with the negative corona.

3.8   Various Phenomena Associated With Corona Discharge

White (1963, p. 87) states that the positive corona is more sensitive to spark-over than the negative, so almost without exception, the electrostatic precipitator industry uses negative corona. The negative spark-over voltage is nearly twice the positive value. This difference is explained by the "streamer" theory of Loeb and Meek (1941). Positive and negative coronas each emit visible and UV radiations. In air, the emission spectrum is due to excited nitrogen molecules, according to Loeb (1965, p. 234). Figure 3.8, from the work of Gallo et al. (1967), is a facsimile of the corona emission spectra. The integrated intensity over the spectrum is estimated at 1.7×10^{-8} W/cm^2 for positive wires and about 10×10^{-8} W/cm^2 for negative. Gallo et al. (1969) studied the effect of humidity and temperature with wire-to-plane coronas. With increasing relative humidity, the effect of electron and ion hydration was observed as a reduction in current at fixed potential, positive or negative. Variations in temperature and absolute relative humidity had little influence on corona current. Uniformity of emission current was also studied as a function of relative humidity; the negative corona uniformity depended on water adsorption to the wire surface, whereas positive corona showed no such effect.

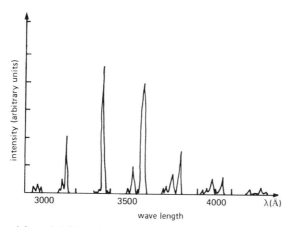

Figure 3.8   Ultraviolet and visible emission spectra for positive and negative corona. The intensity from negative wire is about $6X$ that from positive wire. From Gallo et al. (1967).

Loeb (1965, p. 402) discusses the electrical wind associated with corona discharge. The phenomenon has been known since the late 1600s. A sharp point giving about 100 μA of corona current will blow out a candle at a distance of 1 cm. The gas ions gain momentum from the electric field and collide inelastically with neutral ions; the net wind velocity resulting from this momentum exchange is small (~ 10 cm/sec) compared with ionic drift velocities (5×10^4 cm/sec). Conservation of mass considerations indicate that the electrical wind must lead to gas circulation.

Direct current corona wires exhibit sustained vibrations at frequencies other than the natural resonance in the absence of corona. Wire vibration can reach amplitudes that lead to spark-over of the device if ground electrodes are close to the wire. In practice, vibrations are suppressed by appropriate damping. Davis (1977) discusses a mechanism involving modulation of the electrostatic energy stored in the space charge surrounding the wire as a possible explanation of wire vibration. He rejects modulation of the electrical wind as an explanation, since he states the wind velocity is much too small to drive the wire.

Alternating current corona and impulsive discharges like the Trichel pulse generate radio frequency interferences. Positive corona has no sudden bursts of current and is essentially free of these interferences. The time rate of change of current in Trichel pulses is 10^6–10^7 A/sec, according to Loeb (1965, p. 572), and the resultant electromagnetic fields radiate in the radio frequency spectrum.

As mentioned in the discussion of negative corona, positive ions bombard the cathode at energies on the order of 10 eV, so the cathode material is sputtered away with time. This leads to roughening of an initially smooth surface and to deposition of the sputtered material onto surrounding surfaces. It is therefore necessary to periodically replace negative corona wires, and to clean sputtered metal from surfaces requiring good insulating properties (i.e., the insulating supports for the wires).

Corona also generates corrosive chemicals and conductive salts from airborne molecules, so it is usually necessary to filter the air supply to eliminate unwanted by-products. Ammonia is converted into ammonium nitrate, for example, and this salt is conductive at high humidities.

FOUR

CORONA DEVICES
IN XEROGRAPHY

The physics of corona discharge is reviewed in Chapter 3. In this chapter, corona devices found in xerographic printers and coper–duplicators are treated. Other than the references already cited, additional information on corona devices and applications can be found in the literature on electrostatic precipitation. Oglesby and Nichols (undated) prepared a manual of this technology. Moore (1973) edited a book on applications of electrostatics in which a chapter covers electrostatic precipitators. Each year, the IEEE Industry Applications Society holds a conference offering papers on electrostatics, electrostatic precipitation, and electrophotography. A complete conference record of all papers is printed, and these records are a useful source of information on corona discharge devices.

4.1 The Coaxial Wire

The electric field existing between a long coaxial wire and a conducting cylinder is one of the simplest devices to analyze. Most of the references cited earlier discuss this geometry. In xerographic applications, corona devices are exploited as noncontacting charge injectors for depositing electrostatic charge onto PCs, toner particles, and paper. By necessity, the cylindrical conductor surrounding the wire must have an opening to allow corona ions to escape to the surface of interest. This opening or gap (as it is usually called) distorts the simple geometry of the coaxial wire and cylinder, but the distortion does not offer serious obstacles to a mathematical analysis. In some corona devices, the wire is mounted off-axis in the cylinder to improve the efficiency with which current

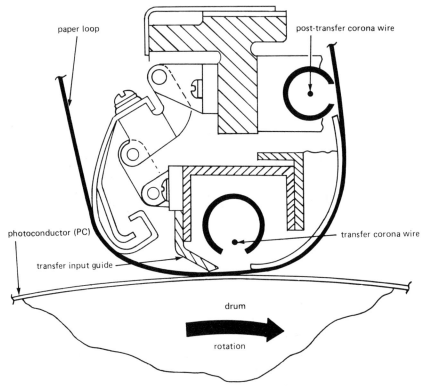

Figure 4.1   The transfer and posttransfer corona geometry of the 3800 printer. A portion of the corona ions flows to the cylinder around the wire, and a portion flows through the cylinder gap. Wire radius is 3.175×10^{-3} cm and cylinder radius is 0.82 cm for each device.

escapes through the gap. Cross sections of a transfer and a post transfer corona unit are shown in Figure 4.1; the function of these devices is discussed more fully in Chapter 10. The discussion in this chapter starts with the simplified geometry of concentric cylinders. The electric field caused by the potential of each conductor is found, then the space charge field of the corona current is accounted for, and a current–voltage relationship is derived and compared with experimental results.

Figure 4.2 is a sketch of concentric cylinders with radii a and b at potential V_a and V_b, respectively. The radius vector r goes from the axis toward the larger

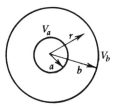

Figure 4.2   Coaxial cylinder geometry.

cylinder at $r = b$. Weber (1965, p. 147) gives the potential at all points between cylinders as

$$V(r) = V_a - (V_a - V_b) \frac{\log_e(r/a)}{\log_e(b/a)} \tag{4.1}$$

however, this neglects any effect arising from space charges. The electric field is the negative gradient of the potential.

$$E(r) = -\frac{\partial V}{\partial r} = \frac{V_a - V_b}{r \log_e(b/a)} \quad \text{for } a \leq r \leq b. \tag{4.2}$$

Equations (4.1) and (4.2) are solutions of Laplace's Equation, $\nabla^2 V = 0$, and are valid for voltages less than the critical value for field ionization, V_c. For V greater than V_c, current flows and a space charge accumulates in the region between conductors. Poisson's Equation $\nabla^2 V = -\rho/\varepsilon$ must be solved when the space charge density $\rho(\text{C/cm}^3)$ is significant. With uniform emission from the central wire, the space charge density per unit length is

$$\rho = \frac{i}{2\pi r \mu E} \quad (\text{C/cm/cm}^3) \tag{4.3}$$

The ion drift velocity away from the wire is $v = \mu E$ (cm/sec) where $\mu(\text{cm}^2/\text{V-sec})$ is the ion drift mobility, and i ($\text{A/cm}^2/\text{cm}$) is the corona current density per unit length of the wire. In cylindrical coordinates, Poisson's Equation is

$$\frac{\partial^2 V}{\partial r^2} + \frac{1}{r}\frac{\partial V}{\partial r} + \frac{\rho}{\varepsilon} = 0 \tag{4.4}$$

which can be written more compactly by recalling that $E = -\partial V/\partial r$. In terms of E, Poisson's Equation becomes

$$\frac{1}{r}\frac{\partial(rE)}{\partial r} = \frac{\rho}{\varepsilon} \tag{4.5}$$

which, by substituting (4.3) for ρ, and integrating for E yields

$$E = \left[\frac{i}{2\pi\varepsilon\mu} + \left(\frac{a}{r}\right)^2 \left(E_c^2 - \frac{i}{2\pi\varepsilon\mu}\right) \right]^{1/2} \tag{4.6}$$

where E_c is the critical field for breakdown at the wire surface. (For E less than E_c, the corona current density $i = 0$.) With $r = a$, $V_b = 0$, and $V_a = V_c$ the critical voltage, (4.2), becomes

$$E_c = \frac{V_c}{a \log_e(b/a)} \quad (\text{V/cm}) \tag{4.7}$$

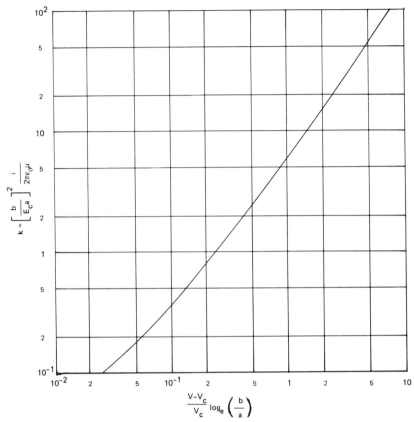

Figure 4.3   Solutions for Equation (4.10) in terms of dimensionless variables. The current–voltage relation is approximately correct for coaxial corona geometry. Adapted from Moore (1973). Copyright 1973, John Wiley & Sons.

Peek (1929) gives a useful semiempirical equation for the critical field.

$$E_c = 31\delta\left(1 + \frac{0.308}{\sqrt{\delta a}}\right) \quad (\text{kV/cm}) \tag{4.8}$$

where δ is the relative air density and a is the wire radius (cm). From Ogelsby and Nichols, $\delta = (T_0 P)/(T P_0) = 1.0$ when $T = T_0 = 293°\text{K}$ and $P = P_0 = 760$ torr. Thompson and Thompson (1969, Vol. 2, p. 550) give a brief derivation of the equation for E_c and show that Peek's result falls in line with those of about five other workers. For (a/r) small, (4.6) reduces to the approximation

$$E = \left(\frac{i}{2\pi\varepsilon_0 mu}\right)^{1/2} \tag{4.9}$$

which is roughly valid for well-developed current flow far beyond the critical level.

The current–voltage relation is found by integrating (4.6). The result, given by M. Robinson in Moore (1973, p. 190), is found by neglecting second-order terms.

$$\left(\frac{V - V_c}{V_c}\right) \log_e\left(\frac{b}{a}\right) = (1 + k)^{1/2} - 1 - \log_e\left[\frac{1 + (1 + k)^2}{2}\right] \quad (4.10)$$

The parameter k is defined as

$$k = \left(\frac{b}{E_c a}\right)^2 \frac{i}{2\pi\varepsilon_0 \mu} \quad \text{(dimensionless)} \quad (4.11)$$

A log–log plot of (4.10) is shown in Figure 4.3; the information is from M. Robinson in Moore (1973, p. 190).

Experimental results for positive and negative corona are given in Figure 4.4. The device was a transfer corona unit similar to that shown in Figure 4.1. The wire radius $a = 3.18 \times 10^{-3}$ cm and the outer cylinder radius $b = 0.82$ cm.

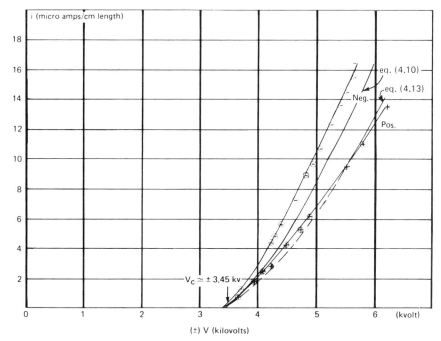

Figure 4.4 Comparison of experiment with Equations (4.10) and (4.13). For computation, an ion mobility of 1.4 cm²/V-sec was used, $a = 3.175 \times 10^{-3}$ cm, $b = 0.82$ cm, $E_c = 200.45$ kV/cm, and $V_c = 3.53$ kV. The wire is not coaxial with the cylinder; it is about 0.6 cm eccentric.

The wire is 0.6 cm ecentric. Using (4.8) with $\delta = 1.0$, the critical field is estimated to be 200 kV/cm, and solving (4.7) for V_c, one finds the critical voltage is about 3.5 kV. Experimentally, V_c is 3.45 kV for positive or negative wires; there is a small difference in V_c for different polarities, but it is less than the data point in Figure 4.4 can resolve. Agreement between theory and experiment is rather good, considering the relative simplicity of (4.7). The predicted current–voltage relationship shown in Figure 4.4 was computed with (4.10) and (4.11). The data in (4.3) were used to find solutions of (4.10).

It is necessary to know the ion drift mobility to find the current per unit length of the wire.

$$i = 2\pi\varepsilon\mu\left(\frac{E_c a}{b}\right)^2 k \quad \text{(A/cm)} \tag{4.12}$$

In Figure 4.4, $\mu = 1.4$ cm^2/V-sec, where the experiments were done in normal laboratory air. White (1963, p. 94) uses 2.2 cm^2/V-sec and Moore (1973, p. 190) uses 2.1 cm^2/V-sec for dry air at standard temperature and pressure; however, they are concerned only with negative coronas for electrostatic precipitation, where the relevant mobility is that of O_2^-. In view of Shahin's work (1966, 1969) showing predominantly CO_3^- ions for negative corona and hydrated protons for positive corona, the size of these ions is larger than the O_2^- ion, so the mobility ought to be reduced. This argument may explain the reduced emission current of the positive corona relative to the negative case. A mobility of 1.4 cm^2/V-sec was chosen to place the computed curve midway between the positive and negative experimental curves. The simple theoretical equations do not include a polarity dependence. With a mobility of 2.2 cm^2/V-sec, the computed curve moves slightly above the negative corona data, but the agreement is still rather good.

In 1915, Townsend worked out a simplified version of (4.10) that is valid at low current/cm for voltages near V_c, and for pressures not far from the normal value 760 torr.

$$i = V(V - V_c)\left[\frac{8\pi\varepsilon\mu}{b^2 \log_e(b/a)}\right] \tag{4.13}$$

By ignoring the logarithmic term on the right-hand side of (4.10), a current–voltage relation for moderate currents/cm and voltages is given by White (1963, p. 95) as

$$i = \frac{4\pi\varepsilon\mu}{b^2}\left[(V - V_c)^2 + \frac{(V - V_c)V_c}{\log_e(b/a)}\right] \tag{4.14}$$

At high currents/cm at $p = 760$ torr, White (1963) gives another useful approximation for the current/cm.

$$i = \frac{2\pi\varepsilon\mu}{b^2}\left(V - aE_c \log_e \frac{b}{12a}\right)^2 \tag{4.15}$$

Equation (4.13) is plotted on Figure 4.4 with the same values as used in (4.10). Once again, the agreement is reasonable.

4.2   The Corotron

In xerographic processes, the charging current must be uniform across the width of the PC or paper, and it must be reasonably stable under a variety of environmental conditions. Corona from a bare wire suspended above a PC would indeed charge the PC surface, but such a simple device suffers from emission nonuniformities; therefore, it has a tendency to overcharge the PC in some regions and undercharge it in others. The *corotron* (see Vyverberg, 1958) was invented to solve the problems encountered with bare corona wires and nonuniform charging.

In essence, the corotron is a corona wire having an auxiliary electrode either above or around the wire to define the electrostatic field geometry and potentials in a controlled manner. Figure 4.5 shows cross sections of a variety of corotrons. This device is also discussed in Schaffert (1975) and in Dessauer and Clark (1965). Springett et al. (1977) modelled the corotron numerically and showed how the total emission current divides between the auxiliary electrode (or shield) and the ground plane. Figures 4.6 and 4.7 are drawn using data from their paper. Since the corotron is used as a current injector, the efficiency is rather low if the wrap angle of the shield is large (i.e., small gap) or if the wire is located too far from the gap opening; moving the wire close to

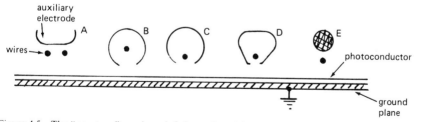

Figure 4.5   The "corotron" can have infinite variety. The wire is usually at very high potential (~ 6 kV) and the auxiliary electrode at very low (or ground) potential. A, B, C, D, and E are each called a "corotron."

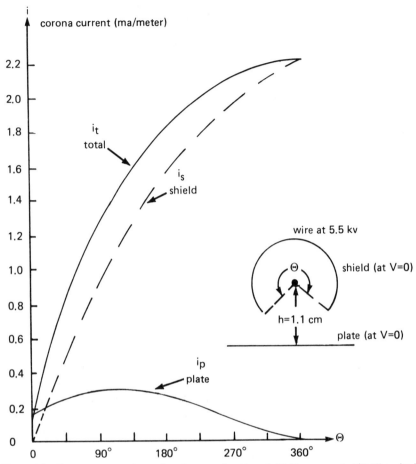

Figure 4.6   Corotron current into a flat plate as a function of shield wrap angle (Θ). The wire is about 50 μm diameter at 5.5 kV; curves are theoretical. From Springett et al. (1977). Reprinted with permission.

the gap improves the injection efficiency. The shield may be biased to control the current passing through the opening. The electric field in the vicinity of the slot is then partly due to the bias potential and partly to the space charge density of the corona current. The effect of shield bias is seen in the data given in Figure 4.8; the slot behaves as a focusing electrode, and increased bias voltage narrows the emission profiles accordingly. The unpublished data are from W. Larson of IBM Corporation.

Wire eccentricity does not alter the form of the current–voltage relation; (4.13) yields reasonable agreement with experimental results from corotrons

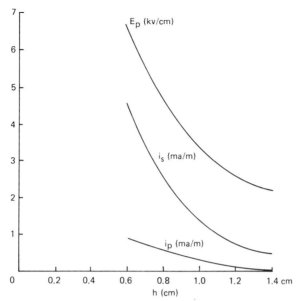

Figure 4.7   Plot of electric field (E_p) at the plate under the wire, shield current/m (i_s), and plate current/m as a function of wire height (h) above plate. Wrap angle Θ is presumably about 90°. Shield and plate at ground, wire at 5.5 kV. From Springett et al. (1977). Reprinted with permission.

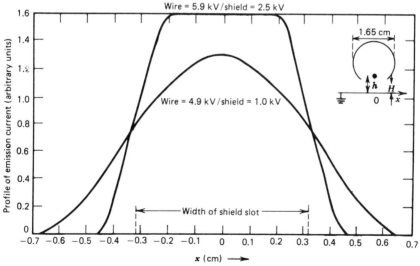

Figure 4.8   Emission current profile of the 3800 transfer corotron. The shield behaves as an electrostatic lens and focuses current flow. The total plate current is about 2.5 μA/cm length in both cases. Wire radius is 3.175×10^{-3} cm ($h \cong 0.8$ cm, $H \cong 0.6$ cm). Unpublished results from W. Larson, IBM Corporation.

like that shown in Figure 4.8, where the eccentricity is about 0.6 cm. Schaffert (1975, p. 237) represents the charging current of a corotron by

$$i_p = AV(V - V_c) \qquad (4.16)$$

where A is a function of the geometry and the ion mobility. With coaxial geometry and no emission slot, A is given by the coefficient in (4.13). Usually, the constant of proportionality between current and voltage is found experimentally. Device characterization is most often done with the device mounted over a metal plate which can be biased to the desired potential. Current flow into the plate (i_p) is a function of the plate (or PC) potential (V_p). The relation for i_p is then modified to account for the increase in surface potential of a PC as it charges up.

$$i_p = A(V - V_p)(V - V_p - V_c) \quad \text{(A/cm)} \qquad (4.17)$$

Current flow to the PC surface diminishes as V_p approaches the wire potential V. In practice, the PC moves at constant velocity past the corotron and the change in V_p caused by the adsorbed corona ions is a small fraction of the wire potential (i.e., $V_p \cong \pm 700$ V and $V \cong +7$ kV). The surface charge density deposited at the PC surface is

$$\sigma = \frac{i_p}{v_{PC}} \quad \text{(C/cm}^2) \qquad (4.18)$$

where v_{PC} is the surface velocity (cm/sec) of the PC. The change in PC potential resulting from this surface charge density is found using (2.5).

$$\Delta V_p = \left(\frac{\sigma}{\varepsilon}\right)d \quad \text{(V)} \qquad (4.19)$$

where d (cm) and ε (C/V-cm) are the PC thickness and permittivity, respectively.

4.3   The Scorotron

The emission uniformity along a corona wire depends on the wire polarity; uniformity is good for positive wires and quite poor for negative wires. This subject is discussed in depth in Chapter 3. Typical emission profiles along a wire are sketched in Figure 4.9. A PC moving at constant velocity would receive nonuniform charge density from a single negative wire, and the variations in surface potential would create objectionable streaking of the developed image. Uniform surface charge density is a prerequisite for good quality printing and copying, and the *scorotron*, invented at Batelle Memorial Institute, was developed to solve the problem of charging a PC with uniform negative potential

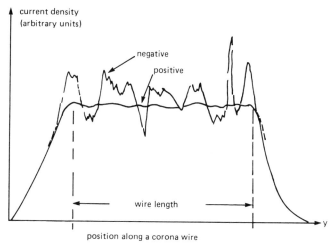

Figure 4.9 Typical emission profiles of positive and negative corona wires along the length of the wire.

(Figure 4.10). The scorotron is composed of a series of corona wires with a screen of larger diameter wires placed between the corona and the PC surface. The screen wires are biased to a potential close to that desired at the PC. Scorotron geometry can have great variety; Dessauer and Clark (1965, p. 205) show a "backing plate" above three corona wires with 15 screen wires placed halfway between the PC and the corona wires. Tateishi and Hoshino (1981) describe control of corona current uniformity by a mesh grid. Schaffert (1975, p. 710) lists over 130 patents on PC charging devices (issued through October 1972).

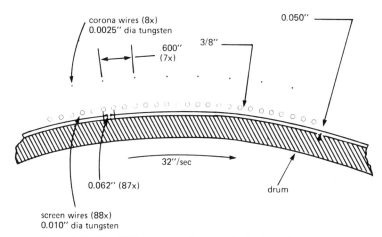

Figure 4.10 The 3800 scorotron. From W. Banks, IBM Corporation.

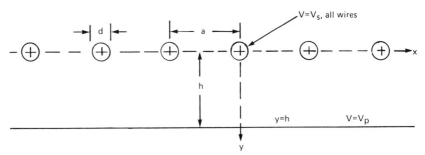

Figure 4.11   The Maxwell grating. An infinite array of parallel coplanar wires of diameter d, equispaced a distance $\Delta x = a$ between centers. The array is at a height h from an equipotential plane ($V = V_p$). All wires are at potential $V = V_s$.

The screen of the scorotron functions analogously to the control grid of a vacuum tube triode. It is a Maxwell Grating, so named after J. C. Maxwell who described and analyzed such a structure in his treatise on electricity. (See Maxwell, 1954, Vol. 1, p. 310). Weber (1965, p. 291) also treats this structure and discusses applications of his analysis. Let the grating lie in the x-z plane and let the y-direction be normal to this plane. The wires are equispaced at a distance $x = a$ between centers, and each wire diameter is d. The grating is a distance $y = h$ from a plane at potential $V = V_p$, and all wires are at the screen potential $V = V_s$. This geometry is given in Figure 4.11. When h is about equal to a or

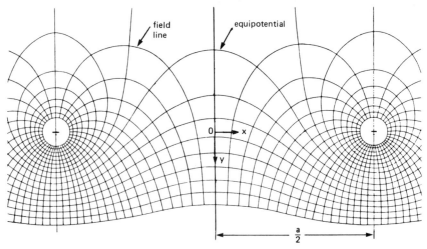

Figure 4.12   Equipotential and field lines near a Maxwell grating. At $y \cong a$, the equipotentials are nearly flat, so the grating appears as a flat continuous plane, and the field is nearly uniform and vertical. The drawing is adapted from Maxwell (1954).

greater, the vertical component of the electric field E_y is approximately given by

$$E_y = \frac{V_s - V_p}{h + (a/2\pi)\log_e(a/\pi d)} \left[\frac{1 - e^{-2\pi y/a}\cos(2\pi x/a)}{1 + e^{-4\pi y/a} - 2e^{-2\pi y/a}\cos(2\pi x/a)} \right] \quad (4.20)$$

This relation ignores space charge effects, but is useful for estimating E_y in the region around, but not including, the wires. At a distance $y = a$ the field is almost uniform, since $\exp(-2\pi) \cong 0.002$, so the grating appears as an equipotential plane at or beyond this distance (Fig. 4.12). This is also true of E_x, although no equations are given here. Ions drift under the influence of the electric field, so a portion will be attracted to the screen wires, with the remainder bypassing the screen to deposit on the plane at $V = V_p$. If the grating is very close to a conducting plane, the effect of that plane must be included to correctly determine the total electric field. This is easily done by the "method of images," a technique treated in most standard texts on field analysis. The ion trajectory around screen wires is best treated by examining the electric field in the vicinity of an isolated wire, including the image of that wire in the ground plane that lies beneath the PC.

4.4 The Isolated Wire and Plane

The electric field of a wire close to a conducting plane is found by replacing the plane with a mirror image of the wire; the image is located an equal distance beneath the location of the plane, and the polarity of the image is reversed. If space charges are present, they can be treated in the same manner. The total potential of the system is the sum of the positive and negative contributions of the two lines or wires. Attwood (1967) discusses the method of images, and his approach is used here. The geometry is defined in Figure 4.13. The potential of a line charge of linear density λ (C/cm) is logarithmic, so the total potential of two lines with opposite polarity is

$$V_t = \frac{\lambda}{2\pi\varepsilon} \log_e \frac{h}{r_1} - \frac{\lambda}{2\pi\varepsilon} \log_e \frac{h}{r_2} = \frac{\lambda}{2\pi\varepsilon} \log_e \frac{r_2}{r_1} \quad (4.21)$$

where r_1 and r_2 are the distances from the center of influence of each wire to a given field point. If the wires are very small, they can be treated as mathematical line charges, and the center of influence coincides with the wire's center. For large diameter wires, the center of influence is off-axis, and the distance h from the ground plane is given by (4.22).

$$h = \left[\left(\frac{D}{2}\right)^2 - R_1^2 \right]^{1/2} \quad (4.22)$$

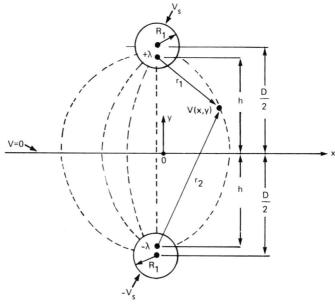

Figure 4.13 Isolated wire and ground plane ($V = 0$). The method of images replaces the plane with another line of opposite polarity at a distance h below the plane.

It is convenient here to write (4.21) in terms of the wire potential V_s instead of the linear charge density. The coefficient defining V_t and the distances r_1 and r_2 to each wire surface are easily found, and (4.21) becomes

$$V_t = \frac{V_s \log_e(r_2/r_1)}{\log_e \dfrac{h + D/2 - R_1}{h - D/2 + R_1}} \tag{4.23}$$

In Cartesian coordinates, $r_1^2 = x^2 + (y - h)^2$ and $r_2^2 = x^2 + (y + h)^2$. The x and y components of the electric field are obtained by differentiation of the total potential V_t; $E_x = -dV_t/dx$ and $E_y = -dV_t/dy$.

$$E_x = \frac{V_s}{\log_e \dfrac{h + D/2 - R_1}{h - D/2 + R_1}} \left[\frac{x}{x^2 + (y - h)^2} - \frac{x}{x^2 + (y + h)^2} \right] \tag{4.24}$$

$$E_y = \frac{V_s}{\log_e \dfrac{h + D/2 - R_1}{h - D/2 + R_1}} \left[\frac{(y - h)}{x^2 + (y - h)^2} - \frac{(y + h)}{x^2 + (y + h)^2} \right] \tag{4.25}$$

Since fields linearly superimpose, a series of isolated lines can be summed algebraically to yield the total electric field. The approximation given in (4.20) is the sum of an infinite series of lines, each of the same polarity. Equation (4.24) and (4.25) are valid for all space above the conducting plane, not including the region occupied by the wire. The solutions are good at the wire surface, if space charge effects are small. The second term in (4.24) and (4.25) results from the image of the wire in the ground plane.

Some numerical examples will help make these concepts more specific. Let the screen voltage $V_s = -750$ V and place a wire of diameter 0.0127 cm (5 mils) a distance $D/2 = 0.127$ cm (50 mils) above a grounded metal plane. Using (4.22), the center of influence is $h = 0.126$ cm from the plane. At $x = y = 0$, the vertical component of the field is

$$E_y(0, 0) = \frac{V_s}{\log_e \dfrac{h + D/2 - R_1}{h - D/2 + R_1}} \left[\frac{-2h}{(h)^2} \right] = \frac{-750 \text{ V}}{\log_e(19.94)} \left(\frac{-2}{0.126 \text{ cm}} \right) \cong 3.98 \text{ kV/cm} \tag{4.26}$$

If one ignores the center of influence eccentricity (i.e., $h = D/2$), then $E_y(0, 0) = 4.01$ kV/cm. This is an error of about 1% for the given wire size. The positive field computed here indicates that a negative ion would move to the plane defined at $y = 0$. If an insulating layer is placed over the ground plane, the ion will be trapped at its surface and the potential will become increasingly negative as ions accumulate. The level of charge density at which $E_y(0, 0)$ vanishes is easily computed, and (4.25) can be modified to account for a surface potential other than zero.

At the wire surface ($x = 0$, $y = h - R_1$), the electric field is

$$E_y(0, h - R_1) \cong \frac{V_s}{\log_e \dfrac{h + D/2 - R_1}{h - D/2 + R_1}} \left(\frac{-1}{R_1} - \frac{1}{2h} \right) \cong 20.7 \text{ kV/cm} \tag{4.27}$$

A field of 20 kV/cm is fairly large, so the wire will attract negative ions readily. In a scorotron like that shown in Figure 4.10, the screen attracts about 70% of the total corona current (W. Banks of IBM Corporation, private communication).

Gallo and Lama (1971) discuss the lateral distribution of current from wire to plane coronas and find their data are described by a relation like (4.25). As a first approximation, corona emission from a wire follows a Lorentzian profile. That is, the current flowing into the plane goes as $f(x) = K/(x^2 + h^2)$; $f(x)$ is a Lorentzian function and has a full width at half maximum $W = 2h$. Gallo and Lama (1971) find experimentally that $W = 1.4h$ and explain their result by accounting for field distortion arising from space charge effects.

The perpendicular field E_y given by (4.25) is the sum of Lorentzians. Normalized plots are given in Figure 4.14 at wire spacings $h = 0.5$, 1.0, and 2.0 with all curves computed at $y = 0$ (i.e., at the surface of the plane). Conservation of

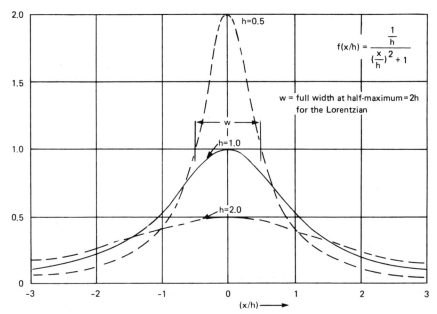

Figure 4.14 The Lorentzian profile of wire-to-wire corona emission. Experimentally, for a given distance (h) between wire and plane, $w \cong 1.4\,h$.

flux (or current) is implicit in the computed curves, since the area under the curves is constant. That is, all current flows to the ground plane for any spacing h. Mathematically, this is proven by integrating the Lorentzian over all x to find the area under a curve; the result is independent of h.

$$\int_{-\infty}^{\infty} \frac{h\,dx}{x^2 + h^2} = \tan^{-1}\left(\frac{x}{h}\right)\bigg|_{-\infty}^{\infty} = \pi \tag{4.28}$$

Much of the behavior of scorotrons and corotrons can be understood qualitatively by ignoring the additional electric field arising from the corona space charge. In Chapter 10, the electric field caused by space charge is included in an analysis of toner transfer using a corotron. Here, space charge distortion has been ignored because to include its effects would unnecessarily burden the analysis and the additional insight gained would be slight. A space charge free analysis gives enough insight to understand the motion of ions from corona wires toward screens and PC surfaces. With complicated geometry, it is usually necessary to use theory and experiment to create effective designs of corona devices.

The charging behavior of a scorotron is shown in Figure 4.15a and b. Photoconductor voltage vs. position is shown for a moving PC; the PC is initially

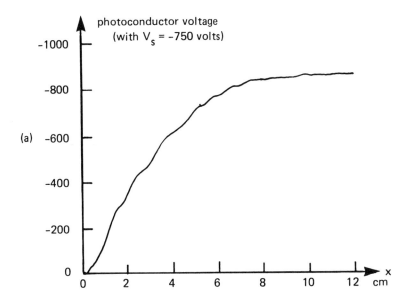

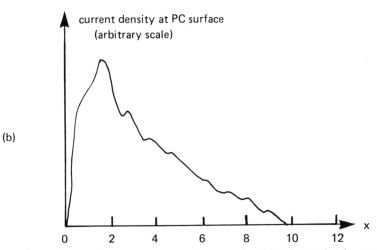

Figure 4.15 (a) Photoconductor voltage vs. position, as estimated by integrating the scorotron current density; (b) current density vs. position. The PC ground plane current for OPC is about −0.75 mA.

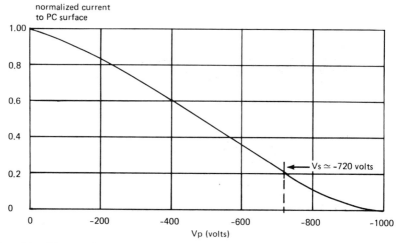

Figure 4.16 Photoconductor charging current vs. surface voltage (V_p) for the 3800 scorotron with screen potential $V_s = -720$ V. See Figure 4.10 for the geometry of the screen. Current flow is essentially cutoff at $V_p = -1000$ V. From W. Banks, IBM Corporation.

uncharged, so the charging current is high at first and then drops off as the surface potential increases. The screen potential is -750 V and the final voltage of the PC is about -850 V. The scorotron geometry is given in Figure 4.10; the screen wires are fairly close to the PC and are placed on centers somewhat greater than the wire–PC distance. This grating draws about 70% of the corona current. The effectiveness of the cutoff behavior of the screen is shown in Figure 4.16; current arriving at the PC approaches zero as the voltage approaches -1000 V for $V_s = -720$ V. The unpublished results are from W. Banks of IBM Corporation.

The current necessary to charge a PC can be estimated using (4.18) and (4.19). With wires 40 cm long, the current arriving at OPC 10 μm thick with $\varepsilon/\varepsilon_0 = 2.6$, would be

$$I_t = \frac{40 V_p \mathrm{v}_{PC} \varepsilon}{d} = (40 \text{ cm})(-850 \text{ V})(81 \text{ cm/sec})\frac{2.6\varepsilon_0}{10^{-3} \text{ cm}} = -634 \ \mu\text{A} \quad (4.29)$$

The experimental value of -700 μA includes leakage and photodischarge from corona wire radiation (see Figure 3.8). These effects apparently reduce the charging efficiency by about 10%. Charging uniformly is improved by using several wires, since the emission node structure of a given wire is uncorrelated with other wires. As the PC travels under a succession of charging wires, the surface charge density smooths out considerably. Emission profiles of four negative wires are shown in Figure 4.17, where each curve is offset for clarity of presentation.

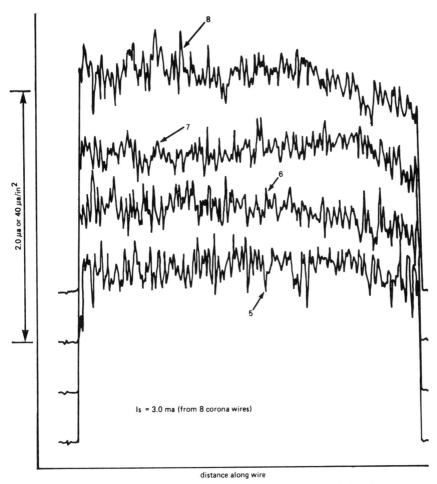

Figure 4.17 Emission profile along four negative corona wires. From W. Banks, IBM Corporation.

4.5 Corona and the Environment

Normally, the atmosphere contains nitrogen, oxygen, oil vapors, Freon, salt crystals, dust, auto emissions, and a wide variety of elements and other chemicals. This air is ionized by the corona devices used in xerographic machines, so the possibility of interesting chemistry and crystal growth on and around corona wires is not surprising. Corona in air generates fair quantities of ozone, so most commercial devices include activated charcoal filters to reduce ozone to acceptable levels.

Ammonium nitrate salts can be created and precipitated by corona devices if the air contains NH_4 at levels around 50 parts per billion. The salt crystallizes and grows on screen wires as well as on the PC surface. At high humidity, these salts become conductive and image quality is degraded because surface charge is transported laterally. Commercial products are readily available for filtering the incoming air.

Airborne dust particles contaminate xerographic systems, especially in the regions where corona devices charge the dust particles. In this aspect, the charging units for the PCs (i.e., scorotrons) are effective electrostatic precipitators, and dust collects on the screen wires. Periodic cleaning of corona devices is a normal part of machine maintenance procedure.

Information on problems and solutions to corona devices is found in the literature on electrostatic precipitators. White (1963) and Ogelsby and Nichols (undated) are useful entry points. Robinson and Robbins (1968) should be consulted for information on atmospheric pollutants.

FIVE

IMAGE EXPOSURE

Electrophotographic printing and document copying are examples of high-contrast image-forming processes. For normal printed text and line drawings, good contrast between background regions and the developed image is desired. Continuous tone reproduction of photographs is possible with some copiers. A PC must be uniformly charged and its surface cleaned of light-absorbing material before the image is exposed; otherwise, unwanted variations in surface voltage of the PC produce electrostatic fields that attract or repel charged toner at undesired locations, and the image quality is degraded. In the image exposure process, PC voltage is selectively altered in proportion to the number of photons absorbed in the charge generation material, and the variations in surface potential lead to variations of electric field in a controlled manner. The purpose of Chapters 5 and 6 is to discuss the relationship between electrostatic fields and the quantity of photons per unit area absorbed by the charged PC. This chapter discusses the exposure per se, and lays the quantitative basis for computing the exposure energy per unit area and the resultant variations in surface potential of a PC. The electrostatic field at and above the PC surface is treated in Chapter 6.

Some laser printers, such as the Siemens ND2 and the IBM 3800, use two methods for PC exposure; the raster scanning laser beam produces characters as a contiguous series of lines and spots, whereas an auxiliary xenon flash lamp produces images of a negative transparency containing fixed images (e.g., on a business form). Other laser printers, such as the Xerox 9700 and the Hewlett-Packard 2680, use laser exposure only, and all fixed information is entered electronically along with the variable information coming from the central processing unit.

Document copiers expose the PC by reflecting light from the original document onto a charged PC. In some high-speed machines, the PC moves on either a drum or a web and the document is scanned by mirrors and other optics onto the PC. In some low-speed machines, the document is moved over a fixed PC. The source of illumination is quite often a tungsten or tungsten–halogen incandescent lamp; some high-speed copiers use a xenon flash lamp for image exposure. The spectral reflectance of papers varies widely; normal xerographic quality white paper reflects perhaps 70 % or more of the visible wavelengths of light. The reflectance of inks also varies widely, depending on color and so forth. The final image of fused toner coming from a high quality machine might reflect 5 % or less of the light energy at visible wavelengths. To cope successfully with a wide variety of inks and papers, office copiers must use broadband illumination sources along with PCs having good electrophotographic behavior over the visible spectrum.

To understand xerographic exposure requirements, it is necessary to comprehend the electric field prerequisites for attaching the desired amount of toner to the PC surface. The discussion necessarily turns to the exposure energy profiles that generate the desired variations in surface potential. Flash exposure, exposure energy, contrast voltage, and voltage transitions between dark and light regions are first introduced, then the discussion proceeds to a quantitative analysis of laser beam exposure.

5.1 Flash Exposure Through a Negative Transparency

A xenon flash tube, collimating lens, negative transparency, and PC plane are shown in Figure 5.1. The effective diameter of the flash source is D, the distance from source to PC plane is d, and h is the distance between the negative transparency and the PC. For simplicity, assume that the transmittance of the negative goes from complete absorption ($T = 0$) to complete transmission ($T = 1.0$) of the light energy from the flash tube. The transition from dark to light at the PC surface is not abrupt at the microscopic level, since the negative transparency contains a gradual transition in optical density and the illuminating source is spread out somewhat. If the negative is very sharp relative to the distances D, d, and h, then the transition length L from dark to light would be given approximately by

$$L \cong \frac{D}{d} h \quad (\text{cm}) \tag{5.1}$$

In the analysis of image exposure, dark–light transition length is a key idea. This length, along with the value of contrast voltage (see Chapter 2), determines the magnitude of the electric field in the neighborhood of an image edge. This concept is treated in more depth in Chapter 6.

The exposure energy/cm^2, or more simply, the *exposure*, is defined as

$$E = \int_0^t I(t)dt \quad (\text{J/cm}^2) \tag{5.2}$$

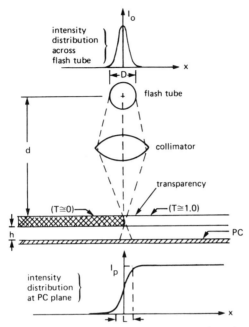

Figure 5.1   Simplified optical system of the 3800 flash exposure station. The transition from dark to light is not abrupt.

$I(t)$ (W/cm^2) is the light intensity as a function of time (in seconds). Intensity is easy to compute with monochromatic radiation such as that from a laser. The light spectrum is much more complicated with sources like the xenon flash tube; Figure 5.2 shows the emission spectrum of a xenon tube. It is composed of a discrete line spectrum superimposed on a continuous radiation spectrum. One can measure the broadband intensity with an appropriately calibrated silicon photodiode. The flash duration for xenon flash tubes depends on the external circuitry; pulses of about 50 μsec are not usual, and the output of a photodiode can be integrated electronically to give the exposure (in J/cm^2 or ergs/cm^2) directly.

The amount of voltage decay attained for a given exposure is found with (2.11). Assume, for example, that OPC receives a flash exposure of $E = 5.0 \, \mu$J/cm^2 (50 ergs/cm^2); OPC is discussed in Chapter 2, where it is shown that this PC has good response over the visible spectrum. The energy constant $E_a = 31.5$ ergs/cm^2 and $V_{sat} = 0$ are given in Figure 2.12. If the dark voltage $V_D = -750$ V, then the light voltage V_L is found with the empirical relation (2.11) $V_L = V_{sat} + (V_D - V_{sat})\exp(-E/E_a) = -750 \exp(-50/31.5) = -153$ V. The contrast voltage $V = V_L - V_D = 597$ V. The exposure profile near a dark–light transition will not change as a step function; if the negative transparency is in intimate contact with the PC, the projected edge will be much sharper, but ultimately the

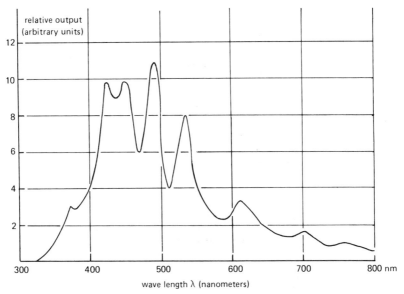

Figure 5.2   Emission spectrum of a xenon flash tube. (Bausch and Lomb monochromator with RCA type 4832 photo multiplier tube.)

edge sharpness will be limited by the spread function of the photographic emulsion itself.

Mees and James (1966) discuss the imagery of lines, points, and edges. Spread functions are also discussed in Biberman (1973) and in Klein (1970). Goodman (1968) treats image formation from a linear systems approach. It is useful to characterize a dark to light transition by some mathematical function that is smooth, continuous, well-behaved, and uncomplicated. The arctangent, hyperbolic tangent, error function, and so forth have great utility for describing transitions from one level to another. The arctangent function is simple and its derivative is a rational algebraic function, so it is particularly useful for approximating the edge transition between dark (V_D) and light (V_L) voltages at the PC surface. The arctangent transition is introduced here, but a full discussion and analysis of electric fields is deferred to Chapter 6. A non-abrupt change in voltage vs. position can be written as

$$V(x) = V_1 + \frac{2V_2}{\pi} \tan^{-1}\left(\frac{x}{a}\right) \quad (V) \qquad (5.3)$$

where a is a parameter defining the sharpness of the transition. If a is extremely small, the transition approaches a step function. Potter (1970) successfully used this function as a description for magnetization transitions in magnetic recording films, and Williams (1982) followed his lead when applying the arctangent to voltage transitions on PCs. A sketch of (5.3) is given in Figure 5.3.

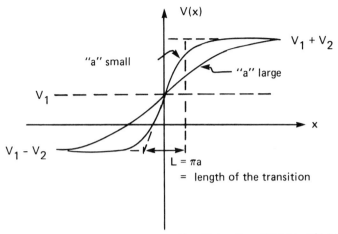

Figure 5.3 The isolated arctangent transition $V(x) = V_1 + (2V_2/\pi) \tan^{-1}(x/a)$.

Here a has the dimension of length (cm), and the length L of this smooth and asymptotic transition can be defined as the equivalent length of a ramp transition whose slope at the center of the transition is equal to the slope of the arctangent transition. This being the case, $L = \pi a$ (cm).

An image edge is formed by one transition from dark to light voltage and an image line is formed by a transition pair. This corresponds to a dark–light–dark variation in a negative transparency placed over a PC, or to the sweep of a scanning laser beam. The voltage transition pair or line is written mathematically as

$$V(x) = V_D + V_c\left[\tan^{-1}\left(\frac{x + W}{a}\right) - \tan^{-1}\left(\frac{x - W}{a}\right)\right]$$

where

$$V_c = \frac{1/2(V_L - V_D)}{\tan^{-1}(W/a)} \quad (V) \tag{5.4}$$

Figure 5.4 is a sketch of $V(x)$ for the line image. The dark and light voltages, V_D and V_L, the line half-width, W, and the transition parameter, a, can be independently adjusted to synthesize a variety of lines images. In flash exposure through a transparency, the value of a would be determined by the geometry of the light source, the optical path, and the distance between the transparency and the moving PC. Ultimately, the sharpness of a voltage transition will be limited by the dielectric breakdown strength of the PC film (about 10^5 V/cm for many good insulating films). This breakdown limit implies that $a \cong 0.01$ cm or greater, and if the exposure system is capable of producing sharper

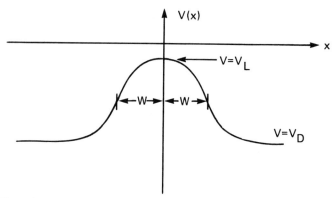

Figure 5.4   Sketch of an image line formed by a pair of arctangent transitions.

transitions, those transitions will relax (broaden) owing to the stress of very high electric fields.

From the engineering viewpoint, a discussion of the exposure of images does not involve an extensive treatment of photoconductivity. The PC is treated as a material characterized by its light voltage vs. exposure energy curve (Figure 2.13) or by the equivalent mathematical (empirical) relation (2.11). This approach is taken in the following analysis of image exposure by a scanning laser beam.

5.2   Image Exposure by a Raster Scanned Laser Beam

Fleischer, Latta, and Rabedeau (1977) described the optical design of the IBM 3800 laser system and Figure 5.5 is from their paper. The laser beam is scanned across the PC surface by reflecting the beam from an 18-facet polygonal mirror rotating about 15,000 rpm. Distance between scan lines is determined by the scan period and the surface velocity of the moving PC drum. In the 3800 printer, the scan start period is about 220 μsec and the drum surface velocity is 80 cm/sec, leading to spacings between scans of 0.0176 cm, or about 144 scan lines per inch in the y-direction. Along the scanned line, or x-direction, the laser beam intensity is modulated acousto-optically by an 80 MHz oscillator whose output is gated by a character generator. The drum, mirror motor, and optical modulator are kept in precise synchronization by a digitally controlled clocking system; thus, the beam modulator turns on or off at integral multiples of a specified data bit period (about 75 nsec in the 3800). Beam velocity along the scan direction is 1.88×10^5 cm/sec at the PC surface, yielding a minimum bit length of 0.0141 cm, or about 180 print elements per inch (PEL). The 3800 is a 144 by 180 PEL printer. Figure 5.6 depicts the manner in which vertical (y-direction), horizontal (x-direction), and diagonal lines are composed in this raster scanning process. Schade (1973) analyzes line raster processes as applied mainly in television scanning.

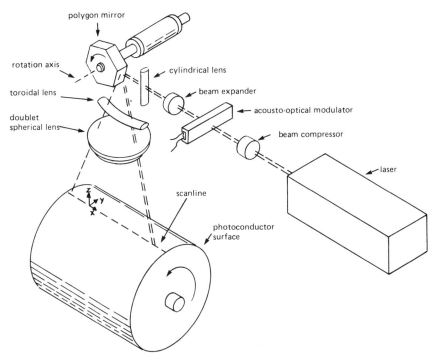

Figure 5.5   The 3800 printer laser exposure system. From Fleischer et al. (1977). Copyright 1977 by International Business Machines Corporation; reprinted with permission.

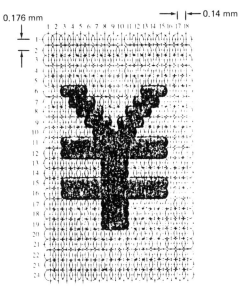

Figure 5.6   The raster process of the 3800 printer. Horizontal lines are continuous. Vertical lines are contiguous short lines or dots. Copyright 1982 by International Business Machines Corporation; reprinted with permission.

Except for a digression on acousto-optical modulators, the rest of this chapter analyzes laser exposure without going into any details of the optical system; Fleischer et al. (1977) should be consulted for this information. Relative to the laser beam diameter, the curvature of the PC drum is quite small, so the PC surface can be regarded as a flat plane in the immediate vicinity of the laser spot. Beam velocity is constant along the x-direction and the PC moves relatively slowly along the y-direction. The z-direction is normal to the PC plane, with $z = 0$ at the film surface.

5.3   Beam Intensity Distribution and Power

Helium–neon lasers are discussed by Lengyel (1966), and those used in most printers emit at a wavelength of 632.8 nm with a Gaussian intensity distribution across the beam. By the time this beam reaches the surface of the PC, it will have passed through and reflected from numerous optical elements, so in general, the beam shape at the PC will be somewhat elliptical. The intensity distribution across the beam, however, will still be Gaussian, but the horizontal and vertical

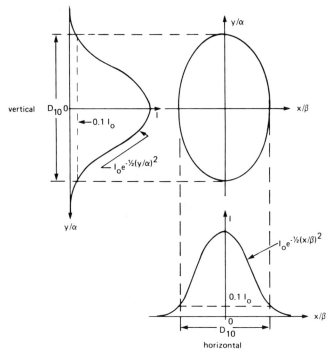

Figure 5.7   The elliptical spot with Gaussian intensity distribution. $D_{10} = 4.30\alpha$ (vertical size); $D_{10} = 4.30\beta$ (horizontal size).

measures of spot size will not necessarily be equal. At the PC surface, the intensity distribution is written

$$I(x, y) = \frac{P_t}{2\pi\alpha\beta} \exp\left\{-\frac{1}{2}\left[\left(\frac{y}{\alpha}\right)^2 + \left(\frac{x}{\beta}\right)^2\right]\right\} \quad (\text{W/cm}^2) \tag{5.5}$$

where P_t = beam power at the PC surface (in J-sec or W), α = vertical spot size parameter (in cm), and β = horizontal spot size parameter (in cm). A sketch of the elliptical spot is shown in Figure 5.7. Beam diameter is often measured between the 10% intensity loci, although some workers use the e^{-2} or 13.5% diameter, and others define beam size at the e^{-1} or 37% intensity loci. In terms of the spot size parameters, the 10% beam diameter is 4.30α (cm) vertically and 4.30β (cm) horizontally. In the system described by Fleischer et al. (1977), the spot is almost circular with $\alpha \cong \beta \cong 8.9 \times 10^{-3}$ cm, nominally, and beam power is about 18 mW at the PC. Raw power at the laser is nominally about 30 mW. The intensity at the spot center is thus about 36.2 W/cm^2 at the PC surface, and this value is sufficient to expose OPC and yield contrast voltages of about 600 V. A layered PC is much more sensitive than an OPC (see Chapter 2) at 632.8 nm, so beam power P_t would be reduced to about 2.5 mW for equivalent contrast voltage.

5.4   Voltage Transitions Caused by the Gaussian Intensity Profile

The laser beam described by (5.5) translates along x at a velocity v that is extremely high compared with the moving PC drum ($v = 1.88 \times 10^5$ cm/sec, $v_{PC} = 80$ cm/sec). For this reason, one can safely ignore motion along y when analyzing exposure along x. A long horizontal line is particularly easy to analyze, since the rise and fall of intensity at a given location on the PC is due only to beam motion and is not complicated by the rise and fall times of intensity from the beam modulator. Intensity modulation is treated in Section 5.6. The exposure (in J/cm^2 or ergs/cm^2) at any position y above or below a long horizontal scan is found by transforming position x to $x = vt$, and integrating (5.5) with respect to time.

$$E = \int_{-\infty}^{\infty} I(vt)dt = 2\int_0^{\infty} \frac{P_t}{2\pi\alpha\beta} \exp\left\{-\frac{1}{2}\left[\left(\frac{y}{\alpha}\right)^2 + \left(\frac{vt}{\beta}\right)^2\right]\right\}dt \tag{5.6}$$

$$= E_0 \exp\left[-\frac{1}{2}\left(\frac{y}{\alpha}\right)^2\right] \quad (\text{J/cm}^2)$$

where

$$E_0 = \frac{P_t}{\sqrt{2\pi}\,\alpha v} \quad (\text{W-sec/cm}^2) \text{ or } (\text{J/cm}^2)$$

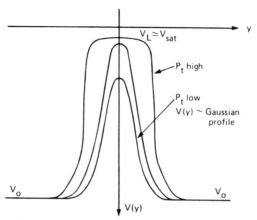

Figure 5.8   High beam power distorts the voltage profile to a non-Gaussian, but symmetric line. At low P_t, the transitions are almost Gaussian.

E_0 is the exposure at $y = 0$; above and below the scan centerline, the exposure profile is Gaussian and constant along x for a given y-position. The PC voltage vs. y-position is, from (2.11)

$$V(y) = V_{sat} + (V_D - V_{sat})\exp\left\{\frac{-E_0}{E_a}\exp\left[-\frac{1}{2}\left(\frac{y}{\alpha}\right)^2\right]\right\} \qquad (5.7)$$

With $P_t = 0.018$ W, $\alpha = 0.0089$ cm, and $v = 1.88 \times 10^5$ cm/sec, (5.6) yields $E_0 = 4.3 \times 10^{-6}$ J/cm^2 = 43 ergs/cm^2. For a dark voltage $V_D = -750$ V and $V_{sat} = 0$, the OPC light voltage along the scan centerline would be $V_L = V(y = 0) = -192$ V for $E_a = 31.5$ ergs/cm^2. With LPC, the energy constant $E_a = 5.0$ ergs/cm^2 for a hydrazone charge transport layer (see Figure 2.12); and if this PC was exposed at $P_t = 18$ mW, the voltage transitions of the scan line would be distorted from a Gaussian profile. This behavior is sketched in Figure 5.8. At low P_t, exposure is small and the exponential discharge curve is reasonably linear, so voltage profiles are only slightly distorted from Gaussians. For large E_0/E_a, the PC voltage approaches the saturation level and the line width broadens. Therefore, overexposure destroys fine detail, and electrophotography, like conventional photography, requires good control over illumination intensity at the image plane. Since LPC is about six times more sensitive than OPC, a beam power of 2.5 or 3 mW would yield adequate contrast voltage without line broadening.

5.5   Exposure Superposition: Adjacent Horizontal Scans

Very little has been written on linear superposition of exposure profiles in electrophotography. By comparison, much has been said in photographic texts on the subject of exposure reciprocity and its failure. Mees and James

(1966, p. 132), for example, give an extensive discussion of reciprocity failure in silver halide photography. In photographic terminology, exposure (E) is intensity (I) multiplied by exposure time (t), or $E = I \times t$. If a film obeys reciprocity in exposure, then $(1.0I) \times (1.0t)$ yields the same film response as $(0.5I) \times (2.0t)$, where response is measured in terms of the optical density of the developed film. Mott and Gurney (1964) explain reciprocity failure as arising from the accumulation of electronic charge in silver halide emulsions. Most PCs used in xerographic applications do not suffer from reciprocity failure, so it is valid to use the principle of linear superposition of isolated exposure profiles to arrive at the total exposure response. This behavior of PCs greatly simplifies the analysis and understanding of image exposure and emphasizes some of the fundamental differences between electrophotography and conventional photography. Schaffert (1971) states that reciprocity is obeyed at least over a range of exposure times from about 3 μsec to 1 sec for OPC. Figure 5.9, from Schaffert (1971), shows the voltage decay of OPC at short and long exposure times, and the curve superimposes quite well.

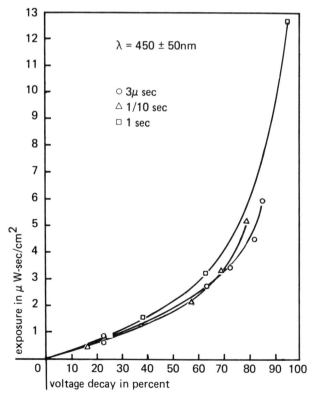

Figure 5.9   Three OPC discharge curves demonstrating the validity of exposure reciprocity. From Schaffert (1971). Copyright 1971 by International Business Machines Corporation; reprinted with permission.

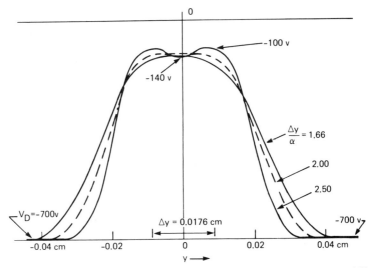

Figure 5.10   Two adjacent horizontal scans, showing about 40 V ripple for $\Delta y/\alpha = 2.70$. $\Delta y =$ 0.0176 cm (constant) ($\alpha = 8.86 \times 10^{-3}$ cm, and $8.86 \times 10^{-3} \pm 20\%$ for the three profiles shown).

Adjacent horizontal scan lines overlap one another by an amount that depends on the relative spot size and scan line separation. The system described by Fleischer et al. (1977) employs a nominal spot diameter of 0.038 cm, whereas scan centers are separated by 0.0176 cm. The additional exposure received in one line (from the energy of an adjacent scan) is computed from (5.6). For a vertical spot size $D_{10} = 0.038$ cm (distance between $0.1I_0$ loci), the size parameter is $\alpha = 8.86 \times 10^{-3}$ cm, and with $y = 0.0176$ cm, (5.6) yields $E = E_0 e^{-2} = 0.135E_0$; that is, the nearest neighbor (nn) interaction is 13.5%. The next nearest neighbor (nnn) interaction is computed with $y = 0.0352$ cm, for which $E = E_0 e^{-8} = 3.4 \times 10^{-4} E_0$. At greater distances along y, the interactions are essentially nil, so one introduces little error by considering only a group of five lines, for which the center line has 2 nn and 2 nnn interactions, so the total exposure at the midline is $E = E_0(1 + 0.27 + 6.8 \times 10^{-4}) \cong 1.271E_0$. For a contiguous series of horizontal scans, exposure uniformity along the y-direction depends on the ratio $\Delta y/\alpha$; total exposure profile is uniform if $\Delta y/\alpha \leq 2.0$, but has a ripple structure if $\Delta y/\alpha > 2.0$. Plots for two adjacent scans are given in Figure 5.10. In this figure, the undersized spot gives a ripple of about 40 V and this variation would yield obvious structure after image development. The oversized spot yields a flat exposure profile for contiguous lines, but at the expense of edge sharpness for isolated lines. The vertical spot size yielding maximally flat exposure with minimum edge blurring is therefore completely defined by the raster spacing. That is,

$$\text{Optimal vertical spot size parameter} = \alpha_0 = 0.50\Delta y$$

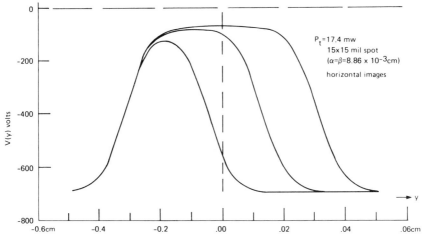

Figure 5.11 Simulated voltage transitions for 1-, 2-, and 3-bit horizontal lines. A PC with $E_a = 2.4\ \mu J/cm^2$ and $V_D = -700$ V was used in the computations.

For computer output page printing, it is preferable to avoid ripple structure and to accept slight degradations in edge sharpness. Figure 5.11 shows plots of simulated voltage transitions for horizontal lines having one, two, and three scan lines. The vertical spot size was set for maximally flat exposure profiles.

5.6   Voltage Transitions Caused by Beam Modulation: The Vertical Line

In raster scan imaging, vertical lines, dots, and diagonal lines involve a rapid change in laser beam intensity. Intensity modulation is conventionally done with acousto-optical modulators. These devices are discussed in Section 5.8. With high contrast line printing, the beam intensity is switched between full and (nearly) zero intensity. That is, the beam is essentially switched between ON and OFF levels, so there is no need to consider analog modulation, although the modulators currently used are capable of analog modulation. At this juncture, the modulator is treated as a black box element that yields an output beam when the device is gated ON electrically, and the intensity falls to zero when the gate closes. The rise and fall of beam intensity depends on the driving circuitry rise and fall times, the beam diameter, and the velocity of sound waves in the modulator material. To a close approximation, beam intensity follows a negative exponential in time. For an ON signal at $t = 0$, the beam intensity is

$$I(t) = I_0\left[1 - \exp\left(\frac{-t}{\tau_r}\right)\right] \tag{5.8}$$

where $I_0 = P_t/(2\pi\alpha\beta)$ (W/cm^2)
 τ_r = rise time constant (sec).

The 10–90% rise time $t_r = 2.20\tau_r$. (In the IBM 3800 printer, t_r is about 75 nsec.) If the beam has been on and the exponential transient has decayed, the intensity is at the full value I_0. If the OFF signal starts at $t' = 0$, the intensity decays with time as

$$I(t') = I_0 \exp\left(\frac{-t'}{\tau_f}\right) \tag{5.9}$$

Rise and fall times are not in general equal, since the sonic energy in the modulator requires a little more time to dissipate itself (because of absorption and scattering) than is required to establish the sonic wave.

The spatio-temporal behavior of the beam intensity $I(x, y, t)$ is described by (5.5) and (5.8) for the ON pulse, and the leading edge exposure is the time integral of the product of these relations. Letting $t = t_0$ be the duration of the ON pulse, and transforming the x position to the travelling coordinate $x - vt$, the exposure is

$$E_1(x, y, t) = \int_0^{t_0} I(x, y, t)dt = I_0 \exp\left[\frac{-1}{2}\left(\frac{y}{\alpha}\right)^2\right]$$

$$\times \int_0^{t_0}\left[\exp\left[\frac{-(x - vt)^2}{2\beta^2}\right] - \exp\left[\frac{-(x - vt)^2}{2\beta^2} - \frac{t}{\tau_r}\right]\right]dt$$

$$= \frac{E_0}{2} \exp\left[\frac{-1}{2}\left(\frac{y}{\alpha}\right)^2\right]\{\operatorname{erf}(A) + \operatorname{erf}(B - A)$$

$$- e^{(C^2 - D)}[\operatorname{erf}(B + C - A) - \operatorname{erf}(C - A)]\} \tag{5.10}$$

where $E_0 = P_t/\sqrt{2\pi}\,\alpha v$

erf = error function

$A = x/\sqrt{2}\,\beta$

$B = vt_0/\sqrt{2}\,\beta$

$C = \beta/\sqrt{2}\,v\tau_r,$

$D = x/v\tau_r.$

The error function is the result of integrating a Gaussian function. It is an anti-symmetric or odd function, $\operatorname{erf}(h) = -\operatorname{erf}(-h)$, and has asymptotic values of ± 1.0. The error function is tabulated in Abramowitz and Stegun (1968) and in Jahnke and Emde (1945).

When the beam turns OFF at $t = t_0$, the intensity has reached a value $I = I_0(1 - e^{-t_0/\tau_r})$. The trailing edge exposure is found by letting $t' = t - t_0 = 0$, $x' = x - vt_0$, and integrating the intensity vs. time according to (5.9).

The result is

$$E_2(x', y, t') = \int_{t'=0}^{t'} I(x', y, t')dt' = (1 - e^{-t_0/\tau_r})\frac{E_0}{2}\exp\left[\frac{-1}{2}\left(\frac{y}{\alpha}\right)^2\right]e^{(F^2-G)}$$

$$\times\ [\text{erf}(H + F - J) - \text{erf}(F - J)] \tag{5.11}$$

where $F = \beta/\sqrt{2}\,v\tau_f$
$\ G = x'/v\tau_f$
$\ H = vt'/\sqrt{2}\,\beta$
$\ J = x'/\sqrt{2}\,\beta.$

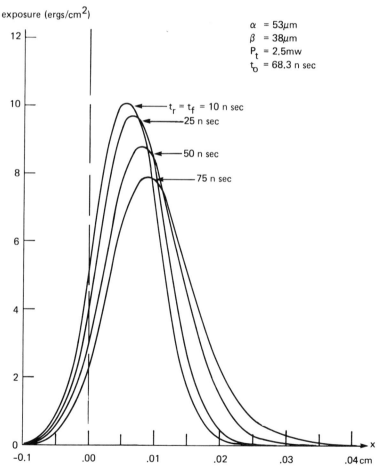

Figure 5.12   A 1-bit (68.3 nsec) spot, showing exposure dependence upon rise and fall times (10–90 %) of the beam intensity. Beam velocity $v = 1.55 \times 10^5$ cm/sec for the computed curves. The spot is elliptical with $\beta < \alpha$, and curves are at the scan centerline, $y = 0$.

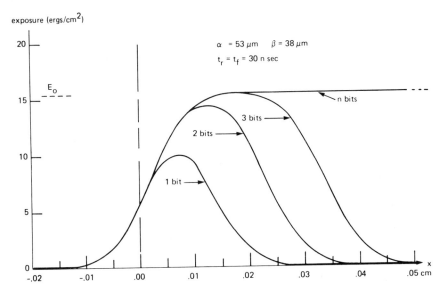

exposure (ergs/cm^2)

20

E_o

15

10

5

0

-.02   -.01   .00   .01   .02   .03   .04   .05 cm

$\alpha = 53\ \mu m$ $\beta = 38\ \mu m$

$t_r = t_f = 30\ n\ sec$

n bits

3 bits

2 bits

1 bit

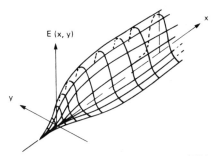

$E(x, y)$

Figure 5.13   Genesis of the line in equal increments or bits of 68.3 nsec each. Rise and fall times are constant. The spot is elliptical ($P_t \cong 3.1$ mW; $v = 1.55 \times 10^5$ cm/sec and $y = 0$ for the computations).

The total exposure at any position (x, y) for a pulse of laser light of duration $t = t_0$ is

$$E_T = E_1 + E_2 \tag{5.12}$$

and has been analyzed in two parts for ease of understanding. The results E_1 and E_2 are convolution products of the space and time functions describing the laser beam intensity. The PC voltage profile depends only on the number of photogenerated charge carriers; that is, the PC is an integrating photon detector and the contrast voltage does not depend on whether the photon flux was varied by moving the beam, changing the beam power (intensity), or both. A few curves describing the behavior of (5.10) and (5.11) (the rising and falling edges of exposure) are shown in Figures 5.12 and 5.13. In Figure 5.12, the exposure pulse length t_0 is constant (68.3 nsec) with $t_r = t_f$, and set at 10, 25, 50, and 75 nsec. As rise (fall) times increase, the peak exposure diminishes and its location shifts along the x-direction, but the area under all curves is equal (conservation of photon energy).

Figure 5.13 shows curves with $t_r = t_f = 30$ nsec, with the pulse length t_0 increasing in increments of 68.3 nsec (i.e., 1 bit equals 68.3 nsec). The inset of this figure gives an isometric view of the exposure profile at the left end of a long line (large n). Exposure level asymptotically approaches E_0, as given in (5.6), and after about 3 bit periods maximum exposure is reached. Photoconductor voltages are computed directly from the exposure equations (5.10), (5.11), and (5.12), using the discharge characteristic equation, (2.11), as before. A long vertical line is composed of a series of contiguous pulse exposures, each of n bits duration and occurring at each sweep of the beam along x. Linear superposition of the isolated exposure profile is assumed as before with the horizontal lines. The vertical line exposure profile differs from the horizontal profile in one important aspect: the edges of vertical lines including the effect of convolution broadening arising from beam translation and modulator rise and fall times, whereas horizontal line edges do not. The transition from dark to light is Gaussian (at low exposures) for the horizontal lines; the vertical transition follows the error function. In other words, the edge sharpness of vertical lines depends on the spatio-temporal behavior of the beam shape and modulator rise and fall times relative to the velocity of beam translation, but the edge sharpness of the horizontal line depends on beam shape only. This difference leads to mismatches between horizontal and vertical resolution. This phenomenon is called resolution anisotropy.

5.7 Resolution Anisotropy

If vertical and horizontal lines are to be equally developed with toner particles, the latent electrostatic image fields must be equal. The electrostatic fields of vertical and horizontal lines will be equal only if the exposure profiles are matched. Because of the raster scan process, a circular laser spot will not yield precisely equal line profiles along the vertical and horizontal directions. This is true even if the modulator rise and fall times are zero. Line profiles for the circular spot are compared in Figure 5.14; the profile of a vertical line is less sharp than that of a horizontal. This difference is usually unimportant for isolated lines, but the effect on line-pairs (formed by the bit sequence

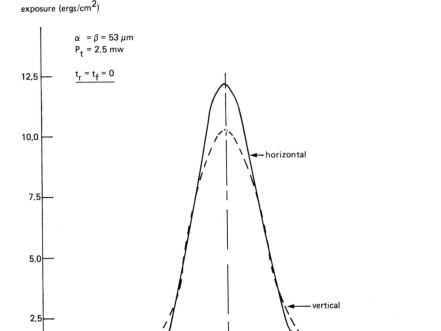

Figure 5.14   Resolution anisotropy finds its main source in beam translation, which broadens the exposure profile. With a circular spot, the vertical line profile is less sharp than the horizontal line ($v = 1.55 \times 10^5$ cm/sec for the computation).

00001010000...) can be obvious. Without proper compensation of the laser spot shape, a vertical isolated line-pair will be poorly resolved after development, and the pair can merge and develop as a single wide line. The exposure profile for the horizontal line-pair, however, develops a well-resolved image of two lines. Spot compensation is achieved by foreshortening the spot diameter along the direction of beam translation and by reducing the rise and fall times of the acousto-optical modulator. Image exposure using the elliptical spot, with the major axis aligned in the vertical direction, yields equal vertical and horizontal resolution. That is, isotropic resolution is achieved with an anisotropic spot, or, exposure with the isotropic (circular) spot produces anisotropic resolution.

The voltage profiles of horizontal and vertical line-pairs are given in Figure 5.15; V_{mod} is the peak-to-valley modulation in voltage between lines and is the

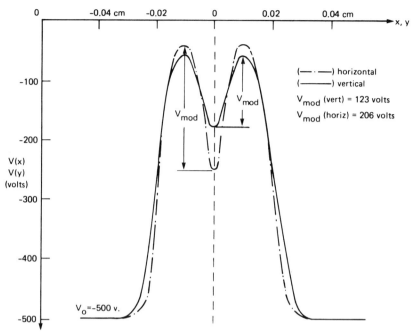

Figure 5.15 Insolated line pair voltage vs. position for horizontal and vertical lines, each very long. Beam parameters are: $\alpha = 0.0053$ cm, $\beta = 0.047$ cm, $P_t f 2.5$ mW, $t_r = t_f = 40$ nsec, $v = 1.55 \times 10^5$, $t_0 = 68.3$ nsec. PC parameters: $V_{sat} = 0$, $V_0 = -500$ V, $E_a = 5.0$ ergs/cm^2.

key attribute determining line-pair resolution. In the plots given, the laser spot is only slightly elliptical (the ratio of vertical and horizontal diameters is 1.125) and the modulator rise and fall times are small ($t_r = t_f = 40$ nsec). A LPC with $E_a = 5.0$ ergs/cm^2 is utilized, beam scan velocity is $v = 1.55 \times 10^5$ cm/sec, and beam power at the PC surface is $P_t = 2.5$ mW. For the vertical and horizontal line-pairs, V_{mod} is 120 and 206 V, respectively. Curves of V_{mod}, normalized by the dark voltage V_d, are given as a function of horizontal beam diameter in Figure 5.16. Values of beam size and t_r, t_f giving equal values of V_{mod} are shown in Figure 5.17. By slight extrapolation, this curve shows the impossibility of matching horizontal and vertical lines, even in the extreme of zero rise and fall times, unless one exploits the elliptical spot with horizontal size smaller than the vertical. In usual practice, modulator rise and fall times are determined by the beam diameter at the modulator and by the sonic velocity of acoustic waves as they travel past the beam. In practical terms, rise and fall times may be limited to about 20 nsec or greater, and such a low value is obtained with a small beam size and concomitant loss in diffraction efficiency in the modulator.

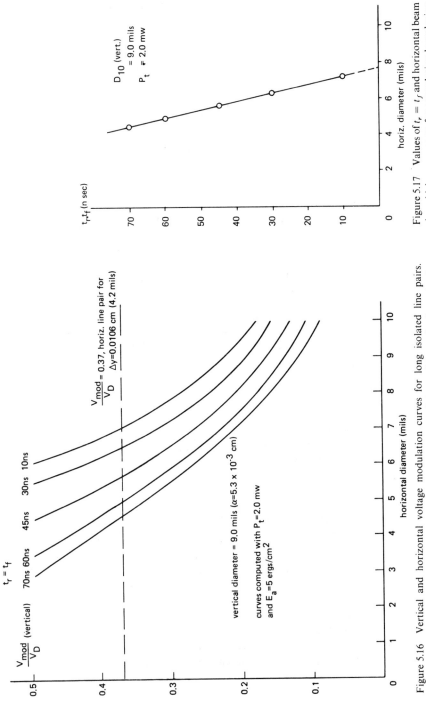

Figure 5.16 Vertical and horizontal voltage modulation curves for long isolated line pairs. Vertical line pair depends on horizontal beam size and on t_r, t_f of the modulator; horizontal pairs are independent of these parameters.

Figure 5.17 Values of $t_r = t_f$ and horizontal beam size which compensate for convolution broadening of a translating beam. Data from Figure 4.16.

92

5.8   Acousto-Optical Modulation

The manner in which laser beam intensity is controlled is interesting and important in its own right. Basically, acousto-optical modulators behave as three-dimensional diffraction gratings for light beams. If the modulator is OFF, the outgoing beam travels undisturbed from the direction of the incoming beam, but if the modulator is ON, part of the beam power is diffracted onto a different angle, called the *first-order diffraction direction*. The remaining power continues along undiffracted in the *zero-order* direction. The ratio of first-order to zero-order beam intensities is called the *modulator efficiency*. Three-dimensional (volume) diffraction gratings are discussed by Smith (1969), and the interaction of light with ultrasonic energy is treated by Born and Wolf (1975, Chapter 12). The bibliography given in Fleischer et al. (1977) lists several references on acousto-optical modulation, and ISOMET Corporation issues application notes on their devices.

Light is diffracted by periodic structures, and in a beam modulator, ultrasonic waves are generated by a transducer bonded onto special glass, TeO_2, or $PbMoO_4$, or other material whose index of refraction is a strong function of pressure. The loci of high and low acoustic pressure travel through the diffracting medium and set up a periodic traveling wave whose crests and troughs correspond to regions of high and low index of refraction (n). The photoelastic constant (p) of a material is a measure of the dependence of n upon stress, and acousto-optical materials are rated by a figure of merit (M), which is a function of n, p, density, and acoustic velocity. Lead molybdate and tellurium dioxide are discussed by Coquin et al. (1971) and by Uchida and Ohmachi (1969), respectively. The intensity of the first order beam (I_1) from a modulator is given by ISOMET (undated) as

$$I_1 = kI_0 \left(\sin^2 \frac{\pi}{\lambda} \sqrt{\frac{M_2 L P_a}{2H}} \right) \left[\mathrm{sinc}^2 \left(\frac{\pi L \Delta \theta}{\Lambda} \right) \right] \qquad (5.13)$$

where k (less than 1.0) depends on modulator design and the optical divergence of the laser beam, λ is the free space wavelength (cm) of the incoming beam, M_2 is the elasto-optic figure of merit of the interaction medium (3.63×10^{-10} cm^2/W for lead molybdate), L is the interaction length (cm) shown in Figure 5.18, P_a is the acoustic power (W) in the medium (P_a = constant × electrical power at the input), H is the width of the acoustic column (cm), $\Delta \theta$ is the error in Bragg angle adjustment (radian), Λ is the acoustic wavelength (cm) in the interaction medium, and $\mathrm{sinc}(x) = \sin(x)/x$. The acoustic wavelength is the acoustic velocity divided by the frequency of the applied signal. For $PbMoO_4$, $v = 3.6 \times 10^5$ cm/sec. With a frequency of 80 MHz, $\Lambda = 4.5 \times 10^{-3}$ cm. The geometry relevant to (5.13) is shown in Figure 5.18.

The intensity of the first-order diffracted beam I_1 depends critically on the orientation of the incoming beam; the condition for maximum intensity is that

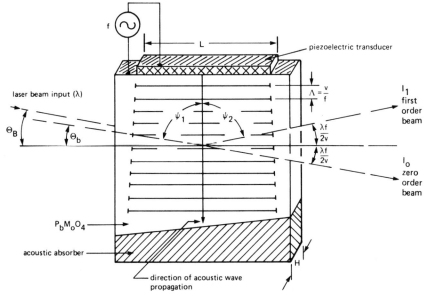

Figure 5.18   Geometry of acousto-optical modulator. Θ_B = Bragg angle in air = $\lambda f 2/v$; Θ_b = Bragg angle in medium = $\lambda f/n2v$; n = index of refraction. When Bragg condition is met, $\psi_1 = \psi_2$. Drawing is adapted from ISOMET Corporation with permission.

the laser beam is precisely aligned to the Bragg angle θ_B in air. Within the modulator medium whose index of refraction is n, the Bragg angle is $\theta_b = \theta_B/n$. The Bragg angle is defined by the Bragg Equation used in discussing diffraction from space gratings.

$$\sin \theta_B = \frac{\lambda}{2\Lambda} \tag{5.14}$$

If the wavelength of the light beam is 632.8 nm (0.6328μ) and the acoustic wavelength is 4.5×10^{-3} cm (45 μm), then $\lambda/\Lambda = 0.014$ and $\sin \theta_B \cong 0.007$ radian (about 0.40°). Small misalignments from the true Bragg angle yield significant loss in first-order intensity. This is shown in Figure 5.19. The interaction length L is approximately 0.5 cm in the modulator described by ISOMET, so a misalignment of $\Delta\theta = \Lambda/(\pi L)$ yields $\text{sinc}^2(1.0) = 0.71$, which corresponds to an alignment error of 2.9 mradians or 0.16°. Criticality in Bragg alignment is reduced by operating at higher acoustic frequencies, which is equivalent to using shorter acoustic wavelengths, or by using shorter interaction lengths. As (5.13) reveals, reducing L means that increased acoustic power is required to achieve a given efficiency of diffraction. A plot of I_1/I_0 vs. input electrical power is shown in Figure 5.20. The data are from R. Holmes of IBM Corporation.

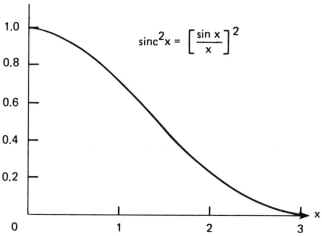

Figure 5.19 The $\text{sinc}^2 x$ function showing how first-order intensity drops with Bragg angle error $\Delta\Theta$; $x = \pi L/\Lambda$ (radian).

Rise and fall times of the I_1 beam are determined by the transit time of the acoustic wavefront through the incoming beam. That is,

$$t_r \cong t_f = C\,\frac{D}{v} \quad \text{(sec)} \tag{5.15}$$

where C is a dimensionless constant, D is the beam diameter in the interaction medium, and v is the sonic velocity. Beam diameter is determined by a *beam*

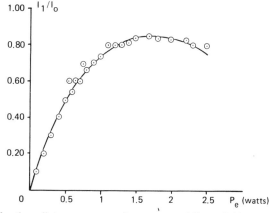

Figure 5.20 Diffraction efficiency vs. power for a commercially available acousto-optical modulator. Solid line is theoretical curve following a $\sin^2 k\sqrt{P_e}$ relation. Data from R. Holmes, IBM Corporation.

compressor just prior to the modulator entrance (see Figure 5.5). The fall time is slightly larger than the rise time because acoustic energy is scattered around by the sides and bottom of the interacting medium, and it takes a little time to dissipate the scattered energy. If one makes the beam diameter very small to obtain short rise and fall times, diffraction efficiency suffers and, according to Rabedeau (1978), driving power must be increased to make up for the loss.

Multifrequency acousto-optical diffraction is utilized in other applications of these devices, but complications arise because of cross modulation and spurious intermodulation frequencies. This subject is discussed by Hecht (1977). Laser beam sweeping and deflection can be accomplished with acousto-optical modulators by sweeping the drive frequency. This application is discussed in ISOMET (undated) and is used in some xerographic printers.

5.9   Unwanted Modulation of Image Exposure

Occasionally, image quality is degraded by unintentional sources of exposure modulation. Fleischer et al. (1977) discuss beam scan displacement errors that lead to objectionable variations in reflectance of developed images. This problem is understood by examining the total exposure profile for contiguous lines, with one line displaced somewhat from the intended location. Figure 5.21 shows exposure modulation for only three lines; the center scan has been displaced 14% away from the center (0.00254 cm displacement) and the two outer lines are separated 0.0356 cm. The laser spot is circular with 10% diameter of 0.0381 cm ($\alpha = 8.86 \times 10^{-3}$ cm). Using (5.6) and linear superposition of three lines, the total exposure is

$$E_t(y) = E_0 \left\{ \exp\left[-\frac{1}{2} \frac{(y - 0.00254)^2}{\alpha^2} \right] + \exp\left[-\frac{1}{2} \frac{(y - 0.0178)^2}{\alpha^2} \right] \right.$$

$$\left. + \exp\left[-\frac{1}{2} \frac{(y + 0.0178)^2}{\alpha^2} \right] \right\} \tag{5.16}$$

Maximum exposure is $E_t = 1.46E_0$ at $y = 0.010$ cm, and minimum exposure is $E_t = 1.02E_0$ at $y = -0.0076$ cm. A small scan displacement error thus generates significant modulation in exposure with subsequent variations in surface voltage. Small variations in PC potential will be significant if the variations occur over small distances, as the resultant electric field is the negative gradient of the surface potential.

Another source of unwanted modulation is attributed to variations in absorbed energy due to OPC thickness variations; this subject is discussed briefly in Chapter 2. Since OPC is not opaque at a wavelength of 632.8 nm, a beam of light is reflected at the conducting ground plane under the photo-generating film and at the OPC–air interface. Multiple reflections of the laser beam create variations in exposure that depend on the phase relation of the

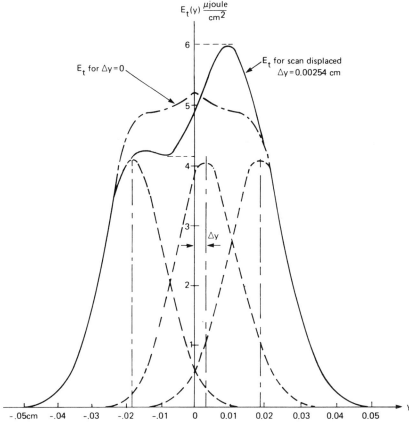

Figure 5.21   Unwanted modulation due to scan displacement error of 1.0 mil (0.00254 cm). Beam is 15 × 15 mils and 17.2 mW; $E_0 = 4.1\ \mu J/cm^2$. Exposure profile without scan error is shown for comparison.

interfering light beams. Phasing between beams is a strong function of OPC film thickness, so the energy absorbed and consequent light voltage form contours (see Chapter 2 on the "wood-grain effect") of constant film thickness. Figure 5.22 gives a plot of relative absorption in the thickness range from 9.0 to 11.0 μm. Note the rapid periodic absorption going from a maximum to a minimum in roughly 800 Å variation in film thickness. At a nominal thickness of 10.0 μm, the exposure modulation index (M) given by B. Schechtman of IBM Corporation (unpublished) is $M = 0.25$, so the variation in absorbed energy is

$$\frac{E}{E_0} = \frac{A \pm M}{M} = 1.0 \pm 0.25. \qquad (5.17)$$

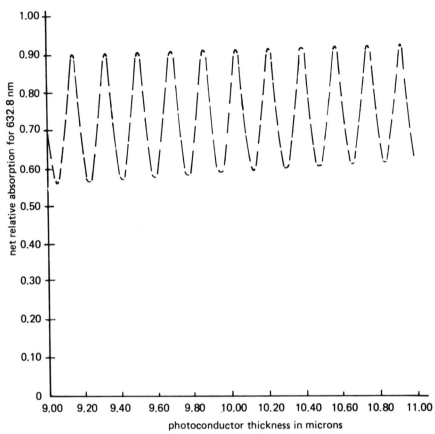

Figure 5.22   Absorption at $\lambda = 632.8$ nm for OPC as a function of film thickness. Modulation is due to interference effects of primary and reflected beams. From B. Schechtman, IBM Corporation.

With $E_0 = 4.17 \times 10^{-6}$ J/cm^2, $E_a = 3.15 \times 10^{-6}$ J/cm^2 (the nominal value for OPC), and $V_D = -700$ V, the modulation given above corresponds to $V(1.25E_0)$ $= -134$ V and $V(0.75E_0) = -259$ V, or 125 V modulation from interference effects. Figure 2.5 shows a facsimile of this effect.

A third source of modulation that degrades print quality is traced to the drive circuitry of the acousto-optical modulator. As shown in Figure 5.20, first-order diffraction intensity has a maximum level, and increasing drive power beyond this point reduces the beam output intensity. Because of variations in operating parameters of high-frequency power transistors, one occasionally finds a modulator driver which turns on rapidly and causes overshoot and ringing of the 80 MHz envelope. Figure 5.23 depicts the phenomenon graphically, showing how the output intensity I_1 would vary with time after the turn-on transient. Noticeable variation in image reflectance results if the overshoot and ringing amplitudes are sufficiently high.

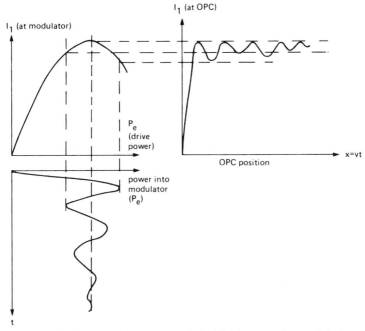

Figure 5.23 Intensity (I_1) vs. position $(x = vt)$ at PC arising from overshoot and ringing of modulator drive power (P_e).

5.10 Modulation vs. Beam Power

In high contrast printing, the amount of modulation produced in PC surface voltage is a key operational attribute. With line-pairs, high modulation in the surface voltage is desirable. With long scans, or with many contiguous horizontal scans, modulation in voltage within the exposed region is undesirable. Desired vs. undesired modulation is often a trade-off in raster-scanned laser exposure, and this chapter closes with a brief analysis of the problem, showing how exposure modulation depends on beam power. The analysis is simplified without loss of insight by using a sinusoidal modulation in exposure.

$$E_t(y) = E_0(C + D \sin ky) \tag{5.18}$$

with $k = 2\pi/\lambda$. If $V_{sat} = 0$, then $V(y) = V_D \exp(-E_t/E_a)$; CE_0 is the average exposure and DE_0 is the base-to-peak variation. Recall the definition of $E_0 = P_t/(\sqrt{2\pi}\alpha v)$, or $E_0 = hP_t$ with h constant, for this discussion. Voltage levels corresponding to maximum and minimum exposure are computed from the exponential discharge characteristics, as before. The difference between peak and valley levels, V_{mod}, is

$$\frac{V_{mod}}{V_D} = e^{-hP_t(C-D)} - e^{-hP_t(C+D)} = 0.5e^{-hCP_t} \sinh(hDP_t) \tag{5.19}$$

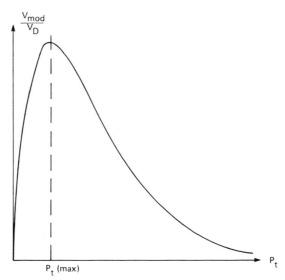

Figure 5.24   A plot of $e^{-AP_t} \sinh (BP_t)$.

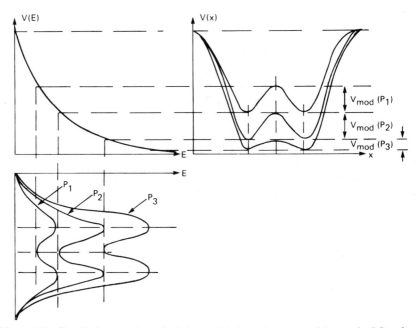

Figure 5.25   Graphical approach to obtaining modulation voltage vs. position on the PC surface. $P_3 > P_2 > P_1$ are the power levels for exposure of a line-pair; the argument is valid for modulation in general.

Therefore, the normalized modulation is the product of a monotonically decreasing function (e^{-hCP_t}) and an increasing function ($\sinh(hDP_t)$), so a maximum or optimum modulation exists. Equation (5.19) is plotted in Figure 5.24. The power at maximum V_{mod} is found by maximizing (5.19).

$$P_t(\max) = \frac{1}{hD} \tanh^{-1}\left(\frac{D}{C}\right) = \frac{1}{2hD} \log_e \frac{C + D}{C - D} \tag{5.20}$$

where $h = (\sqrt{2\pi \alpha v E_a})^{-1}$ (sec/J) or (W)$^{-1}$.

Figure 5.25 adds graphical emphasis to this discussion. Three exposure profiles at different beam power levels are reflected from the exponential discharge curve of a PC, and the resultant curves of voltage vs. position at the PC are given on the right side of the figure. At high power (P_3), the modulation voltage is significantly reduced.

Generally, the maximum power level for good line-pair resolution is not large, so D/C may be 0.2 or less. In this case, (5.20) reduces to the very simple form

$$P_t(\max) \cong \frac{1}{hC} = \frac{\sqrt{2\pi \alpha v E_a}}{C} \quad \text{(W) or (J/sec)} \tag{5.21}$$

For high resolution printing with laser beams, C is within the range of 1.0–1.5 and D is about 0.25. Unwanted modulation can be washed out by high beam power, but fine detail print (e.g., Kanji, etc.) would suffer loss of reflectance and resolution.

This concludes the discussion of PC exposure from the viewpoint of translating variations in beam intensity into surface voltage variations. The next chapter extends the ideas to the electrostatic fields associated with changes in surface voltage.

SIX

ELECTROSTATIC FIELD ABOVE A PHOTOCONDUCTOR SURFACE

The purpose of Chapter 5 was to establish a physical and quantitative basis for the conversion of light energy into variations in surface potential of a charged PC. In this chapter, the connection between surface potential and electric field is treated in more depth. The exposure process in the most fundamental sense creates variations in surface charge density, yet one almost never determines the charge density in any direct manner; the surface potential is routinely measured with vibrating reed electrometers instead, so the treatment of electric field starts as a boundary value problem in which the potential is specified along the surface of the PC. Since the PC behaves as an insulator when in the dark, the surface potential, which corresponds to charge, can vary continuously with position. The electrostatic field in xerography has been treated by Schaffert (1975, p. 476), Neugebauer (1964), Chen (1978), Cheng and Hartmann (1980), and Williams (1982). The electric fields in ionography are discussed by Plewes and Johns (1975) and Fenster, Plewes, and Johns (1974). With the exception of Williams (1982), these references treat periodic images or those having discontinuities in potential or charge density. In this chapter, electrostatic images are treated as smooth, continuous, aperiodic functions specified by the potential along the surface of the PC; that is, the task is defined as a Dirichlet boundary value problem. If the potential $V(x, 0)$ along the boundary ($z = 0$) is known, then the potential everywhere $V(x, z)$ is known, provided $V(x, z)$ is harmonic and analytic. Morse and Feshbach (1953) and Markushevich (1977), for example, discuss the properties and applications of harmonic functions. The potential above the PC is found by using the Green's function for the surface (Morse and Feshbach, 1953, Vol. 1. p. 710). Knowing the potential everywhere, therefore, allows computation of the electric field by taking the gradient of the potential.

6.1   The Electric Field of Arctangent Voltage Transitions

The exposure process, whether with laser beam, flash tube through a negative transparency, or reflection of light from an original document yields changes in PC surface voltage that are smooth functions of position. The mathematical description of a voltage transition from laser exposure, for example, depends on the shape of the intensity distribution of the beam of light and on the characteristic discharge curve of the PC, which is usually a negative exponential function to a close approximation. Exposure by reflection from an already printed document creates voltage transitions whose exact shape depends on the distribution of ink on paper, the roughness of the paper surface, and the spectral characteristics of paper, ink, and illuminating source. To achieve some generality of insight regarding a variety of exposure systems, it is necessary to use an approximating function that is sufficiently flexible to model the surface potential without becoming entangled in the details of a particular exposure system. The function chosen should be continuous, such that all nonphysical singularities in electric field are avoided everywhere (including the surface of the PC) and should also be analytic. Many functions fulfill these requirements, for example, hyperbolic tangent, error function, gudermannian, and arctangent. The arctangent is particularly useful because it is simple, continuous, has continuous derivatives, is asymptotic to finite, nonzero values, and its derivative is a rational algebraic function. The physics of image exposure does not yield arctangent transitions in surface voltage, but the ease, simplicity, and clarity of the arctangent analysis justify its use. Indeed, the numerical estimates of electric field appear reasonable and are fairly insensitive to the exact nature of the transition, provided the slope and contrast values are consistent with physical limitations.

A comparison of transitions resulting from a Gaussian exposure profile and an arctangent approximation are shown in Figure 6.1. Appropriate adjustment of line width ($2W$), edge sharpness, and contrast voltage allows one the freedom to synthesize most voltage profiles of interest in line printing and copying. For an isolated line, such as that shown in Figure 6.1, the surface potential is written as

$$V(x, 0) = V_D + V_c \left[\tan^{-1} \left(\frac{x + W}{a} \right) - \tan^{-1} \left(\frac{x - W}{a} \right) \right]$$

$$(6.1)$$

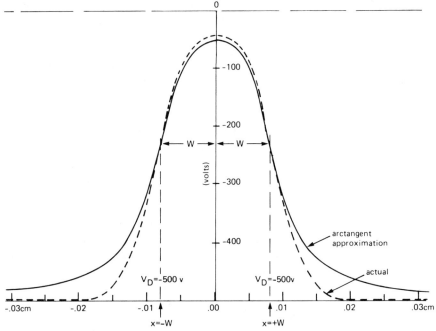

Figure 6.1   A comparison of actual and arctangent transitions for the voltage along the PC surface ($y = 0$). The actual transitions come from a Gaussian exposure profile and thus converge more rapidly to the dark voltage level (V_D) than the arctangent approximation.

where

$$V_c = \frac{(V_L - V_D)}{2 \tan^{-1}(W/a)}$$

The voltage everywhere above the PC surface is found by convolving $V(x, 0)$ with the Green's function for the upper half space. Details of the mathematical derivation are given in the Appendix. The result is

$$V(x, z) = V_D + V_c\left[\tan^{-1}\left(\frac{x + W}{z + a}\right) - \tan^{-1}\left(\frac{x - W}{z + a}\right)\right] \qquad (6.2)$$

The light and dark voltages (V_L and V_D) and the line width ($2W$) are experimentally accessible. The sharpness of the transition from V_L to V_D is set by the transition parameter (a), whose value must be determined indirectly. Methods for estimating a are discussed later. The quantity ($z + a$) in (6.2) reveals that the transition parameter has the identical effect as spacing z above the PC surface. If $a = 0$ (which is physically impossible), the transitions become step functions; Neugebauer (1964) analyzed image lines with step function profiles. In (6.2)

V_c is a dummy variable (in volts) that allows specification of the transition contrast in terms of the light and dark potentials. The potential given by (6.2) is the free-space solution and assumes the PC surface voltage is defined with respect to the underlying ground plane and with all other conductors removed beyond any important influence. If other conductors at fixed potential are brought close to the PC surface, the potential distribution is no longer given by (6.2) and a new problem must be solved. This is illustrated in this chapter during the discussion the effect of the "development electrode" used in developer units. Two-dimensional geometry is assumed here, so the image line is very long in the y-direction (the PC surface forms the x-y plane).

The electric field is the negative gradient of the electrostatic potential. In vector notation, with $\hat{\mathbf{i}}, \hat{\mathbf{k}}$ being unit vectors along x, z directions, the field is

$$\mathbf{E} = -\nabla V(x, z) = -\left(\frac{\partial}{\partial x}\hat{\mathbf{i}} + \frac{\partial}{\partial z}\hat{\mathbf{k}}\right) V(x, z) = E_x\hat{\mathbf{i}} + E_z\hat{\mathbf{k}} \quad \text{(V/cm)} \quad (6.3)$$

The horizontal and vertical components of the field are

$$E_x = V_c\left[\frac{(z + a)}{(x - W)^2 + (z + a)^2} - \frac{(z + a)}{(x + W)^2 + (z + a)^2}\right] \qquad (6.4)$$

$$E_z = V_c\left[\frac{(x + W)}{(x + W)^2 + (z + a)^2} - \frac{(x - W)}{(x - W)^2 + (z + a)^2}\right] \qquad (6.5)$$

A charged toner particle experiences a Coulomb force $\mathbf{F} = q\mathbf{E}$, so the particle would be attracted to or repelled from the PC by the E_z component only. For this reason, E_z becomes the natural basis for electrostatic image analysis; the quantity of toner deposited and the electrostatic adhesive force each scale with E_z. The tangential field E_x translates charged particles along x. Figure 6.2 shows an isolated line voltage profile computed from (6.2) and the resultant field components (6.4) and (6.5), respectively. The PC dark voltage is $V_D = -500$ V and light voltage is $V_L = -150$ V. With $W = 0.02$ cm, $a = 0.01$ cm, the dummy variable $V_c = 158$ V. The inset sketch in Figure 6.2b shows the field lines going from the more positive region to the more negative, that is, from -150 V to the -500 V regions. With this convention, negatively charged toner is attracted to the positive field region ($E_z > 0$), so a line about 0.04 cm wide would develop on this electrostatic image. Positively charged toner would develop two narrower lines separated 0.04 cm and the outer edge of each line would be diffused.

Plots of E_z vs. x for three different line widths are given in Figure 6.3. The field at the line center ($x = 0$) diminishes as the line widens; this behavior is described mathematically in (6.5) by letting $x = z = 0$. The surface field thus goes as

$$E_z(0, 0) = \frac{2V_c W}{W^2 + a^2} \qquad (6.6)$$

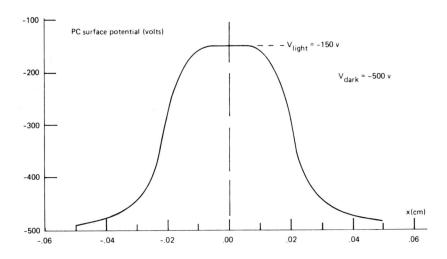

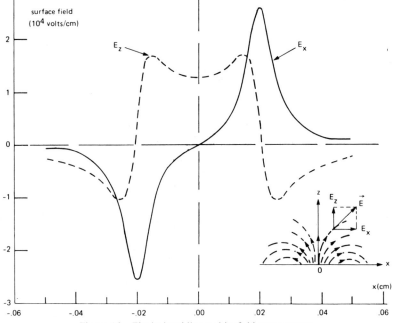

Figure 6.2   The isolated line and its field components.

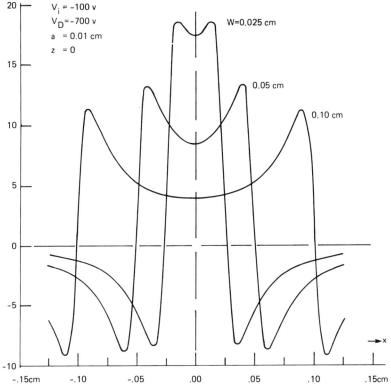

Figure 6.3 Normal field component for the arctangent *transition pair* or *image line*. As the line width ($2W$) increases, E_z diminishes in the center region.

and for sharp edge lines ($a \ll W$), $E_z \cong 2V_c/W$. With very wide lines, the normal field component vanishes in the center region. Near the edges the field can be appreciable, as seen by examining the expressions for the isolated transition or edge:

$$V(x, z) = V_D + V_c \tan^{-1} \frac{x}{z + a} \qquad (6.7)$$

$$E_x = -\frac{\partial V}{\partial x} = -\frac{V_c(z + a)}{x^2 + (z + a)^2} \qquad (6.8)$$

$$E_z = -\frac{\partial V}{\partial z} = \frac{V_c x}{x^2 + (z + a)^2} \qquad (6.9)$$

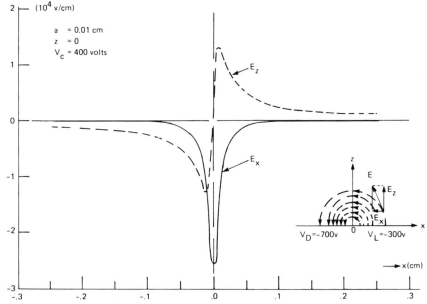

Figure 6.4   The isolatèd edge of one arctangent transition from V_D to V_L. If the transition goes from V_L to V_D, the polarity of the edge is inverted.

Field components for the edge are shown in Figure 6.4. The extreme value for $E_x = -V_c/a$ is at the edge ($x = 0$), and the extremes (at $z = 0$) for $E_z = \pm V_c/(2a)$ are located at $x = \pm a$; the magnitude of E_x is precisely twice the extreme of E_z. If the extreme value of E_x exceeds the dielectric breakdown field strength of the PC surface, charge will conduct along the surface and relax E_x (and E_z) to a lower value.

6.2   Estimates of the Transition Parameter

Peek (1929, p. 254) and Tareev (1975, p. 177) estimate that insulator surfaces, if clean of dusts, salts, scratches, and so on, will withstand tangential electric fields on the order of 10^5 V/cm before breaking down and conducting. Knowing the breakdown field E_{br} allows one to estimate the edge sharpness which, if exceeded, would cause dielectric breakdown of the PC. Since the maximum value of E_x is twice that of E_z, charge conduction along the surface would likely constrain the transition parameter to a minimum value, determined from (6.8), of approximately

$$a < \frac{V_c}{E_{br}} \quad \text{(cm)} \tag{6.10}$$

For an isolated edge with $V_c = 1000$ V and $E_{br} = 10^5$ V/cm, the minimum transition parameter would be about 0.01 cm, or a transition length $L = \pi a \cong$ 0.03 cm. For very narrow lines, the contrast parameter V_c might be 100 V, so the transition parameter could approach smaller values.

If the exposing beam is well-defined, the transition parameter can be estimated directly from exposure profiles like those discussed in Chapter 5. A laser operating in the TEM_{00} mode has a Gaussian intensity profile. For a scan across a PC, the exposure energy/cm^2 profile is written

$$\text{Exposure} = E_0 \exp\left[-0.5\left(\frac{y}{\alpha}\right)^2\right] \tag{6.11}$$

where E_0 is defined in (5.6). This exposure profile yields a voltage profile whose shape depends on the characteristic curve of the PC, but the voltage transition parameter approximately follows the relation

$$a \cong \alpha \quad \text{(cm)} \tag{6.12}$$

provided the beam size is not too small and does not drive the edge field to breakdown limitations.

Transition parameters arising from light reflected from printed documents are generally more difficult to estimate. Reflection microdensitometric scans are necessary to determine the average light intensity profile from a given document type. Statistical fluctuations produce a range of transition parameters, so the analysis of electric fields is more complicated, although the principles are unaltered.

6.3   The Adjacency Effect in Electrostatic Images

The isolated image line is composed of two edges; one edge goes from dark to light and the next goes from light to dark. The electric field of the isolated line is found by linear superposition of the fields of edges whose polarities are reversed. The field of lines and edges extends along the x-axis in both directions, so when line images are moved to closer and closer proximity, the influence of the side field lobes becomes more pronounced. This is shown in Figure 6.3, where two edges are brought closer together to form a narrowed line; the positive portion of the two edges add, so E_z becomes larger for narrow lines. For very wide lines, the field is essentially that of two edges; thus, it is large only in the vicinity of the edges, and charged toner develops the line as two isolated edges, because E_z is very small in the line center region. For this reason, the "development electrode," to be discussed later, is present in xerographic machines. This electrode increases the developing field E_z above the free-space value described previously.

If two or more lines are brought into proximity, the total field is the algebraic sum (i.e., linear superposition) of the field caused by each line, treated as an

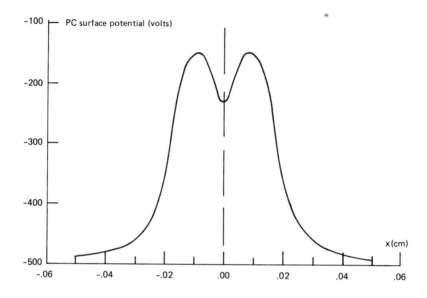

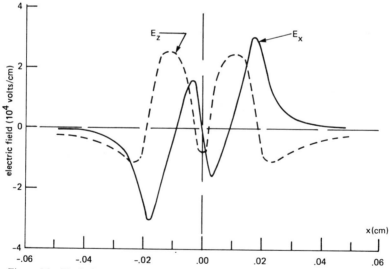

Figure 6.5 The isolated *line-pair*, formed by linear superposition of two isolated *lines*.

isolated source. The effect produced by linear superposition is that of reduction in field strength. This "adjacency effect" in electrostatic images has a profound influence on the ability to develop and resolve individual lines at high spatial frequencies. The line-pair shown in Figure 6.5 would attract negative toner to the positive E_z regions and would repel negative toner from the remaining areas, so two distinct lines would be developed. Should the lines be somewhat closer together, the negative lobe at $x = 0$ would become positive and the two lines would develop with poor resolution, perhaps even merging completely to become one wide line. Figure 6.6 shows a comparison between a line-pair computed for a Gaussian laser beam and an arctangent approximation; the fit is good over the region of interest.

Figures 6.7 and 6.8 show three lines at a center-to-center spacing L of 0.06 and 0.05 cm, respectively. The field at $x = 0$ drops from 11.8 to 9 kV/cm, while the negative field between lines shifts from -16.2 to -2.5 kV/cm, with the small change in L. At $L = 0.047$ cm, the negative field between lines becomes positive and good line resolution is lost. In other words, image resolution crosses the threshold from acceptable to unacceptable with a change in line spacing of 0.03 cm (30 μm, or slightly greater than 1.0 mil).

The principle of superposition holds for the electric field of any number of lines at arbitrary spacing between lines. In the case of an infinite series of identical lines, the total field is the sum as before, but the sum can be evaluated in closed form. Morse and Feshbach (1953, p. 413) show how the sum is replaced

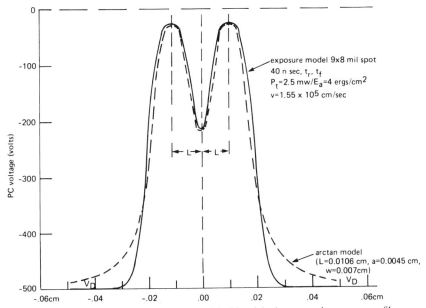

FIGURE 6.6   Comparison of arctan model with original computed exposure profile.

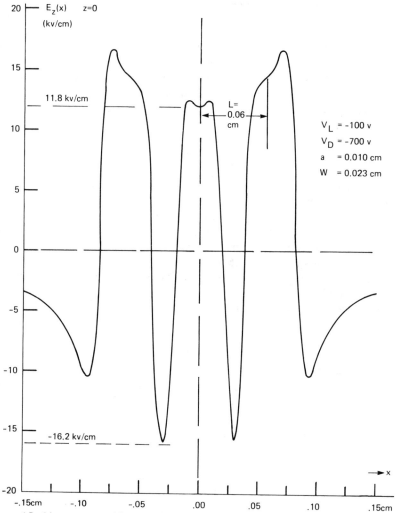

Figure 6.7 Linear superposition of three lines with spacing $L = 0.06$ cm. Properties of each isolated line are identical and are listed above.

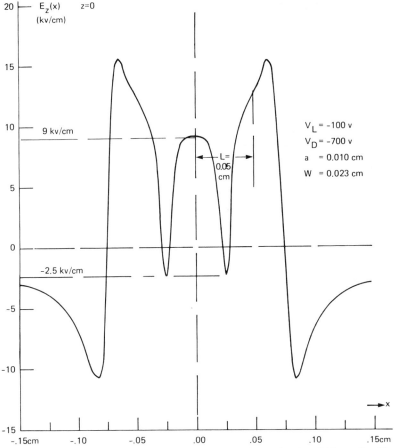

Figure 6.8 Linear superposition of three identical lines with spacing $L = 0.05$ cm. See Figure 6.7 for comparison with $L = 0.06$ cm.

by a contour integral evaluated by the calculus of residues. The derivation of the result is given in the Appendix. At $x = z = 0$, the result is

$$
E_{tz} = \sum_{-N}^{N} E_z(x + nL, z) = \frac{V_c}{L} \sum_{-N}^{N} \left[\frac{(x + W)/L + n}{[(x + W)/L + n]^2 + [(z + a)/L]^2} \right.
$$

$$
\left. - \frac{(x - W)/L + n}{[(x - W)/L + n]^2 + [(z + a)/L]^2} \right]
$$

$$
= \left(\frac{2\pi V_c}{L} \right) \frac{\sin(2\pi W/L)}{[\cosh(2\pi a/L) - \cos(2\pi W/L)]} \tag{6.13}
$$

with $x = z = 0$.

In the limit of very large spacing (L), the influence of adjacent lines will be nil. This is recovered from (6.13) by applying l'Hospital's Rule with the limit $L \to \infty$, and one obtains (6.6), the surface field for an isolated line. Since $(z + a)$ shows up in the starting expression, one can replace a by $(z + a)$ in the final expression to obtain a result that is valid at any distance z above the PC in free space.

6.4   The Modulation Transfer Function (MTF) of Electrostatic Images

Recognizing that the spatial frequency of a series of lines is $f = 1/L$, in (6.13) the total field is expressed directly as a function of spatial frequency, that is, $E_{tz} = E_{tz}(f)$, and $E_{tz}(0)$ is the field of the isolated line (zero frequency). The normalized response $E_{tz}(f)/E_{tz}(0)$ can be interpreted as a frequency response or modulation transfer function (MTF) for electrostatic images. Neugebauer (1965, 1967) introduced the use of E_z as a measure of the xerographic MTF, but he limited applicability to continuous tone reproduction and claimed that MTF theory could not be applied to line images. This is an unnecessary limitation on the concept of the MTF as a compact mathematical description of the information content of a signal. Goodman (1968, p. 114) and Biberman (1973, p. 313), for example, discuss MTF theory and its use in optical systems. Indeed, the MTF for arctangent image lines

$$\text{MTF} = \frac{E_{tz}(1/L)}{E_{tz}(0)} = \frac{\pi(w^2 + a^2)}{LW} \frac{\sin(2\pi W/L)}{[\cosh(2\pi a/L) - \cos(2\pi W/L)]} \quad (6.14)$$

fulfills the requirement for a mathematical description of the free-space field of a periodic array of lines. Graphs of this MTF are given in Figure 6.9 for selected values of a (or $z + a$) with W constant. The function is defined over the interval from zero line width up to $W = L/2$, at which lines are contiguous, thereby yielding a structureless solid area having $E_{tz} = 0$ in free space. The development electrode adds a constant (DC) field sufficiently large to develop toner in solid areas. In raster scanned digitally clocked systems, line frequency f is quantized, so the curves of Figure 6.9 would become a series of unconnected points, each at an allowable spatial frequency.

Schade (1973) exploited the MTF concept when designing line raster television imaging systems, and extension of his ideas to laser beam electrophotographic systems is straightforward. Chapter 5 shows that a circular spot yields anisotropic resolution of lines for digitally modulated raster scanned images because the exposure profile suffers convolution broadening in the direction of beam translation. In consequence, the transition parameter for a vertical line is greater than that produced for the horizontal line (which involves only the spot size). The electrostatic field of the vertical line, composed of contiguous short scans involving the beam modulator, is therefore somewhat smaller

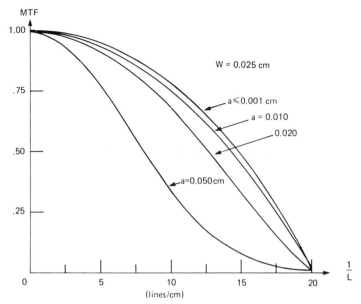

Figure 6.9   Modulation transfer function (MTF) for electrostatic images resulting from arctangent transition profiles in surface voltage of a PC. Curves shown are for line full width $2W = 0.050$ cm; L is the spacing between line centers.

and wider than the field of horizontal lines. Because the MTFs of vertical and horizontal lines are unequal (resolution anisotropy) with the circular (isotropic) spot, the problem is attacked and solved by imaging with an anisotropic spot shape. The elliptical spot, appropriately aligned with the minor axis in the scan direction, restores isotropic resolution. That is, the MTFs are matched by altering the transition parameter a in the horizontal direction. Television scanning suffers in like manner, as the phosphor in cathode ray tubes functions as a beam current integrator that yields convolution broadening in analogy with the PC in electrophotography. Schade (1973) produced equivalent results for television images by introducing a high frequency spot "wobble" perpendicular to the scan direction. The CRT phosphor persistence effectively integrated the beam intensity to yield an elliptical profile that matched the horizontal and vertical MTFs.

6.5   The Electric Field with a Developer Electrode

The free-space electric field is inversely proportional to line width, so wide lines will not attract toner particles in sufficient quantity for uniform darkness across the line image. The edges will be well-developed because the field is

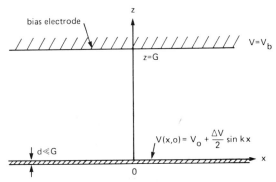

Figure 6.10   Geometry for PC with a bias electrode placed a distance G above.

large. This is the "edge effect" commonly seen in office copiers in the 1960s. Development of large areas or wide lines is much improved by placing a biased electrode close to the PC. The potential difference between the "developer electrode" and the PC voltage gives rise to an additional electric field which, depending on bias polarity, increases or decreases the total electric field normal to the PC surface. With the biased conductor in place, the boundary value problem is altered and a new one must be solved. Schaffert (1975) analyzes in great depth the developer electrode. Here, a simplified geometry is treated that gives useful insight into the function of the electrode, provided the gap distance G, shown in Figure 6.10, is large relative to the PC thickness d. With carrier-toner development (two-component developers), this simplification is justified, since G will be on the order of 1 mm with $d = 10\ \mu\text{m}$ or so.

The bias potential is V_b and the electrode is located at $z = G$. Along the PC boundary, the potential is specified by the desired function. The analysis here is done with a sinusoidal voltage given by

$$V(x, 0) = V_0 + \frac{\Delta V}{2} \sin kx \qquad (6.15)$$

where $k = 2\pi/\lambda$. The potential in the space between the PC and the electrode is found by solving Laplace's Equation for the two-dimensional problem. This is done in the Appendix; the result is

$$V(x, z) = V_b - (V_b - V_0)\left(1 - \frac{z}{G}\right) + \frac{\Delta V}{2}\left(\frac{e^{-kz} - e^{-2kG}e^{kz}}{1 - e^{-2kG}}\right)\sin kx \quad (6.16)$$

At $z = 0$, the PC surface voltage is recovered, and at $z = G$, one obtains $V = V_b$, as required of the solution. As before, the electric field is $\mathbf{E} = -\nabla V$, so the components are

$$E_x = -\frac{\partial V}{\partial x} = -\frac{k\Delta V}{2}\left(\frac{e^{-kz} - e^{-2kG}e^{kz}}{1 - e^{-2kG}}\right)\cos kx \tag{6.17}$$

$$E_z = -\frac{\partial V}{\partial z} = \frac{(V_0 - V_b)}{G} + \frac{k\Delta V}{2}\left[\frac{e^{-kz} + e^{k(z - 2G)}}{1 - e^{-2kG}}\right]\sin kx \tag{6.18}$$

The developing field E_z is composed of two terms; the first term is constant and is the difference between the average PC voltage V_0 and the bias voltage V_b, both divided by the gap length G. This is the bias field. It is uniform, as might be expected from parallel plate geometry. With a small gap, the bias field becomes large. As the bias electrode recedes away toward infinity, the bias field approaches zero, as it should, and one obtains the free-space solution for the PC. The second term is sinusoidal along x and attenuates with increasing distance z above the surface. The magnitude is proportional to the wave number $k = 2\pi/\lambda$, where λ is the wavelength of the sinuosidal fluctuations in surface voltage. At short wavelengths, the electric field can be quite large at $z = 0$. The tangential field E_x has no constant term and disappears at $z = G$, as it should, because the bias electrode is a conductor and will not support a tangential field. At $z = 0$, (6.17) and (6.18) reduce to

$$E_x(x, 0) = -\frac{k\Delta V}{2}\cos kx \tag{6.19}$$

$$E_z(x, 0) = \frac{(V_0 - V_b)}{G} + \frac{k\Delta V}{2}[\coth(kG)]\sin kx \tag{6.20}$$

Coth(kG) converges rapidly to 1.00 with increasing kG; that is, coth(2.0) = 0.96, so at short wavelengths, the effect of the electrode is unimportant for the sinusoidal term.

Bias voltage is normally adjusted to achieve uniformly black large areas, but not such that toner deposits in the background areas. Thus, V_b is set between V_D and V_L, preferably closer to V_D for dark print. If V_b is more negative than V_D, then E_z will be positive in the background region as well as in the images; so negative toner, for example, would deposit everywhere except around the edges of images where E_z is strongly negative (see Figure 6.3). The printed page issuing from an overbiased printer or copier has very black images, white halos around the images, and gray background (toner scattered over the background); overbiased printing is shown in Figure 6.11.

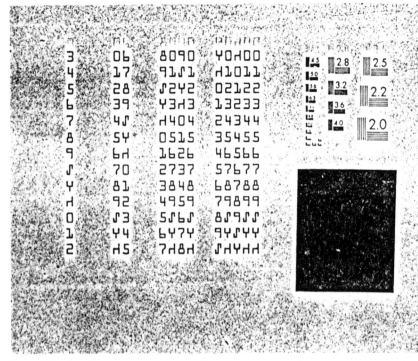

Figure 6.11   Overbiasing causes toner deposition in the background region, except where rejected by the negative field around image edges. In the experiment shown here, $V_D = -700$ V, $V_L = -100$ V, $V_b = -1000$ V, and $G = 0.10$ cm, and exposure was through a transparency.

6.6   Optimizing the Bias Field

Consider the difference between edge or line fields and the relatively low field arising from the bias or developer electrode. In (6.18) or (6.20), $E_b = (V_0 - V_b)/G = 3$ kV/cm with $V_0 = -800$ V, $V_b = -500$ V, and $G = 0.10$ cm (reasonable values). The developing field at an edge might be 10 or 20 kV/cm, so one should expect greater development in the lines and edges. The bias field can be optimized, or at least improved, such that solid areas and lines appear roughly equal in reflectance, and this would require roughly equal bias and edge fields.

$$E_b = \frac{V_L - V_b}{G} = \frac{V_L - V_D}{2\pi a} \tag{6.21}$$

The gap length G can be adjusted to achieve increased E_b, so with the bias voltage set nearly equal to the dark voltage (for maximum large area development), the best gap length would be

$$G \cong 2\pi a \quad \text{(cm)} \tag{6.22}$$

As discussed earlier, a is limited to about 0.01 cm, so G ought to be about 0.06 cm. This is a fairly small gap and reliable operation of a machine would be difficult. The carrier beads in two-component developers would necessarily be quite small (i.e., about 75–100 μm in diameter) so that a layer perhaps 5 beads thick could pass through the developer gap without excessive wear and degradation of the PC. It is difficult to retain small carrier beads in the developer unit, and lost carrier beads might cause image degradation at the transfer unit. These topics are treated in Chapters 7–10.

SEVEN

ELECTROSTATIC IMAGE DEVELOPMENT
PARTICLE CHARGING AND ADHESION

The image exposure process generates a latent electrostatic image at the surface of a PC. This image is converted into a visible one by depositing charged toner particles on the PC surface, where the field polarity relative to the toner polarity selectively deposits toner at the image regions. If the toner particle charge is distributed in a statistical manner, then under certain conditions toner deposits in nonimage regions as well, and the image transferred electrostatically to paper may be degraded. Although several techniques are used to develop electrostatic images, only xerographic development ("dry-writing" in the original Greek) is discussed here, since this approach dominates the world of high speed printers and copier–duplicators. The slower electrophoretic development process found in many small office copiers uses charged particles in a liquid dielectric medium. Image development technology and science includes many diverse topics and is one of the more challenging aspects of electrophotography. Because of its diversity of phenomena, image development is treated in three chapters; this chapter reviews particle charging by contact electrification, measurement of particle charge and its statistical distribution, aerodynamic drag forces on rough particles, and particle adhesion by electrostatic and electrodynamic forces. Chapter 8 addresses micro- and macroscopic models of the image development process by magnetic brush developers, using the information in Chapter 7 as a foundation. Aerosol development is also discussed. Because the magnetic brush successfully opened up xerography to high-speed image development, this device is analyzed in Chapter 9, and some of the problems of competition between electric and magnetic forces are addressed.

Good quality image development may be obtained with two-component (toner and carrier) and monocomponent (toner only) developers. Two-component developers use nonmagnetic toner transported on the surface of magnetic carrier beads, and the toner particles in monocomponent devices are formulated with magnetic pigment. The discussion in this and following chapters specifically addresses two-component development, yet much of the information would apply to monocomponent development as well. In either case, the toner particles are small and are distributed over the range of about 5–30 μm. Carrier beads are much larger, and are usually distributed over the range from about 70 to 250 μm, and are used to charge and transport toner. Carrier beads are made from carbon–steel shot or ferrite particles with a surface coating, often PTFE or a mixture of PTFE and epoxy. This surface must function reliably in two important ways: toner must charge with the appropriate polarity when it touches the carrier surface, and the surface energy must be low to inhibit permanent adhesion of toner. Temporary adhesion of toner is necessary, otherwise toner could not be transported in a controlled manner to the latent electrostatic image. Adhesion and its control is essential to a reliable image development process; for this reason, electrostatic, electrodynamic, aerodynamic, gravitational, and magnetic forces are analyzed in these chapters.

Suppose, for example, that toner receives electrons from an insulated carrier surface and that a positive electrostatic field detaches the toner at the PC surface. Because charge is conserved, the positively charged carrier would be attracted electrostatically to regions of negative field. In the absence of magnetic forces in the opposing direction, the remaining important force would be gravity. Gravity is strong enough to overpower electrostatic forces if the mass of the carrier is sufficiently large. That is,

$$mg > QE_{pc} \quad \text{(dynes)} \tag{7.1}$$

Gravity is a volume force (scales with radius cubed), whereas carrier charge Q is a surface force (scales with radius squared); E_{pc} is the electric field at the PC. Small carriers might be retained on the PC surface against gravitation forces. Carrier flow past the PC would be impeded and small carriers might be removed from the developer unit. Reduced carrier flow and an inability to retain carriers were often a problem in developer units that used gravity to cascade the developer mix over the latent image. The problem was solved by making carrier beads out of magnetic material and pulling them away from the PC with magnets. A sketch of a magnetic brush developer unit is shown in Figure 7.1. Within this device, toner is mixed and charged by contact with carrier beads. The carriers are recirculated by the magnetic brush "pumps" and fresh toner is added to maintain constant toner concentration in the mix. The magnet arrays are fixed while the cylindrical sleeves rotate around the

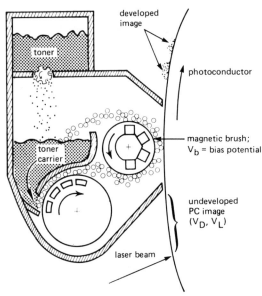

Figure 7.1   Magnetic brush developer unit. Toner is mixed and charged by contact with carrier beads. The carriers are recirculated and fresh toner is added to maintain constant toner concentration in the mix. Magnet arrays are stationary while the cylinders around them rotate, thereby transporting toner and carrier past the electrostatic image at the PC. The cylinder is biased to assist in developing large exposed areas.

magnets, thereby transporting toner and carrier past the PC image. The magnetic brush adjacent to the PC is conducting and is biased to assist in developing large image areas (this is the "developer electrode" mentioned in Chapter 6).

In high-speed machines, the PC velocity might be in the range of 50–100 cm/sec, but the toner–carrier mix velocity relative to the stationary container can reach over 200 cm/sec. Some commercial machines have a series of developer rolls, each set at a bias voltage and mix flow rate that in concert will achieve the desired quality of the developed image. Within the developer unit, a variety of complex phenomena occur simultaneously. Fresh toner drops down onto the recirculating developer mix and is charged by contact with carrier and toner material. Some of the carrier is highly charged, in a polarity opposite to that of the toner; this carrier is neutralized by the flow of current from the developer housing (which must be a conductor connected to system ground) as well as by contact with fresh toner. Under gravitational and magnetic forces, the carrier–toner mix flows at high speed through the device; mechanical agitation, crushing, impacting, shearing, and sliding occur with monotonous regularity (10 kg of mix recirculate every 2 or 3 secs). Adhesive contacts are made and broken, electric charge is donated or accepted at the region of true contact, and carrier beads chain up along lines of magnetic force (crushing toner particles at the interstices) and go whipping or cartwheeling on the magnetic brush as it rotates over arrays of permanent magnets of alternating polarity. As the mix enters the gap at the PC, beads and toner are crushed down to a close-packed array which slides over and develops the latent image. Aerosols of charged toner are created within the developer housing, and this toner is free to deposit on nonimage areas of the PC as well as on grounded conductors. These phenomena, and others not even mentioned, offer an almost bizarre selection of technical challenges. It is a three-ring circus. In the first ring, one finds contact electrification.

7.1 Contact Electrification

There is perhaps no phenomenon more ubiquitous, but less well-understood, than contact electricity. It has been called the oldest branch of electricity; the ancient Greeks were quite aware of the charging of amber (*elektron*, in Greek). The phenomenon is also called triboelectricity and frictional electricity, but Harper (1967) and Loeb (1958) establish clearly that the charging process requires contact between surfaces and that rubbing two objects together only brings more surface into contact. A precise, quantitative theory for insulator charging is still lacking, although considerable progress has been made. Experimental problems arise because surfaces are usually contaminated with unknown substances and the true nature of the contact geometry is most difficult to establish. Other than Loeb and Harper, some additional references are Sanford (1919), Coehn (1898), Faraday (1843), Montgomery (1959), Richards (1923), Seanor (1972), Shaw (1930), Inculet (1973), Ruckdeschel and Hunter (1975), Fabish and Duke (1980), Cottrell et al. (1980), and Lowell and Rose-Innes (1980).

In 1898, Coehn stated that substances of higher dielectric constant become positive when contacted with substances of lower dielectric constant. This statement is known as Coehn's Law, although metals must be assigned a dielectric constant somewhere between 3 and 4 to fit them into this law. See, for example, Sanford (1919, p. 108), Richards (1923), or Loeb (1958, p. 61) for discussions of Coehn's Law. Faraday (1843) investigated at least 30 substances including water, steam, olive oil, turpentine, and dry air; he placed metals between "lac" and sulphur. His ordering of the metals agrees with the much later work of Harper (1967, p. 234), which is given in Figure 7.2. The theoretical line is due to the theory by Harper. It is based on the difference between work functions of two materials and the electron tunneling probability as a function of gap distance between two surfaces. Work functions of metals have been known for a long time, but defining and measuring the work function of insulators has been difficult. Inculet (1973) discusses static electrification of dielectrics and lists the work functions of several materials. Table 7.1 is from his data.

His experiments in vacuum showed that the material with greater work function is left negatively charged relative to the contact of lower work function.

**Table 7.1   Work function
(in eV) of Dielectrics**

Nylon	4.20
Nylon 66	4.08
Glass	4.30–4.60
Polythene	4.70
PVC	4.85
Polyimide	4.36
Polycarbonate	4.26
PTFE	4.26
PET	4.25
Polystyrene	4.22

A well-accepted theory of insulator charging is lacking, although Duke and Fabish (1978) claim to have a model for metal–insulator contacts. Cottrell et al. (1979) criticized the experimental techniques leading to that model, and this criticism launched a series of exchanges in the *Journal of Applied Physics*. Lowell and Rose-Innes (1980) review the latest understanding of contact electricity.

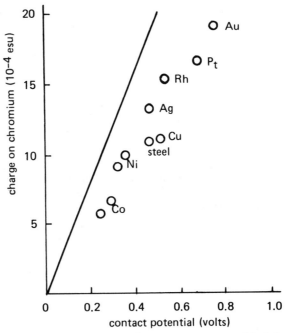

Figure 7.2   Charge on a chromium sphere ($\frac{5}{32}$ in.) vs. contact potential of *Cr* against another sphere ($\frac{1}{2}$ in.) of the given metal. From Harper (1967, p. 234).

7.2 Toner–Carrier Charging Experiments

Most toner used in xerographic developers is based on polystyrene, with other thermoplastic polymers and pigment mixed in. Most commonly, the pigment is carbon black; however, colored pigments are also used. At room temperature, toner is quite brittle and is easily fractured; this is intentional in some toner formulations, since brittleness allows rapid milling of the toner particles in the manufacturing process. Particles are classified according to the desired size range and samples are tested for appropriate charging behavior with carrier beads. Toner and carrier are designed for particular applications in given product lines, and using the wrong toner or carrier usually creates problems in image quality, machine function, and maintenance. On a short-term basis, the functionally important aspect of toner is its surface charge density and polarity after charging it on carrier beads. In the long term, it is important that toner does not contaminate the machine, that it does not cake up and improperly replenish the circulating carrier, or that it does not permanently fuse to the PC or other surfaces. Long-term problems are not analyzed in this book.

Toner charging behavior is measured with an electrometer device having very low leakage current and known input capacitance. Figure 7.3. depicts one such device. In a typical experiment, toner is accurately weighed and mixed with a known mass of carrier beads. The mixing operation charges the toner by contact

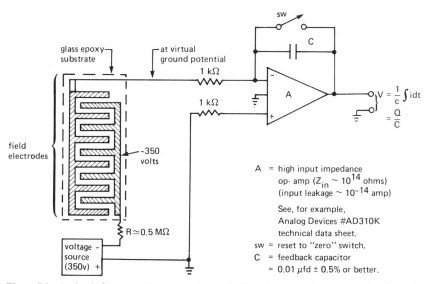

Figure 7.3 A circuit for measuring toner charge Q. Negative toner deposits on the electrodes at virtual ground potential, and current flows until the electrode potential is again at virtual ground in the presence of toner charge. The integrating capacitor C thus charges to a voltage V proportional to the toner charge Q. Leakage across the gap between field electrodes must be kept very low. Design from R. Marrs, IBM Corporation.

electrification with the carrier surface. The toner–carrier mixture is cascaded over the field electrodes of the electrometer device, leaving behind a layer of charged toner on the appropriate field electrode. Because of its high mass, a carrier bead is attracted more strongly by gravity than by the field electrode, so the carrier falls away into a collecting pan after toner is removed from it. If the carrier beads are small enough (i.e., $m < QE/g$, where m = mass, Q = charge, E = field, and g = acceleration of gravity), they will also be retained on a field electrode whose polarity opposes that where toner collects. The field E of the electrometer is adjusted so that carrier does not collect on the field plate. Toner charge Q is derived from the measured output voltage V of the integrator where $V = Q/C$, so the total charge of toner is $Q = VC$ (C). The deposited mass, usually only a few milligrams, is determined with an accurate analytical balance. Toner charge-to-mass ratio is then computed from the results of these two experiments.

$$\frac{Q}{M} = \frac{VC}{M} \quad (C/g) \tag{7.2}$$

In some of the literature, Q/M data are expressed in esu/g, where 3×10^9 esu $= 1.0$ C. The esu of charge is very useful when discussing electrostatic forces, but it is not a familiar unit to those raised in the MKS system. Both systems are used here to help the reader become more at ease with the esu-cgs system. A typical result for toner might be $Q/M = 10 \ \mu C/g = 3 \times 10^4$ esu/g.

When charge/mass is determined by the carrier–cascade technique described above, toner is removed from the carrier when its adhesive junction is disturbed by mechanical shear; those particles in contact with the field electrode are removed first. This means the larger particles support the mechanical load, and they must be removed by the deposition process before smaller particles hiding among the big ones can be deposited. Techniques that blow toner away from the carrier beads are also used for studying toner charging behavior. Toner–carrier mix is placed in a screen cage (a Faraday cage) whose openings are large enough to allow the escape of toner particles, but small enough to retain carrier. The conducting cage is attached to the input of an electrometer, so when air is blown over the mix, the electrometer determines the quantity of charge removed with the toner. Because the aerodynamic drag force on a particle is proportional to its size, large particles detach before small ones, as in the gravitational case described above. At high air velocity, blow-off techniques can remove most of the toner of all sizes; hence, this approach is preferred, since it suffers less from a bias toward the large particles.

Contact charging is a surface phenomenon, so the charge on a toner (carrier) is proportional to the surface area. Particle mass is obviously a measure of the volume, so the charge-to-mass ratio is

$$\frac{Q}{M} = \frac{4\pi R^2 \sigma}{\frac{4}{3}\pi R^3 \rho} = \frac{3\sigma}{\rho R} \ (\text{esu/g}) \text{ or } (C/g) \tag{7.3}$$

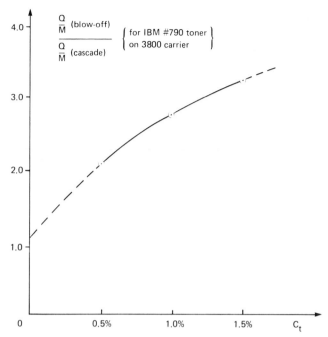

Figure 7.4   Measured charge/mass (Q/M) depends on technique used and the concentration of toner on carrier (C_t). The "blow-off" Q/M is much higher than that found by "cascade" Q/M.

where σ is the surface charge density (C/cm² or esu/cm²), and ρ is the density (g/cm³). With constant σ, particles with small R have the higher Q/M; thus, when measuring the charge and mass, it is also necessary to know the size distribution to make the Q/M data useful.

Figure 7.4 shows the measured Q/M by blow-off technique, normalized by the Q/M of the cascade technique, plotted as a function of the weight percent toner on the carrier (toner concentration). Since the blow-off more readily removes small particles, the measured Q/M is larger in all cases than when measured by carrier cascade or gravity techniques. The carrier and toner in Figure 7.4 are not different, only the measurements differ. The toner concentration C_t is defined as

$$C_t = \frac{\text{toner mass}}{\text{carrier} + \text{toner mass}} \tag{7.4}$$

7.3   Toner Charge/Mass and Mixing Time

Brittle material, like some toners of styrene and butylmethacrylate, are easily fractured. At the fracture interface, charges of both polarities accumulate, so it is not surprising that particles prepared by milling are all charged, some positively and others negatively. The average charge (averaged over all particles) is zero; however, the charge of particles selected at random from a large collection is distributed, very likely according to a Gaussian or normal frequency function. Szaynok (1971) discusses a mechanism that accounts for Gaussian statistics. Experiments with charge spectrometers indicate that toner is always charged; however, the initial distribution (i.e., density) function is symmetrical about zero charge, and when mixed with carrier, the function becomes asymmetrical with a nonzero mean value. The mean charge depends on the mixing or charging time, which is a measure of the number of contact charging events that have accumulated. Figure 7.5 is a plot of toner Q/M vs. mixing time of a sample placed in a small container rotated at 1 revolution per second. Mixing speed in a printer or copier would be greatly increased. Loeb (1958, p. 161) and Ruckdeschel and Hunter (1975) discuss the charging behavior between insulators in rolling or bouncing contact. Their data show that charging is essentially of the form

$$Q = Q_m(1 - e^{-Ct}) \tag{7.5}$$

where Q_m is the maximum charge or asymptotic value, C is a constant that depends on rolling velocity, and t is the elapsed time. Wagner (1956), Peterson (1954), and Ahuja (1976) also discuss the charging behavior of surfaces in rolling or bouncing contact. The simple exponential behavior can be understood as the logical consequence of the charging rate depending on the fraction

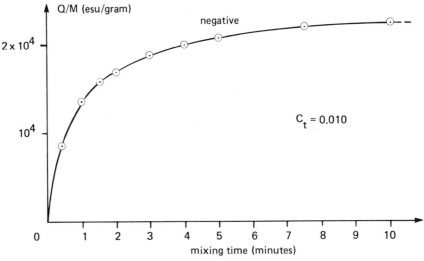

Figure 7.5   Mean Q/M vs. mixing time for 3800 toner and carrier. (This curve is not relevant to mixing time in the printer, which mixes at a much higher rate.) The cascade technique was used for measuring Q/M.

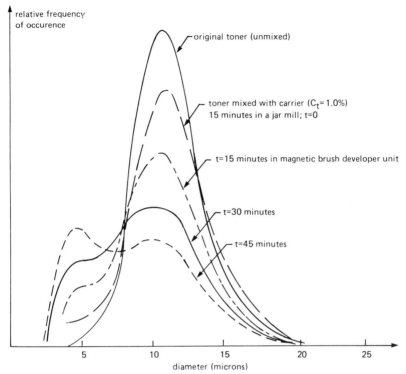

Figure 7.6   The effect of particle milling (comminution) is noticeable even when "gently" mixed with carrier in a jar mill. A magnetic brush developer unit operating at 530 RPM grinds toner down to about 5 μm diameter from the original size of about 11 μm.

of area remaining uncharged and the relative motion serving only to supply uncontacted area.

With very energetic mixing, toner particles may be reduced in diameter and new area created. This milling aspect of mixing is shown in Figure 7.6; the size distribution is bimodal after about 15 min of mixing in a jar mill, with an additional 15 min of mixing in a magnetic brush unit.

7.4   Charge/Mass versus Toner Concentration

The amount of charge/cm^2 given to a toner particle depends on the chance of contacting a neutral area on a carrier surface. At low toner concentration, chances are excellent, but at high concentrations the chances are rather poor; thus it becomes intuitively clear that toner Q/M should be a decreasing function of C_t, the toner concentration.

Experiments with a variety of materials and sizes show that toner Q/M vs. C_t follows the relation

$$\frac{Q}{M} = K \exp\left(-\frac{C_t}{C_{t0}}\right) \tag{7.6}$$

where

$$K = \frac{3\sigma_0}{\rho_t R_t} \quad \text{(esu/g) and} \quad C_{t0} = \frac{\rho_t R_t}{\rho_c R_c}$$

The subscripts t and c refer to toner and carrier, respectively; ρ is the mass density (g/cm^3); R(cm) is the radius; σ_0 (esu/cm^2) is the surface charge density exchanged between toner and carrier surfaces (20–40 esu/cm^2 for xerographic materials); and C_{t0} is that value of toner concentration at which the total surface area of toner particles is equal to the carrier surface area. If N_t is the number of toner particles on one carrier, the toner area is

$$N_t(4\pi R_t^2) = 4\pi R_c^2 \quad \text{(cm}^2\text{)} \tag{7.7}$$

and

$$N_t = \left(\frac{R_c}{R_t}\right)^2 \tag{7.8}$$

The toner concentration is defined in (7.4), so

$$C_{t0} = \frac{N_t M_t}{M_c + N_t M_t} \cong \frac{N_t M_t}{M_c} = \frac{\rho_t R_t}{\rho_c R_c} \tag{7.9}$$

The approximation is valid when the carrier mass M_c is much greater than the mass of all toner $(N_t M_t)$. Here, it is assumed that carrier and toner can be described most simply with an average or mean radius. In actuality, particles are distributed lognormally, so the geometric standard deviation requires specification in addition to the mean size. Chen (1974) discusses the statistics of charged particles; it is a strictly theoretical paper. Benda and Wnek (1981) describe a model of image development that includes a lognormal distribution of particle sizes.

Collins (1977) identifies the exponential factor of (7.6) with the Poisson probability distribution $P(0)$ that a toner particle encounters uncharged carrier surface. His data and those shown in Figure 7.7 fit very well with the negative exponential curves required by the simple theory. In Figure 7.7, the materials have exactly the same chemistry and processing. Only the average sizes are different. By transforming toner concentration to relative fraction of coverage

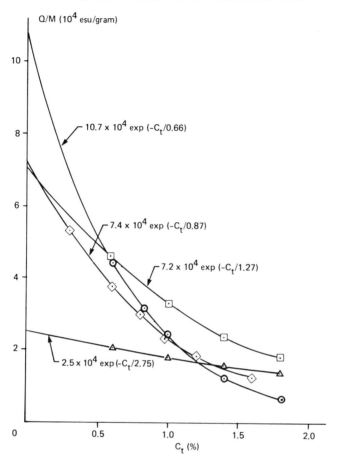

Figure 7.7 Q/M vs. C_t for a variety of toner particle sizes R_t (mean, by number): ⊙ = 3.1 μm; ⊡ = 6.0 μm; ◇ = 4.3 μm; △ = 10.6 μm. Solid curves are empirically matched exponentials.

(f) of the carrier, the four curves of Figure 7.7 fall onto one master curve, as given in Figure 7.8. The fraction of coverage (f) is estimated by dividing C_t by that value of concentration C_t(max) equivalent to a monolayer of cubic close-packed coverage. Under the assumption of identical spheres,

$$C_t(\text{max}) \cong \frac{\pi \rho_t R_t}{\rho_c R_c} = \pi C_{t0} \quad \text{and} \quad f = \frac{C_t}{C_t(\text{max})} = \frac{C_t}{\pi C_{t0}} \qquad (7.10)$$

The four samples plotted in Figure 7.8 fit nicely on one curve. This is true only when the data are transformed according to the measure appropriate to contact charging, that is, surface area.

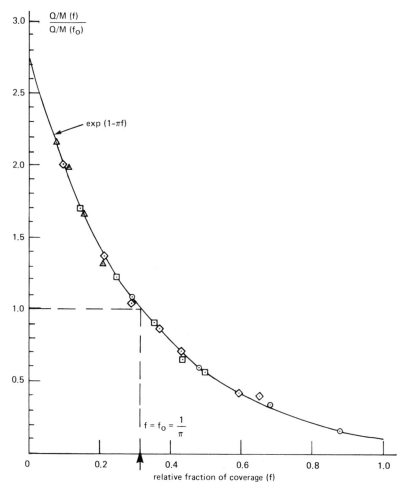

Figure 7.8 Normalized Q/M vs. f, the fraction of coverage of carrier by toner. The data of Figure 7.7 are replotted here; each curve is divided by the value of Q/M where $f = f_0 = 1/\pi$, and C_t for that sample has been transformed to the equivalent value of f.

7.5 Q/M of Toner from Contaminated Carrier

When carrier is recirculated in a magnetic brush device, damage accumulates in several interesting ways. If the carrier beads are coated with a brittle, low-energy material, microcracks develop at the surface and toner particles become pressure-fused to the carrier at the locations of the small cracks. These sites are nucleation centers for growth of toner films which, with continued carrier recirculation and replenishment of fresh toner, grow over the carrier surface and change the contact electrification behavior to toner–toner interactions. If the carrier beads are coated with soft, low-energy material such as PTFE, the coating is gradually abraded away and the underlying high-energy substrate becomes exposed, and toner can fuse to the exposed substrate. Because of high impact pressures, carrier beads will occasionally break up and expose the high-energy surface of a metal or ferrite. All of these aging processes alter the charge/mass behavior of the fresh toner that is periodically added to the mixing region in the developer unit.

A film of permanently attached toner alters the carrier such that no net charge exchange occurs in toner–toner contact; some particles receive electrons, others give electrons back to the carrier in these locations. As a first approximation, the toner that has permanently attached or fused to the carrier can be regarded as an unwanted increase in toner concentration C_t, such that C_t has two components—the available toner and the unavailable film. When one accounts for the fraction of coverage according to these two components, the measured Q/M of the available toner falls rather well on the master curve of Figure 7.8. A film equivalent to $C_t = 0.01 + 1\%$ free toner is equivalent to $C_t = 0.02$; in Figure 7.7, 2% concentration yields less than 2×10^4 esu/g. With this particular toner and carrier system, the print quality would be poor, owing to overdeveloped characters, significant background toner, and loss of fine detail. It would be time to replace the old mix with a new one.

7.6   Neutralization of Carrier Charge

During actual use in a xerographic machine, the carrier beads are recirculated by the magnetic brush and fresh toner is added in controlled amounts to the mix. Since toner receives charge from the carrier, and toner is removed from the developer unit, electric current flows through the conductive housing to the recycled carrier and establishes charge neutrality. Hays (1977) discusses possible mechanisms for neutralizing carrier charge. Basically, carrier and toner are agitated mechanically within the developer unit and toner moves inward from the conductive surface of the housing, thereby leaving the outermost carrier beads essentially clean of toner particles. These clean beads charge up as toner migrates away, so a reasonably high electric field is established between carrier and housing walls. This field causes the neutralizing current flow, provided the housing is connected electrically to the system ground. The flow of charged toner from the outermost developer regions toward the inner region also constitutes a flow of neutralizing current, thus the inner carriers are neutralized as well. The developer sump containing charged carrier is equivalent to a space charge, and the space charge field is highest in the center of the sump.

If the developer unit housing is isolated from the machine system ground, the developer charges up to a high (and hazardous) potential as toner leaves via the PC surface. That is, an ungrounded developer unit is functionally similar to a Van de Graff generator. A numerical estimate of the potential is easily found. Let 10 kg of carrier, each 250 μm in diameter, charge to a surface density of 40 esu/cm^2 or 1.33×10^{-8} C/cm^2. If the carriers are made of steel shot, the density will be about $7 \, g/cm^3$, and using (7.3), the charge/mass of the carrier is estimated at $4.6 \times 10^{-7} \, C/g$. The total charge of 10 kg will be $4.6 \times 10^{-3} \, C$, and with a housing capacitance of 300 pF, the voltage is $V = Q/C = 1.5 \times 10^7 \, V$! Of course, the developer housing would never reach such an incredible level, since the flow of toner would cease when the housing field equaled the development field at the PC surface (about 15 kV/cm). As a result, the housing would charge to a few thousand volts, but one could still receive a nasty jolt.

7.7 Toner Charge Distribution

Up to this point, the discussion has dealt with mean or average values of charge to mass. Particle charging is a statistical event and determining the charge distribution of toner particles is an important study in xerographic theory. Some studies of charged aerosols are relevant to the question of toner charge and its distribution; a few published sources are Gillespie and Langstroth (1952), Kraemer and Johnstone (1955), Kunkel (1950), Röbig and Porstendörfer (1979), and Cho (1964). In most cases, the aerosol charge distribution was symmetrical about a mean value of zero charge. Kunkel (1950) and Szaynok (1971) give arguments for a normal or Gaussian density function. The electrical behavior of aerosols is reviewed by Whitby and Liu (1966), who also mention instrumentation for studying charged particles. Derjaguin et al. (1968/1969), Suzuki and Tomura (1962), Berg and Gaukler (1969), Wuerker et al. (1959), Whetten (1974), and Hendricks and Yeung (1976) each discuss instruments for studying macroscopic charged particles. Lewis et al. (1981) and Stover and Schoonover (1969) describe an instrument specifically designed for studying xerographic toners.

7.8 Charge Spectrometer

A simplified sketch of one type of charge spectrometer is given in Figure 7.9. A fan pulls air through a channel formed by four insulating walls. Conducting plates are attached along two opposing walls and a high potential difference (about 1500 V) is established between these field electrodes. Since the electric field is transverse to the direction of air flow, a charged particle will be deflected toward one electrode or the other, depending on the charge polarity. Gravity will also deflect particles; but if the air flow velocity is high relative to the gravitational terminal velocity of the particle in free fall, then it is fair to ignore gravity. In the studies discussed here, the air flow velocity averaged over 300 cm/sec, whereas the gravitational terminal velocity, as given by Davies (1966, p. 393),

$$v_s = \frac{2R^2 \rho g}{9\eta} \quad (cm/sec) \tag{7.11}$$

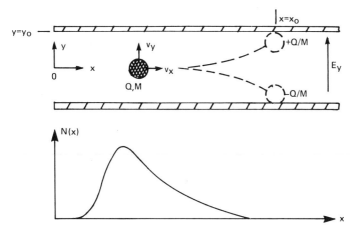

Figure 7.9   The charge spectrometer principle: particle of charge (Q) and mass (M) is transported in an air stream at velocity v_x along x and is deflected along y by the electric field E_y. The particle impacts and adheres at x_0, a position depending on Q and M. The typical number distribution along x is shown as $N(x)$ (usually found by a scanning reflection densitometer).

would be roughly 2 cm/sec for a 20-μm diameter particle. In (7.11), R is the particle radius (cm), ρ (g/cm^3) is the density of the particle, $g = 980$ cm/sec^2 is the acceleration of gravity, and η (g/cm-sec) or (poise) = 1.8×10^{-4} (for air) is the shear viscosity of the gas.

Charged toner particles are removed by blow-off from their carrier host; the carrier beads are held by a permanent magnet at the entrance to the spectrometer. A small diameter hypodermic needle blows a very small volume of air at high velocity over the carrier and removes essentially all of the toner particles; these particles become entrained in the air stream of the spectrometer. The toner aerosol is constrained in a narrow beam about 2 mm wide at the entrance; the air flow is somewhat turbulent over the first few centimeters of travel along the x-direction and becomes laminar within the first 5–10 cm downstream. The distance between field plates is 2.54 cm and their length is 60 cm. The field is reasonably uniform over the volume where toner particles flow down and across the channel. Each particle has a unique charge (q) and mass (m). The net accelerating force along the transverse (y) direction depends on the charge, the electric field (E_y), and the aerodynamic drag force on the particle; thus, a given particle travels a unique distance x_0 (cm) before impacting and adhering to a field plate. Uncharged, or very low charge particles pass through the instrument and are not measured. The instrument by Lewis et al. (1981) collected toner on a sheet of filter paper supported across the direction of air flow, so they were able to collect particles of any charge, including zero. In the instrument of Figure 7.9, particles are intercepted on the field plate at $y = y_0 = 1.27$ cm at a distance x_0 (which depends on the particle q/R or q/m, contingent on the exact nature of the drag force experienced by the particle). In the previously cited references, the validity of Stokes Law (viscous drag) is assumed, so the raw data would yield the charge to radius ratio (q/R), not the charge to mass ratio (q/m). Evidence is given here that the drag force experienced by the rough particles scales with the *square* of the transverse velocity v_y; this kind of retarding force is called *pressure drag*, for lack of a better term. Therefore, the mathematical relationship between particle charge, size, and distance of attachment to the field plate is derived for viscous and pressure drag forces, and the experimental results are compared with the "theories" to see which gives best agreement. Discussions of viscous drag, Stokes Law, and discrepancies between simple Stokesian theory and experiment are found in Goldstein (1929), Pruppacher and Steinberger (1969), and Maxworthy (1965). Fluid dynamics and mechanics are treated by Landau and Lifshitz (1967), for example.

7.9   Viscous Drag on Toner Particles

One way energy can be dissipated in a gas is by transport of momentum through collision processes with the gas molecules. The flow of momentum is transferred by collision between molecules and the process reaches a steady state in a few collisions, so the relaxation time is short (on the order of 100 psec). Shear viscosity is a measure of this transport process and the drag force on a particle for very low velocities or small particles is given by the Stokes drag $F_s = 6\pi\eta\,Rv$ (dyne). The equation of motion for a charged aerosol with an accelerating force is then given by

$$m\,\frac{dv_y}{dt} = qE_y - 6\pi\eta R v_y \quad \text{(dynes)} \tag{7.12}$$

whose solution by direct integration is

$$v_y = \frac{qE_y}{6\pi\eta R}\left(1 - e^{-(6\pi\eta R/m)t}\right) \quad \text{(cm/sec)} \tag{7.13}$$

The result is in the cgs system of units, so q is in units of esu, the field E_y is in esu/cm^2 (300 V/cm $= 1.0$ esu/cm^2), the viscosity of air is $\eta = 1.8 \times 10^{-4}$ g/cm-sec (or poise), particle radius R is in cm, mass is in grams, and time is in seconds. The transverse distance $y(t)$ is limited to $y = y_0$ (cm), and the time required to reach the field electrode is $t_0 = x_0/v_x$, where v_x (cm/sec) is the average air velocity along the x-direction, and x_0 is the measured location of the adherent particle. The distance y is found by a second integration,

$$y_0 = \frac{qE_y}{6\pi\eta R}\left[\frac{x_0}{v_x} + \frac{m}{6\pi\eta R}(e^{-6\pi\eta R x_0/mv_x} - 1)\right] \quad \text{(cm)} \tag{7.14}$$

and this equation is rearranged to obtain the desired relation for the particle charge.

$$q = \frac{6\pi\eta R y_0}{E_y[x_0/v_x + (m/6\rho\eta R)(e^{-6\pi\eta R_0/mv_x} - 1)]} \quad \text{(esu)} \quad (7.15)$$

Very small particles reach their terminal velocity rapidly, so under the condition $m/(6\pi\eta R) \ll 1.0$, the relation (7.15) reduces to a much simpler equation

$$q \cong \frac{6\pi\eta R y_0 v_x}{E_y x_0} \quad (7.16)$$

This equation is found in many of the cited references; it is often called the Suzuki–Tomura Relation. Applying this relation to the instrument described earlier with $y_0 = 1.27$ cm, $v_x = 305$ cm/sec, and $E_y = 2.0$ esu/cm^2 (600 V/cm), one finds that $q/R = 0.67/x_0$; thus, a particle with $R = 5.0 \times 10^{-4}$ cm that deposits at $x_0 = 10$ cm would have a computed charge of 3.35×10^{-5} esu (1.11×10^{-14} C) or a q/m of about 5.5×10^4 esu/g (1.83×10^{-5} C/g) for a density of 1.16 g/cm^3. The discrepancy between (7.16) and (7.15) is about 1% for $R = 5 \times 10^{-4}$ cm and increases to about 19% for $R = 20 \times 10^{-4}$ cm.

The electrostatic cgs system is convenient for force calculations and is used here. Recall that the electrostatic definition of charge was originally done with torque balances, so a force of 1.0 dyne was said to exist between two point charges of 1.0 esu each, separated by a distance of 1.0 cm. That is,

$$F = \frac{qq'}{r^2} \quad \text{(dynes)} \quad (7.17)$$

or the dimensional equivalence is dyne $=$ esu^2/cm^2. Coulomb force normalized by the unit charge is the electric field, so $E = F/q$ and the unit is esu/cm^2, sometimes called the statvolt/cm. Plugging in the appropriate dimensions in (7.16) yields charge in esu, as it should. Most of us do not measure electrostatic forces directly, and our experience is often limited to measurements with voltmeters and other indirect tools that seal us from the sensation of a force. The unit of potential is the esu/cm or statvolt; it is a charge per unit length, and 1.0 esu/cm $=$ 300 V. Sometimes, it is illuminating to flip units around like a kaleidoscope, discovering many unfamiliar identities with more familiar measures. In electrostatics, much investigation was done before 1930, and workers then naturally used the electrostatic cgs system; hence, the old literature is filled with esu's and centimeters.

In (7.15) and (7.16), q/R scales with the ratio $y_0 v_x/(E_y x_0)$, so it is possible to verify the dependence of the drag force on the assumed starting relation (7.12). This is done by experimenting with the instrument parameters y_0, v_x, or E_y while keeping the toner sample invariant. A large sample of toner–carrier mix

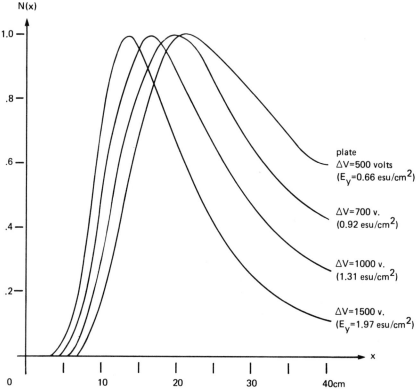

Figure 7.10   Raw normalized data from a charge spectrometer. The four toner samples have nearly identical charge spectra, only the instrument field E_y is different for each curve. Toner–carrier mix is standard 3800 materials at $C_t = 1.0\%$.

is subdivided into equal portions after mixing and charging. The charge distribution of each portion will be reasonably close to that of the remaining portions, so a series of experiments can be performed with the instrument set at different values of applied field E_y, or the air velocity v_x can be changed, or both. Toner is blown into the instrument and the relative frequency (number) of toner particles/cm^2 at any position $N(x)$ is found by counting with a microscope or by measuring scattered light from the toner collection (the field plate has a specular surface and is quite flat). The intensity of scattered light is thus proportional to the number of particles/cm^2 and, as pointed out by D. C. Randolph (private communication), the charge spectrum $N(q)$ is found by deconvolving $N(x)$ from the relation for the spectrometer,

$$q(x) = \frac{K_1}{x} \tag{7.18}$$

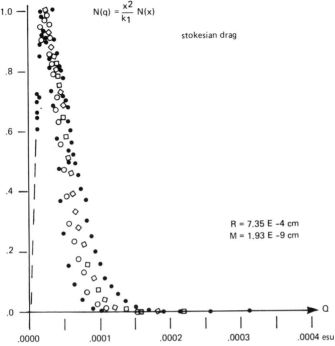

Figure 7.11 Deconvolved spectra for stokesian drag. The four sets of data should agree (self-consistency) if drag force is $F_d = 6\pi\eta R v_y$. The above data are not overwhelming in their agreement.

to obtain the relative frequency of occurrence of particles with a given charge or charge to radius ratio,

$$N(q) = \frac{x^2}{K_1} N(x) \qquad (7.19)$$

A peak in the $N(x)$ vs. x signal therefore does not necessarily correspond to any peak in the $N(q)$ vs. q spectrum, which is the relation actually sought. The data obtained from ostensibly identical toner samples at four different field strengths are given in Figure 7.10. The peaks of the curves have been normalized to 1.0 for ease of comparison. The deconvolved charge spectra are shown in Figure 7.11, and because each sample ought to have the same indicated spectrum, the lack of agreement is evidence that something is wrong. As shown in the next section, the data become much more consistent if the drag force is proportional to v_y^2.

7.10   Pressure Drag on Toner Particles

Stokes' formula, $F = 6\pi\eta Rv$, gives a first-order estimate of drag on a very slow moving sphere in a viscous liquid. Oseen (1927) realized that Stokes' formula was an incomplete description of flow around spheres, but even his correction is insufficient to explain the inconsistency of the data in Figure 7.11. If the dominant drag force is second order in velocity (i.e., a pressure drag), then the equation of motion can be written, according to the nomenclature of Batchelor (1967, p. 339), as

$$m\frac{dv_y}{dt} = qE_y - C_D\pi R^2\frac{\rho_g}{2}v_y^2 \quad \text{(dyne)} \qquad (7.20)$$

where C_D is the drag coefficient (dimensionless, and as yet unspecified), $\pi R^2 =$ the cross-section area (cm^2) of the moving particle, and ρ_g is the density of the displaced gas (1.2×10^{-3} g/cm^3 for air at standard temperature and pressure). The solution of (7.20) is

$$v_y = A\tanh(ABt) \quad \text{(cm/sec)}$$

where

$$A = \left(\frac{2qE_y}{C_D\pi R^2\rho_g}\right)^{1/2} \quad \text{(cm/sec)} \quad \text{and} \quad B = \frac{C_D\pi R^2\rho_g}{2m} \quad (\text{cm}^{-1}) \quad (7.21)$$

Integrating the velocity yields the transverse position which, as before, is limited to $y = y_0$ by the field plate.

$$y_0 = \frac{1}{B}\log_e[\cosh(ABt_0)] \quad \text{(cm)} \qquad (7.22)$$

Inserting the expressions for A, B, and $t_0 = x_0/v_x$ into (7.22) and solving for particle charge, one obtains

$$q = \frac{2m^2v_x^2}{C_D\pi R^2\rho_g E_y x^2}\left[\cosh^{-1}\left(\exp\frac{C_D\pi R^2\rho_g y_0}{2m}\right)\right]^2 \quad \text{(esu)} \qquad (7.23)$$

Experiments with narrow size ranges at $R = 5$, 12, and 20 μm reveal that the drag coefficient scales with the particle size and is approximately linear in R; that is, $C_D = R/L_0$ with $L_0 = 9 \times 10^{-6}$ cm. With $C_D\pi R^2\rho_g/(2m) \gg 1.0$, Equation (7.23) reduces to the much simpler expression

$$q \cong \frac{8\rho_t mL_0}{3\rho_g E_y}\left(\frac{v_x}{x_0}\right)^2\left(\frac{3\rho_g y_0}{8\rho_t L_0} + \log_e 2\right)^2 \quad \text{(esu)} \qquad (7.24)$$

and it is seen that the q/m of the particle can be determined without knowledge of the particle size.

The charge spectrum is determined, as before, by deconvolving the distribution of particles at a given q or q/m according to

$$q(x) = \frac{K_2}{x^2} \qquad (7.25)$$

to obtain the relative frequency of occurrence as a function of charge,

$$N(q) = \frac{x^3}{2K_2} N(x) \qquad (7.26)$$

A representative charge to mass spectrum is given in Figure 7.12; the spectral shape agrees superficially with the shape of spectra determined by Cho (1964)

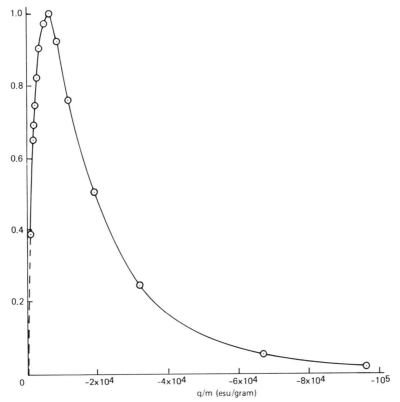

Figure 7.12   Charge/mass spectrum of a toner sample after charging by contact with 3800 type carrier beads.

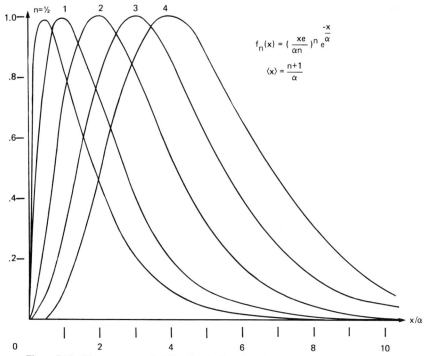

Figure 7.13   The gamma probability density function. See Section 7.10 for its properties.

for small metal particles. Curves of this shape can be subsumed by the family of Gamma Probabability Density functions $f_n(q) = [qe/(q_0 n)]^n \exp(-q/q_0)$, which are plotted in Figure 7.13. See Hastings and Peacock (1974) for further discussion of statistical distributions. Winkelman (1977/1978) shows a q/R spectrum with data reduced under the assumption of viscous drag; he states the distribution is close to a log-normal one. Schein and Cranch (1975) published q/m distributions found by incrementally blowing away toner and measuring the change in both charge and mass in separate experiments. With their technique, the increments of particles detached would likely contain distributions in charge and size, so the spectra would not reveal fine details.

The four separate scans given in Figure 7.10 are deconvolved according to (7.24) and (7.26) and the results are plotted in Figure 7.14. The consistency is much improved over that shown in Figure 7.11, so the evidence supports the assertion that the aerodynamic drag force goes as

$$F_d = \frac{\pi R^3}{2L_0}\rho_g v_y^2 \quad \text{(dyne)} \tag{7.27}$$

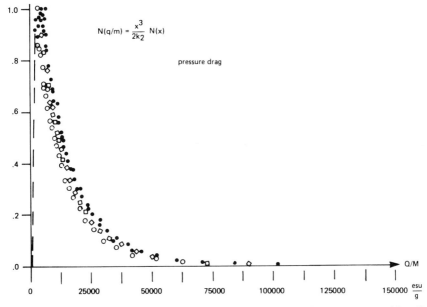

Figure 7.14   Deconvolved spectra for pressure drag. The four sets of data are reasonably self-consistent, giving support to the claim that the drag force is $F_d = (\pi R^3/2L_0)\rho_g v_y^2$.

7.11   An Interpretation of the Drag Coefficient

Behind the development of viscous dissipation or Stokes's Law lies the idea that the gas in which the charged particle moves is composed of molecular billiard balls. The molecules collide and translate only; thus, they carry momentum only. This view is justified for monatomic gases such as He, Ne, A, Kr, or Xe. The normal atmosphere, however, is composed primarily of the diatomic molecules N_2 and O_2 with important polyatomic molecules like H_2O and CO_2 as well. These molecules have internal degrees of freedom, namely vibration and rotation, so they can and do absorb energy directly from collisions with other bodies. Kneser (1933, 1954, 1961), in discussing relaxation and transport phenomena, establishes the fundamental idea that momentum and energy are coupled when the direction of momentum exchange and transport coincide. That is, translational energy can be transformed into vibrational or rotational energy, and the lifetime of these excited states is quite long, in some cases, so the collision process stores energy in the diatomic and polyatomic molecules. The stored energy flows or relaxes to a steady state and is converted back to translational energy (heat). With molecules such as O_2 and H_2O, the relaxation time is extremely long (about 1 msec) and the presence of these molecules in air leads to the "anomalous" sound absorption behavior studied by Knudsen (1931, 1933, 1935) and Henderson and Herzfeld (1965). Ingard (1969) and Morse and Ingard (1968) can be consulted for discussions on anomalies in sound transmission and internal energy loss mechanisms in gases. Kneser (1954) attributes the anomalous sound absorption in air to long relaxation times of polyatomic molecules and identifies the effect with an incompletely developed volume viscosity. In shear viscosity, momentum only is taken up by the gas, so the relaxation time is roughly equal to the mean free path divided by the molecular velocity (an approximately correct estimate is $6.5 \times 10^{-6} \, \mathrm{cm}/5 \times 10^4 \, \mathrm{cm/sec} = 1.3 \times 10^{-10}$ sec). Jeans (1940) and Loeb (1961) should be consulted for more exact estimates of classical relaxation times. Chapman and Cowling (1970, p. 215) and Herzfeld and Litovitz (1959, p. 47) discuss volume viscosity and relaxation effects.

A small, rough toner particle accelerated at several hundred g's to a velocity of perhaps 100 cm/sec creates a pressure gradient in the displaced gas and the excess energy (owing to molecular absorption of kinetic energy from the particle) is carried away by the gas. In air, absorption is largely due to vibrational modes of oxygen and water molecules; the excited molecules gradually relax (msec) and degrade the energy to heat (i.e., the thermal velocity increases). Henderson (1963) has written an excellent tutorial paper on this subject. As a first approximation, the excess energy (E_g) given to the gas is

$$E_g = \frac{m_g v^2}{2} \tag{7.28}$$

where m_g = mass of the gas displaced by the particle = particle volume times the gas density. The drag force is identified with the work per unit distance done on the gas. That is, the gas resists changes in density (the volume viscosity is a measure of this resistance), but the change in density is highly localized. The drag force can be expressed as

$$F_d = -\frac{\Delta E_g}{\Delta y} = -\frac{2\pi R^3 \rho_g v^2}{3 L_e} \tag{7.29}$$

where L_e is the effective distance over which the pressure gradient exists. Equating (7.29) with the previous expressions (7.20) or (7.27), one discovers a relationship between the drag coefficient C_D and a property of the gas, namely

$$C_D = \frac{4R}{3 L_e} \tag{7.30}$$

and the empirical constant L_0 used earlier to reconcile experiments with (7.23) or (7.24) becomes

$$L_0 = \frac{3 L_e}{4} \quad \text{(cm)} \tag{7.31}$$

Since the empirical value was $L_0 = 9 \times 10^{-6}$ cm, the effective distance L_e for excess energy storage is about 1.2×10^{-5} cm, which is about two times the mean free path of N_2 at standard temperature and pressure. (The *CRC Handbook of Chemistry and Physics*, 59th ed., gives a value of 6.5×10^{-6} cm for the mean free path of N_2 at STP.) This interpretation of the drag for accelerating particles is perhaps at odds with much of the literature on the behavior of aerosols. Indeed, the implications of this interpretation are broad and require a thoroughness of investigation that goes much beyond the scope of this book.

7.12   Particle Adhesion

Particle adhesion occurs at every opportunity in xerographic processes. In the development step, toner adheres to the carrier surface, is attached to the PC surface, and is transported out of the development system. At the transfer unit, toner is attached to paper, and those particles not transferring are removed from the PC by a cleaning device and are transported aerodynamically to a collection receptacle. The forces involved in adhesion are primarily electrostatic and electrodynamic in nature. Krupp (1967), Zimon (1969), Patrick (1967), and Derjaguin et al. (1968–1969, 1978) are good entry points to the literature on adhesion. Krupp, who specifically addresses particle adhesion, considers electrostatic and dispersion forces as dominant between adherents and builds a physical theory in his review of the subject. He classifies interactions between solids into three types. Type I interactions result from long-range forces (i.e., inverse square and inverse cube laws) such as electrostatic and dispersion forces. These act not only at the area of contact but extend to regions beyond the immediate adhesive junction. Dispersion forces are very important at distances of perhaps 0.05 μm or less between surfaces; electrostatic forces dominate at greater distances. Type II interactions are short-range chemical and hydrogen bonding forces that arise only if an adhesive area has already been created by long-range forces. Type III interactions include such effects as sintering, diffusion, dissolution, and alloying between adherents. Krupp states that Type I and III interactions are most important in particle adhesion, because they establish the size of the contact area between particle and substrate. Viewing adhesion kinetically, particle and substrate first contact one another at one point of atomic dimensions, then the long-range forces generate a torque on the particle which acts about the contact fulcrum and rotates the particle until contact with several other regions is formed. Elastic and plastic deformation in the contact regions must be treated dynamically, as material often creeps and flows viscously until equilibrium is reached. The process increases the contact area and, with some materials, requires several months to reach equilibrium.

The importance of adsorbed films is discussed by Corn (1966); he reviews particle adhesion and experimental techniques for measuring adhesive forces. Corn regards dispersion forces, electrostatic forces, and the surface tension of adsorbed films as the major factors in particle adhesion. Other factors like particle shape, surface roughness, and the nature of surface contact relate to the (usually) unknown area of true contact between particle and substrate. Bowden and Tabor (1964) did the pioneering work on the nature of true contact between real surfaces. Loeb (1958), in fact, dedicates his book on static electricity to F. P. Bowden and his associates because they clarified "... the more baffling aspects of static electrification..." Therefore, a serious study of adhesion would necessarily include Bowden and Tabor's classifical investigations.

7.13   Dispersion Forces

Kittel (1966, p. 83) speaks of the van der Waals–London equation and the interaction of isolated molecules through fluctuating dipole–dipole fields. This interaction leads to a potential energy of the form

$$V(R) = -\frac{K}{R^6} \quad \text{(ergs)} \tag{7.32}$$

and a force that goes as

$$F(R) = -\frac{dV}{dR} = \frac{6K}{R^7} \quad \text{(dynes)} \tag{7.33}$$

Forces of this type are always present and play an essential role in such phenomena as the organization of biological membranes, the hydrophobic effect, physical adsorption, the behavior of soap films, friction, adhesion, surface tension, the strength of solids, and the behavior of real gases. Israelachvili (1974) has done much to clarify the subject of van der Waals forces. He says,

> van der Waals forces have also remarkably varied properties: they may be attractive or repulsive; they may align molecules relative to each other; they may deform the shapes of large bodies, and they may promote the migration of molecules across interfaces.

When molecules organize into macroscopic solid objects, the van der Waals or London dispersion force no longer follows the inverse seventh power, as in (7.33), and computation of the interaction between a particle and substrate can be quite protracted. In this section, some very simple formulas are given, although one must read the literature to appreciate the effort behind the simple equations. Some of the important references are Mahanty and Ninham (1971), Krupp, Schnabel, and Walter (1972), Richmond and Ninham (1972), Theodorovich (1978), Keifer, Parsegian, and Weiss (1978), Dorris and Gray (1979), Landau and Lifshitz (1960), and Langbein (1969, 1971).

The dispersion interaction between two bodies results from fluctuations in electromagnetic fields caused by electronic motion about the nucleus. As all materials absorb and emit electromagnetic radiation, the oscillating molecule can be thought of as a transmitter and receiver of radiation, so the field equations used to derive an interaction necessarily become (in classical language) those of a dipole interacting with another dipole. In the language of quantum mechanics, one speaks of electromagnetic fluctuations. Mahanty and Ninham (1976) call these electrodynamic interactions "dispersion interactions." The word "dispersion" is used because Fritz London—one of the first to have a theory of such interactions—computed the forces based on the dispersion of optical absorption spectra of materials. A link is thus established between the optical properties of solids and the electrodynamic force between particles and substrates. Two regimes are discussed in the literature on dispersion forces. The *nonretarded* regime is for materials separated by a distance less than 100 Å; the *retarded* regime is for separations greater than 500 Å. The nonretarded regime is of primary interest in toner adhesion. Retardation effects can be understood in classical language by considering a Bohr atom as an instantaneous dipole sending a signal to another Bohr atom which polarizes in response to the signal. This response creates another signal which is sent back to the first atom, so the two atoms shake hands through their fluctuating dipole fields. It takes a little time for radiation to transit the distance between atoms; hence, the phase relationship between atoms is a function of the distance. The attractive interaction weakens as the transit time increases (i.e., retardation effects become important), or equivalently, as the distance increases between atoms. For the retarded regime, the exponent in (7.33) increases to an inverse eighth power interaction.

Israelachvili (1972, p. 44) treats the problem of summing up all of the interactions between two macroscopic bodies. Given two dielectric slabs that are very thick and wide, separated by a distance D, the force per unit area for two half-spaces is

$$f = \frac{A}{6\pi D^3} \quad \text{(dynes/cm}^2\text{)} \tag{7.34}$$

where A is the Hamaker Constant (erg). Krupp (1967, p. 113) develops an equivalent relation and calls it the van der Waals pressure, and, giving some credit to Lifshitz, writes the equation as

$$P_{vdW} = \frac{\hbar\bar{\omega}}{8\pi^2 z_0^3} \quad \text{(dynes/cm}^2\text{)} \tag{7.35}$$

and calls $\hbar\bar{\omega}$ the Lifshitz–van der Waals Constant; z_0 is the distance between plates or "half-spaces." Comparing (7.34) and (7.35), one finds the relation between the Hamaker Constant and the Lifshitz–van der Waals Constant.

$$\hbar\bar{\omega} = \frac{4\pi}{3} A \quad \text{(erg)} \tag{7.36}$$

Tabulations of interactions for various pairs of materials are found scattered through the literature. Table 7.2 has been collected from several sources: Krupp (1967), Krupp, Schnabel, and Walter (1972), and Israelachvili and Tabor (1972). For order-of-magnitude estimates, the Hamaker constant does

**Table 7.2   The Hamaker Constants (A)
of Materials in Vacuum**

Material	$A \, (10^{-12} \, \text{erg})$
Quartz (SiO_2)	0.8–1.0
Hydrocarbons	0.5 (liquid); 0.9 (solid)
Water	0.36–0.63
Polystyrene	0.61–0.79
Mica	1.35
Silver	4.0
Gold	1.83–4.5
Copper	2.5

not vary widely; it is roughly 1×10^{-12} erg for many materials, whether liquid, insulator, metal, or polymer. This observation greatly simplifies the situation, but it also underscores the futility of searching for materials that might dramatically reduce the adhesion between particles and substrates.

Israelachvili and Tabor (1972) showed the transition from nonretarded interaction to the retarded regime. In a beautiful series of experiments with crossed mica cylinders (which have the same contact geometry as a sphere on a plane), they measured the dispersion force over distances from 15 to 1300 Å by a resonance technique, with the distance measured by an interferometer. The power law of the interaction was extracted from their data and was shown to go from an inverse square law to an inverse cube law. Their result is plotted in Figure 7.15. Freshly cleaved mica surfaces are smooth at the molecular level over large areas, thus the true contact geometry and area can be accurately determined. In the retarded regime, the force per unit area of two plates (half-spaces) is

$$f = \frac{B}{D^4} \quad (\text{dynes/cm}^2) \tag{7.37}$$

where B is the "retarded" Hamaker Constant. Israelachvili and Tabor found the experimental value for mica was $B = 9.7 \times 10^{-20}$ erg-cm, and this verified the essential correctness of the theory that predicted $B = 9.3 \times 10^{-20}$ erg-cm.

To find the dispersion force between curved surfaces, a geometrical factor is used. Langbein (1969, 1971) gives the factor for two spheres whose radii (R_1

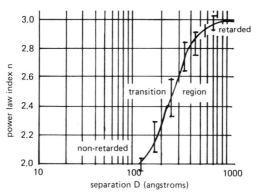

Figure 7.15 Variation of the power law n for van der Waals force between crossed mica cylinders with distance D. From Israelachvili and Tabor (1972).

and R_2) are much greater than the separation D. Using his relation, the total dispersion force between spheres is

$$F_d = \pi D \left(\frac{R_1 R_2}{R_1 + R_2} \right) f \quad \text{(dynes)} \tag{7.38}$$

A sphere with a very large radius approximates a flat plane, so letting $R_1 \to \infty$ and $R_2 = R$, the dispersion force for a sphere on a plane is

$$F_d = \frac{AR}{6D^2} \quad \text{(dynes)} \tag{7.39}$$

for the nonretarded regime. For distances D greater than about 500 Å, the power law is close to an inverse cube and (7.37) must be used, so

$$F_d = \pi D \left(\frac{R_1 R_2}{R_1 + R_2} \right) \frac{B}{D^4} = \left(\frac{R_1 R_2}{R_1 + R_2} \right) \frac{\pi B}{D^3} \quad \text{(dynes)} \tag{7.40}$$

and letting R_1 become large, as before, the dispersion force in the retarded regime for a sphere and plane becomes

$$F_d = \frac{\pi B R}{D^3} \quad \text{(dynes)} \tag{7.41}$$

When two bodies come into intimate contact, D does not go to zero. One must remember the limitations of a derivation, and in this case the oscillating dipoles are treated as point sources; thus, molecular or atomic size does not enter into the final equations. If a finite size is assigned to the atom or molecule, say 3 or 4 Å, then the distance of closest approach between two atoms is just that size given to the atomic oscillators. In this manner, physically absurd situations are avoided, and singularities in dispersion forces do not arise when objects come in contact. Krupp uses 4.0 Å as the minimum distance of approach; Tabor and Israelachvili use 3.0 Å. At this stage in the development of adhesion theory, it is not crucial to the argument what value of D is chosen when bodies touch. This is largely because the level of ignorance about the relevant value of R, and the number of contacting asperities of real surfaces, overwhelms any possible ignorance about $D(min)$. Other than freshly cleaved mica, almost no surfaces are molecularly smooth over large areas, as has been amply demonstrated by Bowden and Tabor (1964). To reconcile theory and experiment, Krupp assigns small radii of curvature to the several contact asperities of a larger particle attached to a substrate. For toner particles with a radius of about 5 μm, the asperities might be in the range of 0.1 μm, with three asperities (a tripod is the minimum stable configuration) supporting the particle on the substrate. With numbers such as these, one can make order-of-magnitude estimates of the dispersion force between a toner particle and a carrier bead surface. Letting the Hamaker constant $A = 1 \times 10^{-12}$ erg, a perfect sphere resting on a flat plane would adhere with a force

$$F_d = \frac{AR}{6D^2} = \frac{1 \times 10^{-12} \text{ erg} \times 5 \times 10^{-4} \text{ cm}}{6 \times (4 \times 10^{-8} \text{ cm})^2} = 0.05 \quad \text{dyne} \quad (7.42)$$

If one amortizes the contact over three asperities, each with a radius of 0.1 μm, then the estimated dispersion force would be

$$F_d = \frac{3AR'}{6D^2} = \frac{3 \times 1 \times 10^{-12} \text{ erg} \times 1 \times 10^{-5} \text{ cm}}{6 \times (4 \times 10^{-8} \text{ cm})^2} = 0.003 \quad \text{dyne} \quad (7.43)$$

"Back-of-the-envelope" estimates such as this are quite useful, since they give an order of magnitude for the force under question, and this allows the assignment of a priority to the amount and kind of attention or effort given to the phenomenon. Since toner particles are charged, the electrostatic component of the adhesive force also requires attention.

7.14 Electrostatic Force

The electrostatic force between toner and carrier is Coulombic in nature. The derivation of forces between charged spheres is found in numerous sources. Jackson (1962, p. 31) and Maxwell (1954), for example, give very readable accounts. The geometry is given in Figure 7.16; here, $f = R_t + R_c + \ell$, where ℓ is a very small distance approaching $D(min)$, as discussed earlier. This small distance is included here only as a reminder that dispersion forces are important,

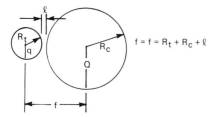

$f = f = R_t + R_c + \ell$

Figure 7.16 Toner–carrier geometry for computing electrostatic forces. Toner charge is q; carrier charge is Q; Distance between surfaces is ℓ.

but that no singularities exist. It is ignored in most of the succeeding arguments. The external field of a uniformly charged sphere is indistinguishable from that of a point charge q at the center of the sphere. Here, it is assumed that a toner particle is uniformly charged at its surface. The carrier is presumed to be a good conductor covered with a very thin insulating skin (which is not shown in the figure). With these approximations, the electrostatic force between toner and carrier is

$$F_c = \frac{q^2}{f^2}\left(\frac{Q}{q} - \frac{(f/R_c)^3}{(f^2/R_c^2 - 1)^2}\right) \tag{7.44}$$

where

$$f = R_c + R_t + \ell \cong R_c + R_t, \text{ since } \ell \ll R_c \text{ or } R_t.$$

This is the form Jackson (1962) gives (Figure 7.17). It can be rewritten as

$$F_c = \frac{qQ}{(R_c + R_t)^2} - \frac{q^2(1 + R_t/R_c)}{(2R_t + R_t^2/R_c)^2} \tag{7.45}$$

which in the limit of very large R_c relative to R_t becomes

$$F_c \cong -\frac{q^2}{4R_t^2} \tag{7.46}$$

This equation is the so-called "image force" attracting a charged particle toward a conducting plane. If the plane is a dielectric with dielectric constant k, and the system is in a medium with $k_0 = 1.0$ (i.e., air or vacuum), then the image force is written as

$$F_c = -\frac{[(k - 1)/(k + 1)]q^2}{4R_t^2} \tag{7.47}$$

Good conductors are equipotentials in static electric fields, so they polarize in a field such that the internal field is zero. This requires that $(k - 1)/(k + 1) = 1.0$ for conductors, which is only mathematically true for infinite k.

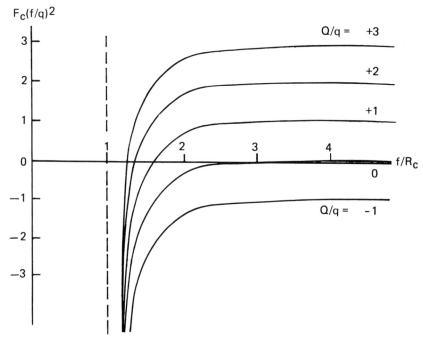

Figure 7.17 Plot of coulomb force between a small charged body (q) and a larger, conducting sphere of charge Q and radius R_c. $f = R_t + R_c + /$. From Jackson (1962), Copyright 1962, John Wiley & Sons.

An unfortunate double usage of the word "image" exists in electrophotography. The usage as given above refers to the polarization of one material by the external field of another body, with this polarization giving rise to an additional field such that the total field is indistinguishable from that of the original charged body plus a mirror image charged body, opposite in polarity and spaced, in the case of a conductor, a distance R_t beneath the surface of the plane. This image force is always attractive.

The image force given by (7.44) is also attractive when f/R_c is close to 1.0, irrespective of the polarities of Q (the carrier charge) and q (the toner charge). That is, particles of the same polarity attract if they get close enough, but repel if the spacing is increased slightly. For a numerical estimate of the coulomb force (F_c), let $R_c = 1.25 \times 10^{-2}$ cm, $R_t = 5 \times 10^{-4}$ cm, $Q = 0$, and $q = -3 \times 10^{-5}$ esu [computed from (7.6) with $\sigma_c = -26$ esu/cm^2 and $C_t = C_{t0}$]. From (7.45), one obtains

$$F_c \cong -8.9 \times 10^{-4} \text{ dyne} \tag{7.48}$$

whereas, the simpler equation (7.46) yields

$$F_c \cong -9.0 \times 10^{-4} \text{ dyne} \tag{7.49}$$

Comparing the estimate of F_c with the earlier statement of F_d, dispersion forces clearly dominate adhesion for this simple case. Mastrangelo (1982) finds that adhesion is indeed controlled by van der Waals' dispersion forces. However, Donald (1969), Kottler et al. (1968), and Donald and Watson (1970) claim that adhesion is dominated by electrostatic forces. The discrepancy is removed when one examines the experimental techniques. The evidence supports the claim of Mastrangelo, but there are regimes where electrostatic forces can dominate. The influence of slight mechanical agitation could easily separate toner a small distance such that F_c dominates. The distance D where the dispersion and electrostatic forces are equal is found by comparing (7.38) and (7.46). For the present case, this distance is

$$D \cong \left(\frac{2AR^3}{3q^2}\right)^{1/2} \cong 3 \times 10^{-7} \quad \text{(cm) (30 Å)} \tag{7.50}$$

In other words, if toner and carrier are immersed in an electric field and given a little agitation, the adhesive bond can be sheared enough to separate the particles such that the electric force then dominates. This action becomes the basis of image development. In his studies with an ultracentrifuge, Mastrangelo (1982) finds that 50% of the toner particles ($R = 5\ \mu$m) can be removed with a force of 0.045 dyne (dispersion component) plus 0.005 dyne (electrostatic component).

It is known from experiments with magnetic brush developers and cascade devices that image development requires mechanical assistance to detach toner electrically. If the carrier–toner mix does not actually touch the PC, the toner stays attached to the carrier and no image development is achieved. This phenomenon is true also of image transfer from the PC to a sheet of paper, where physical contact is imperative for successful transfer. The same physics apparently operates at the cleaning device, where a rotating brush or a stationary blade must touch the toner particles to dislodge them. These observations are consistent with the claim that dispersion forces are indeed important to particle adhesion, and that mechanical assistance is required to shear the adhesive junctions, thereby freeing the toner, so its motion can be directed by electrical or aerodynamic forces.

EIGHT

ELECTROSTATIC IMAGE DEVELOPMENT
MODELS OF THE PROCESS

Chapter 7 establishes the basis for xerographic development of latent images by discussing electrostatic and electrodynamic adhesive forces. The ideas presented in that chapter are taken for granted here, and quantitative models of the development process are analyzed. Various workers have treated cascade development and magnetic brush development. Cassiers and Van Engeland (1965), Bickmore et al. (1970), and Herbert et al. (1975), for example, discuss various aspects of cascade development theory and practice. Magnetic brush development is treated by Schein (1975), Harvapat (1975), Williams (1978), and Benda and Wnek (1981). Thourson (1972) reviews xerographic development processes and his bibliography gives 63 entries.

Magnetic brush development is first analyzed microscopically, under the assumption that sufficient mechanical shear exists to break the dispersion force component of the adhesive junction between toner and carrier beads. In addition, it is assumed that toner and carrier can be represented by an average size, although it is well known that the sizes are distributed lognormally. Benda and Wnek (1981) give a model for development that includes distributions in toner size and charge, and, as they point out, the good agreement with experiment is bought at the expense of simplicity.

8.1 A Microscopic Analysis of Electrostatic Development

Schein (1975) and Williams (1978) built models of image development that are conceptually simple, highlight the underlying processes, and give reasonable agreement with experiment. Schein's model specifically addressed large area development and Williams compared the results of modeling with line image and large area development experiments. These models address the process from the viewpoint of a carrier bead covered with charged toner, and sum the electrostatic forces acting on toner to decide whether a particle will deposit on the PC or remain attached to a carrier surface. Both models assume the deposited toners do not substantially alter the development field; Schein's hypothesis yields a linear relation for the toner mass/cm^2 vs. applied field and Williams obtains a nonliner, threshold relationship. The data given in Thoursen (1972), attributed to Seimiya and Mitsuhashi (1966), show nonlinear behavior for some toner–carrier combinations and nonlinear, threshold behavior for other toners and carriers. Benda and Wnek (1981) show linear and nonlinear behavior, depending on experimental circumstances.

The mass of toner deposited on a unit area of a latent image can be broken down into three factors:

$$\left(\frac{\text{toner mass}}{\text{cm}^2 \text{ of image}}\right) = \left(\frac{\text{toner mass}}{\text{carrier}}\right) \times \left(\frac{\text{number of carriers}}{\text{cm}^2 \text{ of image}}\right)$$

$$\times \left(\begin{array}{c}\text{fraction of toner removed}\\ \text{from one carrier}\end{array}\right)$$

Factor for factor, the analytical result of Williams's model is

$$\frac{M}{A_{im}} = \left(\frac{C_t M_c}{1 - C_t}\right) \times \left[\frac{2V_c}{\sqrt{3}D_c^2 V_{pc}}\right] \times \frac{1}{2}\left[\frac{FE_0/E_{a0} - 1}{FE_0/E_{a0} + C}\right] \quad (8.1a)$$

$$= \left[\frac{\pi\rho_c D_c V_c C_t}{(1 - C_t)6\sqrt{3}V_{pc}}\right]\left[\frac{FE_0/E_{a0} - 1}{FE_0/E_{a0} + C}\right] \quad (\text{g/cm}^2) \quad (8.1b)$$

The first two factors in (8.1a) refer to the quantity of toner–carrier mix transported to the PC surface; these are mechanical factors, where C_t is the toner concentration, M_c is carrier mass, V_c is the linear velocity of carrier relative to a fixed reference, D_c is the carrier diameter ($2R_c$), and V_{pc} is the linear velocity of the PC relative to a fixed reference. The units are cgs. The third factor addresses the amount of toner removed from a carrier by the electrostatic field (E_0) at the PC surface acting on a charged toner particle. A toner particle adheres both electrostatically and electrodynamically, but for simplicity it is assumed that the mechanical shear separates toner and carrier perhaps 100 Å or so, and the dispersion force can be ignored. The remaining force is electrostatic, which becomes equivalent to an adhesive field (E_{a0}) when normalized by the toner charge. Finally, F is a field enhancement factor resulting from the shape and dielectric properties of the carrier. Schein (1975) claims the development field is increased almost 15-fold by the carrier in large area development. For line images of approximately the same width as a carrier bead, the enhancement would be $F \leq 3$, as the image field is highly nonuniform and drops off with distance from the PC surface. In Equation (8.1), C is a constant given by

$$C = \frac{2n_0 R_t^2}{f^2} = \frac{2(R_c/R_t)^3 (\rho_c/\rho_t)C_t R_t^2}{(R_c + R_t)^2} = \frac{2\rho_c R_c^3 C_t}{\rho_t R_t (R_c + R_t)^2} \qquad (8.2)$$

where n_0 is the original number of toner particles on a carrier prior to the particle deposition, and is related directly to the toner concentration. All other symbols have been defined in Chapter 7. With R_t much smaller than R_c, the constant C reduces to

$$C \cong \frac{2C_t}{C_{t0}} \qquad (8.3)$$

Recall that C_{t0} is defined in (7.9).

Most of the physics of image development is involved in the third factor. The first factor is self-explanatory, and the second is based on Schein's work, with the additional observation that carrier beads arrange in a close-packed array when pressed down at the nip between the magnetic brush and the PC surface. Harvapat (1975) discusses a model of development where toner can deposit from carriers not touching the PC. This model uses an adjustable constant that describes the depth of development within the packed carrier beads.

The fraction of toner removed electrostatically from a carrier depends on the tug-of-war between the Coulomb force attaching a toner to a carrier, and the Coulomb force of the PC image attracting the toner. The inward adhesive force scales with q^2 (toner charge $= q$) and the outward radial force as qE_r, where E_r is the radial component of electric field at the carrier surface. As shown in Figure 8.1, E_r is altered (increased) by the shape and dielectric constant of the carrier; for simplicity of notation, $R_c = a$ and $R_t = b$ in this drawing and in the following two equations. The field outside a polarized sphere in an otherwise uniform external field is given by the relation (ignoring the tangential component)

$$E_r = E_0 \cos \theta \left[1 + 2\left(\frac{\varepsilon - 1}{\varepsilon + 2}\right)\left(\frac{a}{r}\right)^3 \right] \qquad (8.4)$$

If the body of the carrier is conductive, then $\varepsilon \to \infty$ for static fields, and the radial field at a distance $r = a + b$ from the carrier center is

$$E_r(r = a + b) = E_0 \cos \theta \left[1 + 2\left(\frac{a}{a + b}\right)^3 \right] \qquad (8.5)$$

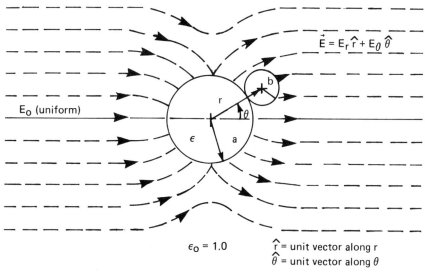

Figure 8.1   Uniform external field polarizes a carrier sphere which distorts the field to that of a dipole field plus the uniform field. Distortion caused by toner charge and polarization is not shown.

Treating the toner particle as a point charge q, the force at r is increased because of the enhancement of the total electric field by the polarized carrier. The field enhancement factor F is

$$F = \frac{E_r}{E_0 \cos \theta} = 1 + 2\left(\frac{a}{a + b}\right)^3 \quad \text{or} \quad F \cong 3 \text{ for } a \gg b. \tag{8.6}$$

This factor depends entirely on the geometry of the carrier and, for a sphere, $F = 3.0$ at $r = a$ (the surface of the carrier). For prolate ellipsoids and oblate ellipsoids, the factors can be computed also. Stoner (1945) and Osborn (1945) computed and tabulated demagnetizing factors for magnetically permeable ellipsoidal bodies. Their work can be applied to electrostatic problems by recognizing that the magnetic permeability (μ in cgs units) and the electrical permittivity (ε or dielectric constant k in cgs units) are direct analogs in magneto-static and electrostatic problems. A sphere is a degenerate ellipsoid; for non-spherical or pathologically shaped carrier beads, the field enhancement factor F is large at sharp edges or bumps and is very small elsewhere.

It is convenient to define the adhesive field between toner and uncharged carrier ($Q = 0$); that is, $E_{a0} = F_c/q$. Reading directly from (7.46),

$$E_{a0} = -\frac{q}{4R_t^2} = -\pi\sigma \quad \text{since } q = 4\pi R_t^2 \sigma. \tag{8.7}$$

By simple force–balance reasoning, toner deposition occurs where E_r exceeds E_{a0} and is of the correct polarity. A developing field E_0 according to this analysis pulls toner away from one hemisphere of a spherical carrier and presses toner more firmly down on the opposite hemisphere. The condition for image development is, therefore

$$|E_r| \geq |E_{a0}| \tag{8.8a}$$

and opposite in sign, or

$$|E_{a0}| \leq |FE_0| \tag{8.8b}$$

or

$$\cos \theta \geq \left| \frac{E_{a0}}{FE_0} \right| \tag{8.8c}$$

and these relations define a "polar cap" on the carrier surface, within which toner particles are development candidates. Under the proviso that mechanical shear exists and disrupts the dispersion force adhesive bond, the fraction of toner removed from a carrier will be given by the relation

$$\mathscr{F} = \frac{1}{2}(1 - \cos \theta) = \frac{1}{2}\left(1 - \left| \frac{E_{a0}}{FE_0} \right|\right) \tag{8.9}$$

with $\mathscr{F} < 0$ undefined.

The shaded region in Figure 8.2 corresponds to the region defined by (8.9). A threshold phenomenon is implicit in the derivation, and development begins when the image field just exceeds the adhesive field, as reduced by F; that is, $E_0 = E_{a0}/F$ and in a direction opposite to E_{a0}. Distributions of toner charge are discussed in Chapter 7, so any threshold behavior could be detected experimentally only with particles having a narrow statistical distribution. Broad distributions would likely mask the threshold behavior. Surface charge density (i.e., the adhesive field $E_{a0} = -\pi\sigma$ esu/cm^2) is the functionally important quantity, and electric field threshold behavior could be expected for particles of a variety of sizes, provided they each had the same charge density. The total charge of a particle depends on surface area, with big particles having most of the charge. Meaningful comparisons between toner samples would require that the q/m data be transformed to values of surface charge density.

When identical toner particles, each of charge q, leave the carrier surface, the carrier charges up to $Q = -nq$, where n is the number of departed toners.

$$n = n_0 \mathscr{F} = \frac{n_0}{2}\left(1 - \left| \frac{E_{ad}}{FE_0} \right|\right) \tag{8.10}$$

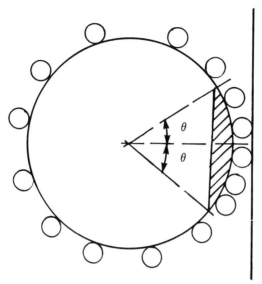

Figure 8.2   The fraction of toner removed from a carrier is defined as $\mathscr{F} = \frac{1}{2}(1 - \cos \theta)$, where θ depends on toner charge density and the external electric field E_0 of the latent image.

The number of original particles n_0 on the carrier is given by

$$n_0 = \left(\frac{R_c}{R_t}\right)^3 \frac{\rho_c}{\rho_t} C_t \tag{8.11}$$

As the carrier charges up, the adhesive field also increases. Reading from (7.44), the adhesive field E_{ad} with $Q \neq 0$ is

$$E_{ad} = \frac{F_c}{q} = \frac{Q}{f^2} - \frac{q(f/R_c)^3}{f^2(f^2/R_c^2 - 1)^2} \tag{8.12a}$$

$$= -\frac{nq}{f^2} - \frac{q(f/R_c)^3}{f^2(f^2/R_c^2 - 1)^2} \cong -\frac{nq}{f^2} - E_{a0} \quad \text{for } R_c \gg R_t. \tag{8.12b}$$

Substituting (8.10) for n in (8.12b) and using (8.11) for n_0, the adhesive field can be rewritten in terms of the fraction of toner removed.

$$E_{ad} = -\frac{n_0 q \mathscr{F}}{f^2} - E_{a0} \tag{8.13}$$

A new equation for the fraction removed is now discovered:

$$\mathscr{F} = \frac{1}{2}\left(1 - \left|\frac{E_{ad}}{FE_0}\right|\right) = \frac{1}{2}\left[1 - \frac{q n_0 \mathscr{F}/f^2 + E_{a0}}{FE_0}\right] \tag{8.14}$$

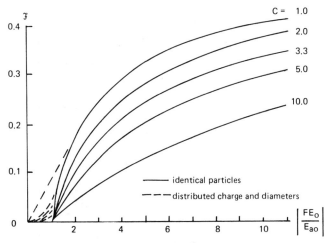

Figure 8.3   The behavior of $\mathscr{F}$ with reduced developing field $|FE_0/E_{a0}|$.

When (8.14) is rearranged, the solution appearing in (8.1) is found.

$$\mathscr{F} = \frac{1}{2}\left(\frac{|FE_0/E_{a0}| - 1}{|FE_0/E_{a0}| + C}\right) \tag{8.15}$$

As before, C is a dimensionless constant proportional to C_t. This is the final result; the reduced field FE_0/E_{a0} is written inside vertical bars to remind the reader that E_0 and E_{a0} are actually vectors, and development of toner is toward the PC when their signs are opposed, or toward the magnetic brush when their signs are of the same polarity.

The behavior of (8.15) with reduced field is plotted in Figure 8.3 for selected values of C. Mathematically, this function is a hyperbola with translated origin, and in all cases the asymptotic value is 0.50 (i.e., with extremely high development field E_0, only half of the toner can be removed in this model). The mass per unit area developed onto an image is linear in ratio of velocities V_c/V_{PC}, is almost linear in toner concentration C_t, and is nonlinear, threshold in reduced developing field FE_0/E_{a0}. Recall from (7.6) that E_{a0} is also a function of C_t:

$$E_{a0} = \pi\sigma = \pi\sigma_0 e^{-C_t/C_{t0}}$$

where

$$\sigma_0 = \lim_{C_t \to 0} \sigma \text{ and } C_{t0} = \rho_t R_t/(\rho_c R_c), \tag{8.16}$$

The experimental results of Schein (1975) verify the relation V_c/V_{PC} for carrier flow counter to the PC direction. At $V_c/V_{PC} = +1.0$ there is a curious

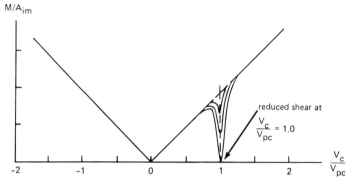

Figure 8.4   Behavior of M/A_{im} with ratio of carrier and PC velocities. The dip at $V_c/V_{PC} = +1.0$ is indicated here, although the model does not explicitly predict it. The dip would presumably be due to the role of dispersion forces in toner adhesion.

anomaly in the experiment, as the quantity of deposited mass is less than expected. This is shown schematically in Figure 8.4. Schein attributes this dip to lack of sufficient mechanical motion between toner and PC. On the other hand, Vahtra (1982) treats a generalized flow model of toner and carrier and assigns the dip to a depletion of toner concentration.

Theory and experiment are compared in Figures 8.5 and 8.6. The test vehicle was an experimental laser printer. Developing field E_0 was computed from measured dark and light voltages, bias voltage, and developer gap length. Chapter 6 discusses electrostatic fields and their computation. Line images

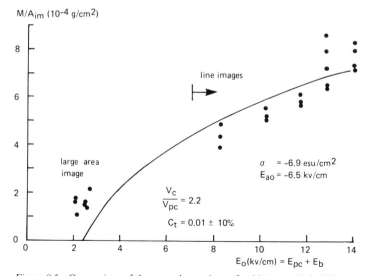

Figure 8.5   Comparison of theory and experiment for M/A_{im} vs. E_0 in kV/cm.

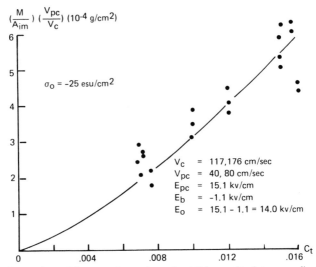

Figure 8.6   Comparison of theory and experiment for M/A_{im} vs. C_t; data normalized by (V_c/V_{PC}).

were printed with the laser beam and large areas were obtained by flash exposure. The solid curve in Figure 8.5 was computed using the values listed in Table 8.1.

Table 8.1   Test Parameters

Toner density $= \rho_t = 1.16 \, \text{g/cm}^3$
Toner radius $= R_t = 6 \times 10^{-4}$ cm (number average)
Charge density $= \sigma = -6.9 \, \text{esu/cm}^2$ (at $C_t = 0.01$)
Carrier density $= \rho_c = 7.2 \, \text{g/cm}^3$
Carrier radius $= 1.25 \times 10^{-2}$ cm (number average)
Carrier velocity $= V_c = 117; 176$ cm/sec
PC velocity $= V_{PC} = 40; 80$ cm/sec
Toner concentration $= C_t =$ variable
Adhesive field $= E_{a0} = -6.5 \, \text{kV/cm}$ (at $C_t = 0.01$)

Agreement between theory and experiment is good at the higher development fields of the line images; agreement is not very good for large areas, and this could be due to distributions in surface charge density of the toner. Models such as this and Schein's are useful as guides in bringing out the roles played by geometry and electrostatics. Benda and Wnek (1981) achieve very good agreement between theory and experiment with a level of sophistication that at times obscures insight. The data in Figure 8.5 show that roughly four times the toner

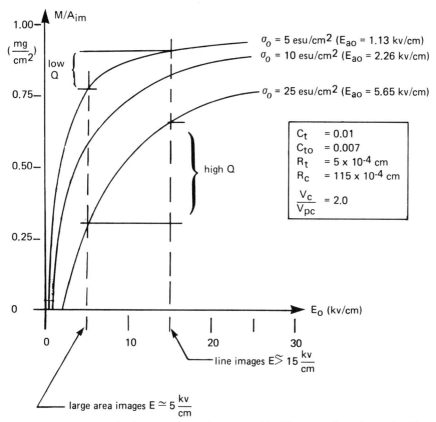

Figure 8.7 Computed development curves for toner with different surface charge densities. Parameters are given in the inset. Low σ_0 toner saturates in M/A_{im} vs. E_0 much sooner than high σ_0 material.

mass/cm² will deposit at $E_0 = 14\,kV/cm$ than at $E_0 = 2.5\,kV/cm$ (large areas). In principle, it is possible to exploit the threshold development, saturation characteristic of M/A_{im} vs. E_0 to obtain increased deposition at low applied fields. Toner with a low surface charge density has a reduced adhesive field E_{a0} and would readily develop at low E_0. This is sketched in Figure 8.7, and curves of medium and high surface charge density are given for comparison.

Problems arise when attempting to use low-charge densities, as nonelectrostatic development modes exist in the rather aggressive magnetic brush environment. Most notably, aerosol development occurs and toner dust develops nonimage regions to cause objectionable background on the transferred image. This subject is addressed shortly. Some of the problems with low-charge density come from the breadth of the distribution; zero charge and opposite polarity toner coexist with the low (average) charge material, so much of it is very

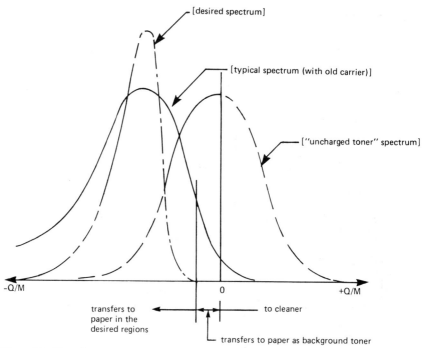

Figure 8.8   Three hypothetical charge spectra. The "desired" spectrum has low mean and small variance on the low side of the modal value, thus eliminating material that would lead to background toner.

loosely held to the carrier. Classifying toner to narrow size and narrow charge density ranges would alleviate some of the dusting problems. Three hypothetical curves of charge distributions are depicted in Figure 8.8. One curve is for toner not yet charged on carrier; it is symmetrically distributed about the zero average charge. This toner would overdevelop an image and it would also place copious amounts of opposite polarity toner on the background regions of the PC. The image would transfer to paper, and the opposite charge toner would stay on the PC and overload the cleaning device. The middle (typical spectrum) curve shows toner charged on old carrier beads. The small positive tail is the result of toner contacting toner that has fused to the carrier surface. A region of low, but negative charge toner exists which would develop both image and background (because of aerosol development), so the quality of the final print would be poor (excessive background toner). The third curve (desired spectrum) is drawn to depict a charge spectrum (or more correctly, a charge density spectrum) that would give good image development for lines and large areas without the annoying presence of background toner or cleaner overload.

It is now clear that careful study of toner charge distributions reveals the characteristics desired for good image development. Narrow distributions of toner charge density with low mean value could in principle offer a new solution to the old problem of unequal reflectance between lines and large areas, without the bothersome side effect of background toner.

8.2   A Macroscopic Analysis of Development with Space–Charge Limits

In the previous analysis, no provision was made for the accumulating charge of the developed toner. As charged toner piles up on the PC surface and oppositively charged carrier resides on the magnetic brush, the total electric field causing image development is reduced in magnitude. In large area development, the applied electric field is usually low, relative to the fields of narrow line images; thus, the presence of space charges arising from the toner and carrier is a significant, if not dominant, influence on the developing process. The analysis of large area development given here is from the work of C. E. Rasmussen, formerly of IBM Corporation. Rasmussen chose to analyze large area development from a macroscopic viewpoint, reasoning that the developing field was neutralized by the charged toner piling up at the PC, and that development stopped when the total electric field became zero. Figure 8.9 sketches the geometry and defines the nomenclature, all in cgs units. Toner and carrier are treated as continuous media because the granularity is quite small relative to the size of a large area image.

When toner deposits on the PC, a layer of material h centimeters thick is present; this is a space charge whose density is

$$\rho_t = \frac{q}{m}pd_t \quad (\text{esu/cm}^3) \tag{8.17}$$

where the q/m is in esu/g, p is the packing fraction of the toner ($p = 0.5$, approximately), and d_t is toner mass density (g/cm^3). Note that ρ_t is now the space

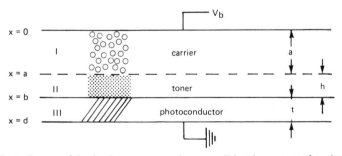

Figure 8.9   A diagram of the development zone where ε_c = dielectric constant of carrier medium = 4.5; ε_t = dielectric constant of toner medium = 2.5; ε_{PC} = dielectric constant of PC = 2.7; ρ_c = carrier space charge density (esu/cm^3); ρ_t = toner space charge density (esu/cm^3); σ_{PC} = PC surface charge density (esu/cm^2); a = magnetic brush to PC spacing = 0.14 cm; t = PC thickness = 0.0015 cm; h = height of toner layer (cm); V_b = bias voltage (electrostatic units) (esu/cm).

charge density in esu/cm^3, whereas earlier it was defined as the mass density. After giving up toner, carrier beads are left with a space charge density of opposite sign

$$\rho_c = -\left(\frac{hv_{PC}}{av_c}\right)\rho_t \quad (\text{esu/cm}^3) \tag{8.18}$$

where v_{PC} and v_c are the velocities of PC and carrier (cm/sec), respectively, and a is the thickness (cm) of the carrier pack in the developer nip formed by the magnetic brush and PC surfaces.

Poisson's Equation ($\nabla^2\phi = -4\pi\rho/\varepsilon$) is solved for each of the regions—I, II, and III. Upon applying the necessary boundary conditions and grouping terms, Rasmussen gives the electric field at the carrier–toner boundary as

$$E = \frac{2\pi a\rho_c}{\varepsilon_c} - \frac{2\pi h\rho_t}{a}\left(\frac{h}{\varepsilon_t} + \frac{2t}{\varepsilon_{PC}}\right) + \frac{1}{a}\left(V_b - \frac{4\pi t\sigma_{PC}}{\varepsilon_{PC}}\right)$$

$$= \frac{V_c}{a} - \frac{V_t}{a} + \frac{(V_b - V_{PC})}{a} \quad (\text{esu/cm}^2) \tag{8.19}$$

This is the field driving image development, and since the three terms have a common denominator, they may be grouped to yield the expression

$$E = \frac{(V_c - V_t + V_b - V_{PC})}{a} \tag{8.20}$$

Before toner deposition starts, the initial field is

$$E = \frac{(V_b - V_{PC})}{a} \tag{8.21}$$

and development will occur until $E = 0$, which is a condition implying that

$$V_t = V_c + V_b - V_{PC} \tag{8.22}$$

This relation says that toner deposition stops when the potential well formed at image exposure is filled back up. It says nothing about toner mass, or how the charge is distributed, and so forth. It is a macroscopic result. The potential resulting from a layer of toner (V_t) is measured by placing an electrometer probe (vibrating reed electrostatic voltmeter) above the pile of charged toner. Experimental results with a printer are given in Figure 8.10; the PC potential V_{PC} was fixed and the bias voltage V_b was varied. The data and macroscopic

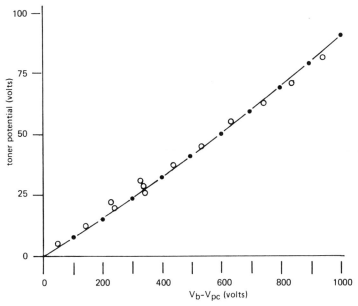

Figure 8.10   Comparison of Rasmussen's large-area theory with experiment; $q/m = -9.0 \times 10^4$ esu/g (-3.0×10^{-5} C/g) was used in the computed ($— \cdot —$) curve.

theory are in good agreement. The toner q/m was 9.0×10^4 esu/g or 3.0×10^{-5} C/g. Equation (8.22) can be rewritten in terms of the toner q/m and the other parameters given in Figure 8.9.

$$V_t = \frac{(V_b - V_{PC})^2}{2\pi\varepsilon_t(q/m)(pd_t)(aV_{PC}/\varepsilon_c v_c + 2t/\varepsilon_{PC})^2} + \frac{2t(V_b - V_{PC})}{\varepsilon_{PC}(av_{PC}/\varepsilon_c v_c + 2t/\varepsilon_{PC})} \quad (8.23)$$

To obtain good agreement with experiment, Rasmussen used a value of $\varepsilon_c = 4.5$, where as Schein (1975) used 17 and Hays (1978) used values between 10 and 18. The effective dielectric constant of carrier beads is difficult to compute theoretically, as the computation involves interactions between polarized conducting bodies that are not always perfectly spherical. Measurements of the dielectric constant of a packed assembly of carrier beads yield the average value, but image development would likely depend on the peak value, as pointed out by Hays (1978).

The important idea in Rasmussen's model is that the development of large areas is space-charge limited; toner with high space-charge density (high q/m, packing factor, and mass density), easily neutralizes the development field. A thin layer of high charge density yields the same space-charge potential as a thick layer of low charge density material. Taking (8.18) and (8.19), and solving for h by using the binomial expansion for the square root, the toner film thickness is

$$h \cong \frac{V_b - V_{PC}}{2\pi\rho_t(av_{PC}/\varepsilon_c v_c + 2t/\varepsilon_{PC})} \tag{8.24}$$

where all values are in cgs units. Recall that the potential is in esu/cm or stat-volts, where 1.0 esu/cm = 300 V, and dielectric constants are dimensionless in the cgs system. Toner mass per unit area is usually measured instead of directly measuring h, so the appropriate conversion factor gives

$$\frac{M}{A} = \frac{V_b - V_{PC}}{2\pi(q/m)(av_{PC}/\varepsilon_c v_c + 2t/\varepsilon_{PC})} \quad (\text{g/cm}^2) \tag{8.25}$$

From a systems viewpoint, macroscopic equations such as (8.25) force attention to the role of toner q/m in a manner that reveals its impact on system performance much more directly than does the microscopic counterpart (8.1). Toner concentration does not appear in (8.25), although q/m has a strong dependence

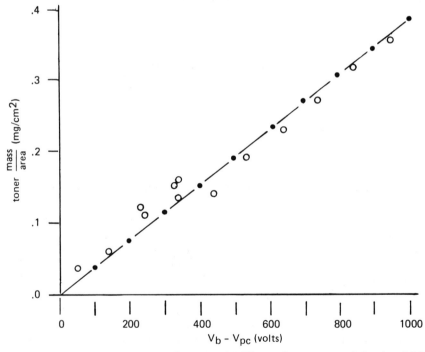

Figure 8.11   Large-area toner mass/cm^2 vs. potential difference between magnetic brush and PC surface. From Rasmussen.

on C_t, as shown in (7.6). A plot of (8.25) and some experimental results are given in Figure 8.11. The linearity of M/A with $V_b - V_{PC}$ is in agreement with Schein (1975).

In the derivation of (8.19), Rasmussen assumed that toner was removed from carrier beads throughout Region I of Figure 8.9, such that the space charge density of the carrier beads was uniform within this volume. There is very strong experimental evidence that toner comes only from carriers actually touching the PC surface, so the space charge density for carriers ρ_c is high and is limited to the volume occupied by one layer of beads. In magnetic brush developers, it is usual to set the developer gap (a, in Figure 8.9) equal to about five layers of beads; however, the beads are rather constrained to their relative positions while in the developer gap, so there is little opportunity for charged and uncharged beads to intermix during image development. Therefore, the carrier space-charge density remains high if the beads are good insulators. Benda and Wnek (1981) discuss conductivity of the carrier in magnetic brushes and show experimental results of E. J. Gutman of Xerox Corporation. For insulative carriers, the data for M/A vs. development voltage are linear. With carriers of various conductivities (the conductivity is in general nonohmic), the curves of M/A vs. development voltage are nonlinear, and the quantity of toner developed is greatest for carriers having the highest conductivity. Jewett (1977) also mentions conductive carrier and its influence on the development of large area images.

8.3   Multiple Magnetic Brush Development

If carrier beads are not free to move away from the PC, and if they are insulating, then space charge accumulates and large area images will not develop to the extent achieved with conductive carrier. Multiple magnetic rolls can be used to dissipate the carrier space charge and to improve the reflectance of large area images; some devices pass the carrier from one magnetic roll to another, still other developer units contain several independent magnetic brushes, each having its own sump for carrier and toner mix. Multiple developer rolls allow mixing and agitation of the carrier as it moves from one roll to the next; thus, the carrier has the opportunity to neutralize its charge by touching the conductive surface of the roll and by receiving toner from other carrier beads. The motion of toner from one bead to another is often called "toner migration," and this motion constitutes the flow of a neutralizing current also. High-speed flow studies show that carrier beads do not move around much within the developer nip, and it is only after passing through the developer gap that beads intermix from layer to layer, thus spreading out the space charge of the carriers that developed the image. The toner space charge resides at the PC surface, so it is unaltered, but the effect of carrier space charge can be determined indirectly by measuring the quantity of toner at the PC after each development cycle. Rasmussen estimated that each additional magnetic brush (with constant bias

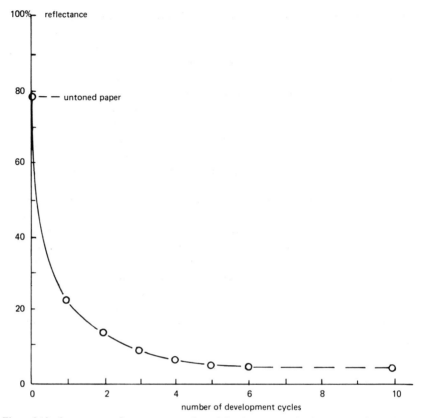

Figure 8.12   Large-area reflectance vs. number of development cycles for an experimental laser printer.

potential V_b) can develop approximately 45 % of the amount developed by the previous brush. Indeed, the toner space charge builds up toward a value that would exactly oppose the initial development field, so a law of diminishing returns can be applied, if additional developer brushes are installed. This is shown in Figure 8.12 where the reflectance of the printed page is plotted as a function of the number of image development cycles. Reflectance does not decrease appreciably after about four cycles.

8.4   Aerosol Generation and Background Toner

Because toner charge is distributed, a range of adhesive forces hold toner onto carrier beads in a developer unit. With magnetic brushes rotating at several hundred revolutions per minute, the whipping of bead chains and impacting of carriers on the magnetic roll and other surfaces generate sufficient force to detach toner particles with low electrostatic adhesion. Once free of adhesive forces, toner moves according to aerodynamic forces combined with the Coulombic "image" forces given by $F_c = -q^2/4x^2$, where x is the distance between the particle of charge q and an imaging surface.

In the geometry shown in Figure 7.1, carrier and toner are conveyed from the mixing sump to the magnetic brush by magnetic forces. The carrier–toner mix is thrown from the conveyor to the magnetic brush where nearly all material is captured. Upon impact at the magnetic brush roll, the rapid deceleration is sufficient to detach toner, thus generating a toner aerosol. Upon exit from the developer gap, carrier beads reform into magnetic chains with significant carrier–carrier impacting, once again generating an aerosol of toner. The immediate environment inside a developer unit can be rather dusty, and the dust is quite highly charged relative to normal atmospheric aerosols. Some of this dust attaches to the PC surface subsequent to the principle magnetic brush development process, so at least two development modes exist. The aerosol mode provides a pathway for background toner. Schaffert (1975) and J. T. Bickmore in Dessauer and Clark (1965) discuss aerosol or "powder cloud" development, and the technique is used for development of xeroradiographic images, although it generates objectionable background toner.

The force between colliding spherical carrier beads can be analyzed with elastic (Hertzian) theory. Timoshenko and Goodier (1970, p. 420) derive the force at the instant of maximum compression between colliding spheres and find that

$$F = C^{2/5} \left(\frac{5}{4} m_e v^2 \right)^{3/5} \quad \text{(dynes)}$$

where

$$C = \left[\frac{16 R_1 R_2}{9\pi^2 (K_1 + K_2)^2 (R_1 + R_2)} \right]^{1/2} \quad (\text{dyne} - \text{cm}^{-3/2}) \qquad (8.26)$$

$$K_i = \frac{1 - v_i^2}{\pi E_i} \quad (\text{cm}^2/\text{dyne}) \quad \text{and} \quad m_e = \frac{m_1 m_2}{m_1 + m_2} \quad (\text{g})$$

The symbols R_1 and R_2 are the radii (cm) of the spheres, v_1 and v_2 are the Poisson's Ratios (about 0.3 for metals and 0.2 for polymers), E_1 and E_2 are the Young's Moduli (dynes/cm^2), m_e is the effective mass (g) in the center-of-mass frame, and $v = v_1 + v_2$ (cm/sec) is the initial relative approach velocity of the colliding spheres. A sphere colliding with a stationary plane is found by letting R_2 and m_2 approach infinity and setting v_2 at 0. Young's Moduli for a few selected materials are: aluminum $= 7 \times 10^{11}$ dynes/cm^2, carbon steel $= 2.1 \times 10^{12}$ dynes/cm^2, and polyethylene terephthalate (PET) $= 4.8 \times 10^{10}$ dynes/cm^2. Let two steel carriers collide with $v = 175$ cm/sec, and let $R_1 = R_2 = 0.0125$ cm, with the mass densities both equal to 7.2 g/cm^3. Using (8.26), the maximum compressive force is approximately $F_{max} = 2.9 \times 10^4$ dynes, and the deceleration becomes $a = F/m_e = 1 \times 10^9$ cm/sec^2, or about $10^6 g$.

This deceleration is quite sufficient to detach toner from the carrier. If a carrier impacts a flat plane of PET (where the PET properties can roughly be used to approximate the PC), the impact force, with R_2, m_2 both infinite and $v_2 = 0$, becomes $F_{max} = 1.4 \times 10^4$ dynes, and the deceleration is $a = F/m_1 = 2.4 \times 10^8$ cm/sec^2, or about $2.4 \times 10^5 g$. This is also sufficient to detach toner appropriately situated on the carrier bead. For carrier impacting aluminum, the maximum force becomes roughly 3.8×10^4 dynes with a maximum deceleration of about $6.5 \times 10^5 g$. These are ball-park estimates, but they show that aerosol generation ought to be the rule, not the exception, in a developer unit operating with linear velocities on the order of about 100 cm/sec.

The electrical behavior of charged aerosols has received much scientific attention over the years. Millikan (1917) measured the charge of the electron in his classic oil drop experiment. Fuchs (1964) reviewed the determination of particle mobility in his well-known book on the mechanics of aerosols. Hidy and Brock (1970), Whitby and Liu (1966), Loeb (1958), and Zimon (1966) were each cited earlier. Loeb has an extensive treatment of dust electrification, and he reviews experiments and techniques, showing how often results can be misleading or be misinterpreted.

Corbett and Bassett (1971) discuss field measurements in clouds of charged particles; they describe a ballistic probe system that fires ball bearings through charged clouds and catches the balls in a Faraday cage for charge measurement. It sounds like exciting work, especially if you are the one chosen to hold the Faraday cage.

NINE

THE MAGNETIC BRUSH
ANALYSIS OF MAGNETIC FORCES

The magnetic brush is found in high-speed xerographic image developer units. The "brush" part of this device is composed of magnetizable carrier beads transporting nonmagnetic toner on a rotating cylinder placed about a stationary array of permanent magnets. In monocomponent development processes, the magnetic brush is also used; however, the toner particles are themselves magnetic, and carrier beads are not used. In either case, the magnetic forces attract the magnetizable bodies to the magnets and, therefore, constrain the material against centrifugal, gravitational, and electrical forces. In this chapter, these forces are analyzed for two-dimensional arrays of permanent magnets. When the magnetic particles (carrier or toner) are immersed in a magnetic field, they also become little magnets that interact with one another, and this is manifested by the chaining behavior typical of all magnetic materials in magnetic fields. It is therefore appropriate to discuss carrier–carrier forces (or toner–toner forces, if the toner is magnetic) while examining competition between electric and magnetic forces.

9.1 Magnetic Energy and Force

A two-dimensional treatment of magnetic forces is justified for long magnets with the axis of magnetization perpendicular to the long axis. The equations so derived are useful over about 90% of the magnet length, provided the magnet is about 10 times longer than it is wide or thick. Like some other forces, a magnetic force is the negative gradient of a potential energy, where the potential is sought in terms of the magnetic characteristics of the materials in question. It is therefore necessary to find the magnetostatic energy (W_m) of a body and take its derivative in space. The force (F_m) is

$$F_m = -\nabla W_m \quad \text{(dynes)} \tag{9.1}$$

where the gradient operator in two dimensions is

$$\nabla = \left(\frac{\partial}{\partial x}\hat{\mathbf{i}} + \frac{\partial}{\partial y}\hat{\mathbf{j}}\right) \tag{9.2}$$

Strictly speaking, the magnetostatic energy W_m is the change in energy in space arising from the presence of a magnetized body. More clarification on this subject is found in Jackson (1962, p. 176).

$$W_m = \frac{1}{8\pi} \int_V (\mu - \mu_0)\, \mathbf{H} \cdot \mathbf{H}_0 \, dV \quad \text{(ergs)} \tag{9.3}$$

The volume of interest is $V = (4\pi/3)b^3 \text{ cm}^3$, where b is the radius of a sphere that is assumed for the discussion. The internal field of this sphere is $\mathbf{H}$ (in oersteds or gauss), $\mathbf{H}_0$ is the external field with the sphere removed a great distance, μ and μ_0 are the intrinsic permeability of the sphere and that of the surrounding medium (unity, for air or vacuum).

If the external field does not change greatly over the volume occupied by the sphere, then all of the factors in the integrand of (9.3) will be reasonably constant, so the integral becomes

$$W_m = \frac{1}{8\pi}(\mu - 1)\mathbf{H} \cdot \mathbf{H}_0\left(\frac{4\pi}{3}b^3\right) = \frac{(\mu - 1)}{6}b^3 \mathbf{H} \cdot \mathbf{H}_0 \quad \text{(ergs)} \tag{9.4}$$

A comment is in order here: letting H_0 be constant over the volume of integration greatly simplifies the derivation; however, if H_0 were exactly constant, then W_m would not change with position in space; the negative gradient would be zero, and no force on the particle would result. For many of the magnetic brushes in use today, field gradients are on the order of -1000 G/cm; so, given a carrier sphere about 0.01 cm in diameter, the field would change only 10 G across this body. Since H_0 is about 500 G, the variation in field across a diameter is about 2%, and the assumption made above is easily justified.

The field inside the sphere (**H**) can be found in terms of the external field (H_0), provided the body magnetizes in linear proportion to the applied field.

If the body is permanently magnetized, then the next few equations do not apply. Two well-known equations are used:

$$\mathbf{B} = \mathbf{H} + 4\pi\mathbf{M} \quad (G) \tag{9.5}$$

and

$$\mathbf{B} = \mu\mathbf{H} \quad (G) \tag{9.6}$$

Equation (9.5) is a cgs equation where B is in gauss, H is in gauss or oersteds, and M is in emu/cm^3 (and $4\pi\mathbf{M}$ is in gauss). McCraig (1977) gives a very clear discussion of magnetic units. The field inside a body is the vector sum of the external field and the demagnetizing field (H_d), where $H_d = -NM$ and N is the demagnetizing factor whose value depends only on the shape of the body.

For spheres, $N = 4\pi/3$; therefore, the internal field is

$$\mathbf{H} = \mathbf{H}_0 - \frac{4\pi}{3}\mathbf{M} \tag{9.7}$$

Using (9.5) and (9.6), $\mathbf{M}$ can be written in terms of $\mathbf{H}$,

$$\mathbf{M} = \frac{\mathbf{B} - \mathbf{H}}{4\pi} = \frac{(\mu - 1)\mathbf{H}}{4\pi} \tag{9.8}$$

and inserting this expression into (9.7), one obtains

$$\mathbf{H} = \mathbf{H}_0 - \frac{4\pi}{3}\left[\frac{(\mu - 1)\mathbf{H}}{4\pi}\right] = \mathbf{H}_0 - \frac{(\mu - 1)}{3}\mathbf{H} \tag{9.9}$$

and (9.9) is solved for H in terms of H_0.

$$\mathbf{H} = \left(\frac{3}{\mu + 2}\right)\mathbf{H}_0 \tag{9.10}$$

The demagnetizing factors for prolate, oblate, and general ellipsoids are tabulated in Stoner (1945) and Osborn (1945). There are no analytical demagnetizing factors for geometries other than surfaces of the second degree, since these are the only mathematical shapes that can support (in mathematical rigor) uniform magnetization. Many ferrite carrier beads have pathological shapes and look more like tiny chunks of broken concrete or grains of sand. The magnetization would not be uniform in this case; but to a first approximation, one would necessarily treat these rough bodies as ellipsoids for analytical purposes.

Substituting (9.10) into (9.4) yields the desired expression for the *induced magnetostatic energy of a sphere.*

$$W_m = \frac{1}{2}\left(\frac{\mu - 1}{\mu + 2}\right) b^3 H_0^2 = \frac{1}{2}\mathbf{m}\cdot\mathbf{H}_0 \quad (\text{erg}) \tag{9.11}$$

where **m** is the *dipole moment* (in emu or ergs/G) of the sphere. The magnetization **M** is the dipole moment per unit volume; therefore, in terms of **M**, the total dipole moment **m** is

$$\mathbf{m} \equiv (\text{volume}) \times \mathbf{M} = \left(\frac{\mu - 1}{\mu + 2}\right) b^3 \mathbf{H}_0 \tag{9.12}$$

In (9.11), the factor H_0^2 comes from $\mathbf{H}_0 \cdot \mathbf{H}_0 = H_0^2$ and the units are $\text{G}^2 = \text{erg/cm}^3$; that is, a field squared has dimensions of energy density. Since 1.0 erg = 1.0 dyne-cm, energy density is equivalent to dyne/cm², which is a pressure. Indeed, magnetized bodies are in a state of stress that equals the energy density. Maxwell (1954, Vol. 2, p. 278) discusses the forces acting on and within a body when placed in a field.

The magnetic force acting on a magnetic carrier is found by taking the negative gradient of W_m given in (9.11).

$$\begin{aligned}
\mathbf{F}_m = -\nabla W_m &= -\left(\frac{\partial}{\partial x}\hat{\mathbf{i}} + \frac{\partial}{\partial y}\hat{\mathbf{j}}\right)\left[\frac{1}{2}\left(\frac{\mu - 1}{\mu + 2}\right) b^3 H_0^2\right] \\
&= -\left(\frac{\mu - 1}{\mu + 2}\right) b^3\left[\left(H_x\frac{\partial H_x}{\partial x} + H_y\frac{\partial H_y}{\partial y}\right)\hat{\mathbf{i}} + \left(H_x\frac{\partial H_x}{\partial y} + H_y\frac{\partial H_y}{\partial y}\right)\hat{\mathbf{j}}\right] \\
&= F_x\hat{\mathbf{i}} + F_y\hat{\mathbf{j}}
\end{aligned} \tag{9.13}$$

In more compact notation, this expression is written

$$\mathbf{F}_m = -(\mathbf{m}\cdot\mathbf{V})\mathbf{H}_0 \tag{9.14}$$

and in vacuum or air, $H_0 = B$ in the cgs system of units, so (9.14) can be written in a more general form

$$\mathbf{F} = -(\mathbf{m}\cdot\mathbf{V})\mathbf{B} \tag{9.15}$$

In this form, the force on magnetic toner used in monocomponent developers can be found. Equation (9.15) is applicable to permanently magnetized bodies also. For example, if the dipole moment of the body is **m** = 1.0 emu, and it is aligned with a magnetic field having a gradient $\mathbf{VB} = 1000$ G/cm, then the force on the body is 1000 dynes in the direction of increasing field.

Examination of (9.13) shows the magnetic force scales with the cube of the radius (b), so the magnetic force is a *volume force*. Later, this is contrasted with electrostatic forces that are *surface forces* (scaling with the square of the radius). The dependence of $\mathbf{F}_m$ on the permeability of the sphere goes as $(\mu - 1)/(\mu + 2)$, and this ratio is plotted in Figure 9.1a. If the intrinsic permeability is about 30 or greater, $\mathbf{F}_m$ is almost independent of μ. The permeability of magnetic

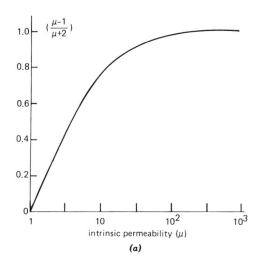

(a)

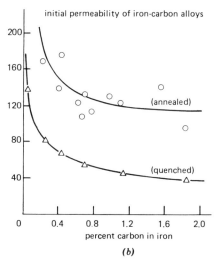

(b)

Figure 9.1 (*a*) Computed curve for $(\mu - 1/\mu + 2)$. (*b*) Experimental permeability (initial) for iron–carbon (steel) alloys vs. percent carbon. From Bozorth (1968).

toners is quite low (about 2.5) and these materials more appropriately belong in the category of permanent magnets, although (9.13), (9.14), or (9.15) are applicable. Equation (9.15) is perhaps the least ambiguous, and it is preferred when working with permanent magnetic materials. Steel carrier beads are used in many magnetic brush developers, and this material is not permanently magnetic. Molten steel is sprayed from a shot tower and the droplets freeze into spheroidal shapes. This process quenches the material and yields an intrinsic permeability somewhere between 40 and 80, depending on the carbon content. Bozorth (1968, p. 368) gives experimental values of initial permeability for iron–carbon (steel) alloys; his data are shown in Figure 9.1b.

The magnetic moment m (or $m/V = M$, the magnetization) of a carrier is linearly related to the applied field, until the carrier approaches magnetic saturation. This relation is found in (9.12) or (9.8). Provided the material is not saturated or entering saturation, the magnetic moment depends on the applied field, not on the particular material of the carrier body. The carrier must of course, be sufficiently magnetic; that is, $\mu > 30$, a condition that applies to the ferromagnetic materials iron, nickel, cobalt, and gadolinium, to all ferrites of the class $MeFe_2O_4$, where $Me = $ Fe, Co, Mn, Ni, Cu, and Mg, and to yttrium iron garnet (YIG). Nonmagnetic and paramagnetic materials have a permeability very close to unity. Table 9.1 gives measured magnetic force per unit volume of four different materials. The nickel, iron, and cobalt spheres were vacuum melted from 99.995% purity material; the steel sphere

Table 9.1   Magnetic Force per cm^3

Sample	M_s (emu/cm^3)	F/Volume (dynes/cm^3)
Ni	490	1.68×10^5
Fe	1714	1.62×10^5
Co	1422	1.28×10^5
Steel	1470	1.62×10^5

contained 1.0% carbon. Measurements were made at a field of about 800 G, with a gradient of about 1000 G/cm. The force per unit volume for Co is 20% lower than the other samples; this is due to the low intrinsic permeability (about 10) of cobalt, which arises from high magnetocrystalline anisotropy.

Magnetic permeability is found by magnetizing a body in a field H_0, computing the internal field H, and measuring B; the permeability is $\mu = B/H$. If H is very small, then one has determined the *initial permeability*. With increasing H (internal field), the material eventually begins to saturate (i.e., B no longer increases linearly with H), so the measured permeability decreases. With spheres, the field at which saturation begins is approximately

$$\mathbf{H}_s \cong \frac{4\pi}{3} \mathbf{M}_s \quad \text{(G)} \qquad (9.16)$$

and for pure Fe, Ni, and Co H_s is, reading from Table 9.1, about 7200, 2100, and 6000 G, respectively. The ferrites Fe-, Co-, Mn-, and $NiFe_2O_4$ have saturation fields of approximately 2000, 1800, 1700, and 1100 G, respectively; thus, all of these materials would function equally well in a magnetic brush developer with $H_0 = 1100$ G or less. Because the magnetic force per volume is almost independent of the magnetic material, the criteria for selecting one material over another will be mechanical, not magnetic. The mass density of ferrites ranges between 5 and 5.4 g/cm^3; that for the metals is perhaps 1.6 times greater, so ferrite carrier beads are to be preferred if impact forces, centrifugal forces, or total mass of the development mix are of concern. Van Engeland (1979) mentions additional criteria for selecting carrier beads.

By further examination of (9.13), one notes that the magnetic force F_m is proportional to the product of the field and field gradient. Since F_m is a dipole force, there will be no force in a uniform field (the gradient is zero). Torque can exist in a uniform field, but torques cause rotation only, not translation of the body. Magnetic field gradients are highest near the edges of magnets, so carrier beads, iron filings, and so forth are preferentially attracted to edges.

In summary, the magnetic force on a sphere is specified by the volume, its permeability, the applied field, and the field gradient. Carrier radius is in centimeters, permeability is dimensionless in the cgs system used here, the field is in gauss or oersted, and the field gradient is in gauss per centimeter or oersted per centimeter. The force is in units of dynes or ergs per centimeter (the gradient of the energy.)

9.2 Magnetic Field of a Rectangular Magnet

In this section, the magnetic field outside a long rectangular permanent magnet is derived, and the field equations found can be substituted into (9.13) to compute the force. Figure 9.2 describes the coordinate system used for this analysis. The magnet is uniformly magnetized in the positive y-direction; this assumption is justified within engineering accuracy for most anisotropic (oriented) permanent magnetic materials of the ALNICO-8 and barium ferrite (ceramic) class whose coercivities exceed roughly 1000 G. Isotropic permanent magnets may not withstand the high demagnetizing fields that exist near edges, so the magnetization becomes nonuniform to a greater extent than with anisotropic magnets. Experiments in the author's laboratory show that the calculated and

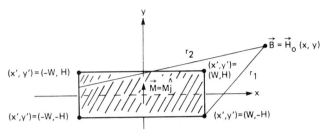

Figure 9.2 Permanent magnet with uniform magnetization $\mathbf{M} = M\hat{\mathbf{j}}$, in (emu/cm^3). Field points are (x, y) and source points are (x', y'). Source full width $= 2W$ and full height $= 2H$, both in cm. The magnet is very long in the z-direction (perpendicular to this page).

measured forces are within 10% agreement, thereby justifying the initial assumption of uniform magnetization.

In Figure 9.2, $\mathbf{M} = M\hat{\mathbf{j}}$ is a vector along the y-axis. The field equations are easily applied to other orientations of $\mathbf{M}$. The only restriction is that $\mathbf{M}$ is along one of the four Cartesian directions in two-dimensional space. In these equations, a field point is (x, y) and a source point is (x', y'). The magnetic field is derived from the vector magnetic potential $\mathbf{A}_z$. Smythe (1968) is a useful reference for this subject. Since $B = H_0$ in free space (air, in this case), the field is the curl of the vector potential.

$$\mathbf{H}_0 = \mathbf{V} \times \mathbf{A}_z = H_x\hat{\mathbf{i}} + H_y\hat{\mathbf{j}} \tag{9.17}$$

and from Smythe (1968), the relation between $\mathbf{A}_z$ and $\mathbf{M}$ is

$$\mathbf{A}_z = \iint_S \frac{\mathbf{M} \times \hat{\mathbf{n}}}{r}\, dS \tag{9.18}$$

where $\hat{\mathbf{n}}$ is a unit vector in the outward normal direction on the surface of the magnet, dS is an element of surface area ($dS = dy'\, dz'$ or $dx'\, dz'$) depending on the surface of interest, and r is a distance from source point to field point.

$$r = [(x - x')^2 + (y - y')^2 + (z - z')^2]^{1/2} \tag{9.19}$$

Since $\mathbf{M}$ is given as $+M\hat{\mathbf{j}}$, then $\mathbf{M} \times \hat{\mathbf{n}}$ is zero everywhere, except along the two surfaces $\hat{\mathbf{n}} = +\hat{\mathbf{i}}$ and $\hat{\mathbf{n}} = -\hat{\mathbf{i}}$, where $x' = +W$ and $x' = -W$, respectively. The full width of the magnet is $2W$ and the elementary area $dS = dy'\, dz'$ along these surfaces. The magnet is very long in the z-direction, so the field equations an independent of z after integration along z'. Equation (9.18) is integrated in a straightforward manner. Tables in Dwight (1961) or Gradshteyn and Rhyzhik (1965) can be consulted for assistance.

$$
\mathbf{A}_z = \iint_S \left(\frac{\mathbf{M} \times \hat{\mathbf{n}}}{r_1} + \frac{\mathbf{M} \times \hat{\mathbf{n}}}{r_2} \right) dy'\, dz'
$$

$$
= \int_{-\infty}^{\infty} \int_{-H}^{H} \left[\frac{-M\hat{\mathbf{k}}}{\sqrt{(x-W)^2 + (y-y')^2 + (z-z')^2}} \right.
$$

$$
\left. + \frac{M\hat{\mathbf{k}}}{\sqrt{(x+W)^2 + (y-y')^2 + (z-z')^2}} \right] dy'\, dz'
$$

$$
= \int_{-H}^{H} 2M\hat{\mathbf{k}}[-(y-y')\log_e \sqrt{(x-W)^2 + (y-y')^2}
$$

$$
- \log_e \sqrt{(x+W)^2 + (y-y')^2}]\, dy'
$$

$$
= 2M\hat{\mathbf{k}}\left\{ -(y-y')\log_e[(y-y')^2 + (x-W)^2] + 2(y-y') \right.
$$

$$
- 2(x-W)\tan^{-1}\left(\frac{y-y'}{x-W} \right) + (y-y')\log_e[(y-y')^2 + (x+W)^2]
$$

$$
\left. - 2(y-y') + 2(x+W)\tan^{-1}\left(\frac{y-y'}{x+W} \right) \right\} \Bigg|_{-H}^{H}
$$

$$
= 2M\hat{\mathbf{k}}\left\{ (y+H)\log_e \frac{[(y+H)^2 + (x-W)^2]}{[(y+H)^2 + (x+W)^2]} + 2(x-W)\tan^{-1}\left(\frac{y+H}{x-W} \right) \right.
$$

$$
- 2(x+W)\tan^{-1}\left(\frac{y+H}{x+W} \right) - (y-H)\log_e \frac{[(y-H)^2 + (x-W)^2]}{[(y-H)^2 + (x+W)^2]}
$$

$$
\left. - 2\tan^{-1}\left(\frac{y-H}{x-W} \right) + 2(x+W)\tan^{-1}\left(\frac{y+H}{x+W} \right) \right\} \tag{9.20}
$$

Field components are found by taking the curl of $\mathbf{A}_z$.

$$
\mathbf{H}_0 = \mathbf{B} = \nabla \times \mathbf{A}_z = \left(\frac{\partial}{\partial x}\hat{\mathbf{i}} + \frac{\partial}{\partial y}\hat{\mathbf{j}} + \frac{\partial}{\partial z}\hat{\mathbf{k}} \right) \times A_z \hat{\mathbf{k}}
$$

$$
= \frac{\partial A_z}{\partial x}\hat{\mathbf{i}} \times \hat{\mathbf{k}} + \frac{\partial A_z}{\partial y}\hat{\mathbf{j}} \times \hat{\mathbf{k}} = -\frac{\partial A_z}{\partial x}\hat{\mathbf{j}} + \frac{\partial A_z}{\partial y}\hat{\mathbf{i}} \tag{9.21}
$$

or

$$H_x = B_x = +\frac{\partial A_z}{\partial y} \quad (G) \tag{9.22}$$

$$H_y = B_y = -\frac{\partial A_z}{\partial x} \quad (G) \tag{9.23}$$

Upon taking the derivatives of (9.20), doing some algebra, and rearranging terms, the desired field equations are

$$B_x = 2M\left[\log_e \frac{(x-W)^2 + (y+H)^2}{(x-W)^2 + (y-H)^2} - \log_e \frac{(x+W)^2 + (y+H)^2}{(x+W)^2 + (y-H)^2}\right] \tag{9.24}$$

$$B_y = 4M\left[\tan^{-1}\left(\frac{y+H}{x+W}\right) - \tan^{-1}\left(\frac{y+H}{x-W}\right) + \tan^{-1}\left(\frac{y-H}{x-W}\right)\right.$$

$$\left. - \tan^{-1}\left(\frac{y-H}{x+W}\right)\right] \tag{9.25}$$

The required field gradients are obtained directly from (9.24) and (9.25).

$$\frac{\partial B_x}{\partial x} = 4M\left[\frac{(x-W)}{(x-W)^2 + (y+H)^2} - \frac{(x-W)}{(x-W)^2 + (y-H)^2}\right.$$

$$\left. + \frac{(x+W)}{(x+W)^2 + (y-H)^2} - \frac{(x+W)}{(x+W)^2 + (y+H)^2}\right] \tag{9.26}$$

$$\frac{\partial B_x}{\partial y} = 4M\left[\frac{(y+H)}{(x-W)^2 + (y+H)^2} - \frac{(y-H)}{(x-W)^2 + (y-H)^2}\right.$$

$$\left. + \frac{(y-H)}{(x+W)^2 + (y-H)^2} - \frac{(y+H)}{(x+W)^2 + (y+H)^2}\right] \tag{9.27}$$

The magnetic vector potential is harmonic and analytic because A_z is a solution of Laplace's Equation. These properties of A_z are exploited to save unnecessary labor. From Laplace's Equation

$$\nabla^2 A_z = \frac{\partial^2 A_z}{\partial x^2} + \frac{\partial^2 A_z}{\partial y^2} = 0 \tag{9.28}$$

so it is obvious that

$$\frac{\partial^2 A_z}{\partial x^2} = -\frac{\partial^2 A_z}{\partial y^2} \tag{9.29}$$

Equations (9.22) and (9.23) are used in conjunction with (9.29) to show that

$$\frac{\partial B_x}{\partial y} \equiv \frac{\partial B_y}{\partial x} \tag{9.30}$$

and

$$\frac{\partial B_x}{\partial x} \equiv -\frac{\partial B_y}{\partial y} \tag{9.31}$$

These latter two identities could be proved by working directly with (9.24) and (9.25).

The field equations have been experimentally checked with high energy magnets like ALNICO-8, ALNICO-8HE, CERAMIC-5, and CERAMIC-5H. In all cases, the agreement was within 10% for magnets about $1.0 \times 1.0 \times 10$ cm^3. End effects became important at about 0.5 cm from the end of a magnet, so the analytical results were useful for nearly 90% of the magnet length.

9.3   Permanent Magnets

Most technical data for permanent magnets are given in terms of the magnetic flux density or induction B plotted as a function of the applied magnetic field. The material is first saturated at a high field, then the induction B is plotted for the second quadrant of the hysteresis loop in the B, H plane where the field H opposes the direction of B. The curve so generated is called the "de-magnetizing" curve of the material, because B drops from its fully magnetized "residual" or remnant state, B_r, down to zero induction ($B = 0$) in this second quadrant. The field at which $B = 0$ is called the "coercivity" H_c. Two demag-netizing curves are shown in Figure 9.3; one curve is for ALNICO-8HE, which is an alloy of Fe, Ni, Co, Al, and small additions of other elements, and the other is for a barium ferrite ceramic material (BaFe$_{12}$O$_{12}$ plus small amounts of other elements) called INDOX 5, Feroba, Ferroxdure, Ferrimag, and so forth. Both materials are highly anisotropic (oriented magnetic structure) magnets appropriate for use in magnetic brush developer units. The straight lines labeled B/H or "permeance coefficient" values show how the operating point (the small circles on the curves) of a magnet depends on its shape. If a magnet is long and thin like a rod, and is magnetized along the long direction, the permeance co-efficient is large. If magnetized perpendicular to the long direction, B/H is small. For example, a magnet $1.27 \times 1.27 \times 10$ cm^3 has a permeance coefficient $B/H = 0.9$ approximately along the 1.27 cm direction, and $B/H = 30$ in the 10 cm direction. Permeance coefficients are directly related to the demagnetizing

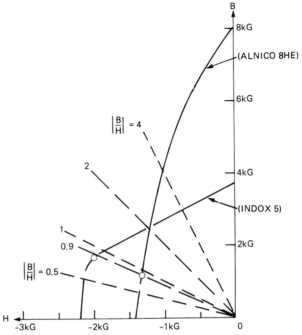

Figure 9.3   The demagnetizing curves of two permanent magnetic materials, ALNICO 8HE and INDOX 5 (a barium ferrite ceramic). The lines (——) are operating slopes ($|\mathbf{B}/\mathbf{H}|$ or permeance values) that depend on the magnet shape. The "○" on each curve indicates the approximate operating point (B_0, H_0) for $1.27 \times 1.27 \times 10$ cm^3 magnets.

factors discussed earlier, and calculations are possible for only a few simple cases. Usually, adequate estimates of operating points are found by measuring B (or H_0) with a gaussmeter probe held flush with a magnet pole face. For a square cross section $(B/H = 0.9)$, the flux density at the surface of a pole is about $0.7B_0$, where B_0 is the flux density at the magnet center (an inaccessible location). The precise value found with (9.24) is $B(x, y)/B(0, 0) = 0.7048$ with $x = 0$ and $y = H$, the half height of the magnet ($8 \tan^{-1}(2)/4\pi = 0.7048$). In this manner, one does not measure M directly; $B(0, y = H)$ is measured, B_0 is calculated, and M is given by

$$M = \frac{B_0}{4\pi} \tag{9.32}$$

In the remainder of this chapter, further reference is not made to the magnetization M of a permanent magnet, but to its flux density B or to the field outside (H_0) the magnet where $B = H_0$ in the cgs system.

Some representative values of measured fields might help create a sense of proportion about magnets in magnetic brushes.

$$\text{ALNICO-8HE:}\quad B(y = H) = 800\text{--}850 \text{ G}; \ B_0 = 1135\text{--}1205 \text{ G}$$

$$\text{INDOX 5:}\quad B(y = H) = 1150\text{--}1250 \text{ G}; \ B_0 = 1630\text{--}1770 \text{ G}$$

These values were measured with the magnets in free space, and the dimensions were $1.27 \times 1.27 \times 10 \text{ cm}^3$, magnetized along a 1.27 cm direction. If the magnets are placed on an iron or other magnetically "soft" pole piece, the value of $B(y = H)$ increases about 13% because of the magnetic image effect of that pole piece. That is, one magnet on soft iron looks magnetically like two magnets, and the polarity of the magnetic image is opposite (mirror image) to the external magnet. Magnetic fields with iron poles are easily computed by the method of images, as discussed in Chapter 4 on electrical corona devices.

9.4 Normalized Field, Gradient, and Force Equations

In the field equations (9.24) and (9.25), B_x and B_y scale with B_0 (the flux density) at the magnet center. It is convenient to normalize all of the relevant equations by dividing each by B_0. This leaves a set of equations that depend only on the geometry and location of the magnetic source. The resultant equation for magnetic force becomes

$$\mathbf{F}_m = -\left(\frac{\mu - 1}{\mu + 2}\right) b^3 B_0^2 \left[\left(b_x \frac{\partial b_x}{\partial x} + b_y \frac{\partial b_y}{\partial x}\right)\hat{\mathbf{i}}\right.$$

$$\left. + \left(b_x \frac{\partial b_x}{\partial y} + b_y \frac{\partial b_y}{\partial y}\right)\hat{\mathbf{j}}\right] \tag{9.33}$$

where $b_x \equiv B_x/B_0$ and $b_y \equiv B_y/B_0$. When written this way, the behavior of $\mathbf{F}_m$ is separated into the material and the geometrical aspects of the problem. In (9.33), the coefficient multiplying the normalized field and gradient terms contains the magnetic part of the equation, and it will be called the "force constant" K_f.

$$K_f = \left(\frac{\mu - 1}{\mu + 2}\right) b^3 B_0^2 \quad \text{(ergs)} \tag{9.34}$$

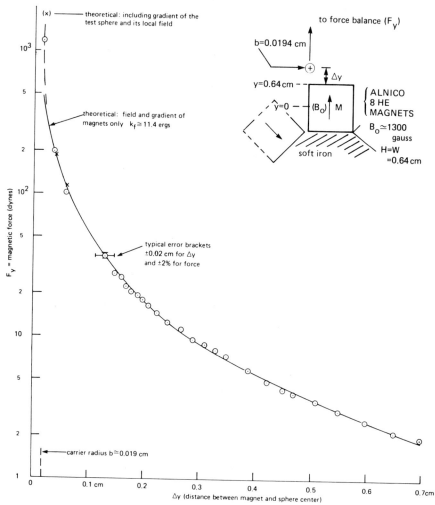

Figure 9.4 Comparison of theory and experiment ($\odot \odot \odot$) for steel sphere ($b = 0.0194$ cm) attracted to the edge of an ALNICO 8HE permanent magnet resting on a soft iron pole piece. The negative sign convention has been ignored for this plot.

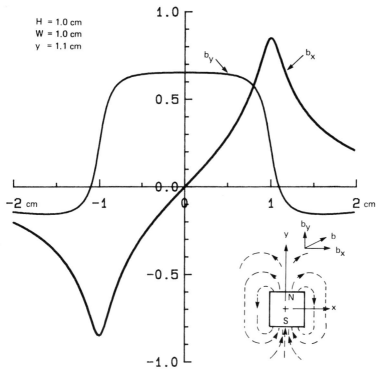

Figure 9.5   Normalized field components of a uniformly magnetized body [2.0 × 2.0 cm² in cross section ($H = W = 1.0$ cm)] plotted versus x.

The cgs dimension of K_f is ergs, and the dimension of the normalized force $\mathbf{f}$

$$\mathbf{f}_m = \frac{\mathbf{F}_m}{K_f} \tag{9.35}$$

is therefore cm^{-1}

A numerical example is helpful at this point. A steel sphere with $b = 0.0194$ cm and $\mu = 40$, with an ALNICO 8HE magnet of $B_0 = 1300$ G yields a force constant $K_f = 11.4$ ergs. The 1300 G value assumes the magnet has been placed on an iron slab with the magnetic orientation perpendicular to the plane of the slab. The magnet is square with $2W = 2H = 1.27$ cm, and the normalized field–field gradient is computed with these values. Theory and experiment are compared in Figure 9.4, and the agreement is excellent until the carrier sphere comes within one diameter ($2b = 0.038$ cm) of the magnet surface. Accounting for the large field gradient at the surface of the carrier, theory and experiment agree once again. The small carrier bead was attached to an electrobalance that measured equivalent mass units (mg). The force in dynes was obtained from the

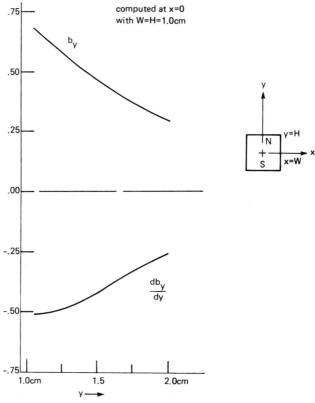

Figure 9.6 Normalized field and gradient vs. separation y. At the top pole face, $y = 1.0$ cm $= H$. Half-width $W = 1.0$ cm.

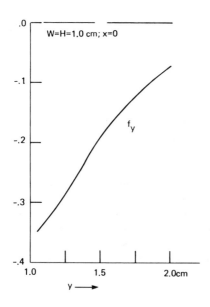

Figure 9.7 Normalized force f_y vs. separation for a 2.0×2.0 cm^2 cross section ($W = H = 1.0$ cm). Negative f_y means a sphere is attracted in the $-y$ direction for y positive.

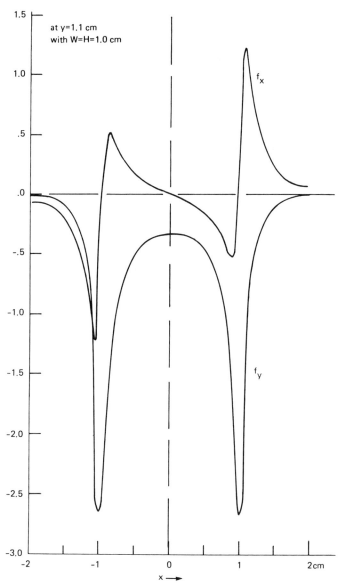

Figure 9.8 Normalized force f_x and f_y vs. x. A sphere is attracted toward a magnet edge, so f_x is positive when a sphere is attracted in the negative x-direction.

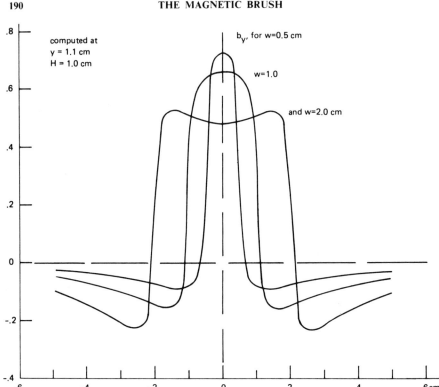

Figure 9.9   Normalized field b_y vs, x for $W = 0.5$, 1.0, and 2.0 cm. Curves computed at fixed spacing $y = 1.1$ cm with H constant at 1.0 cm.

measured apparent increase in carrier mass using a value $g = 980 \text{ cm/sec}^2$, so F_m (dynes) = equivalent mass (g) $\times$ 980 cm/sec^2. For most engineering work, it is acceptable to think of 1 mg under earth's attraction as equivalent (within 2%) to a force of 1 dyne. The tone arm of a good phonograph turntable tracks at 1g, or about 1000 dynes.

In Figure 9.4, the measured force at a separation of one bead radius is nearly 1200 dynes, whereas the simple equations predict 484 dynes. This discrepancy arises because the derivation ignores the local field perturbation in the immediate vicinity of the sphere. The range of this perturbation, as shown later, is roughly one bead diameter, so the simple theory is quite adequate for distances greater than this amount.

The curves given in Figures 9.4–9.8 were computed for magnets $2.0 \times 2.0 \text{ cm}^2$ in cross section. Studying these curves gives a fair idea of the way real magnets behave. $K_f f_y$ yields the attractive force in dynes; K_f is about 23.2 ergs for INDOX 5 magnets with $B_0 = 1850$ G on the iron plate. This is about twice the value of K_f determined for ALNICO 8HE. Figures 9.9 and 9.10 show the

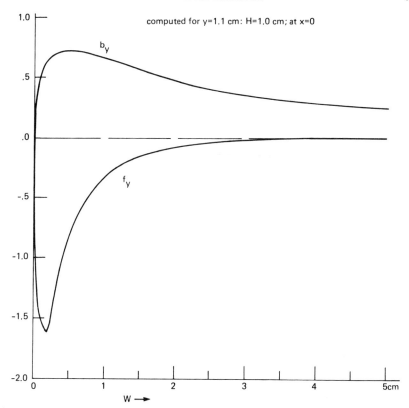

Figure 9.10 Normalized force and field vs. magnet *half-width* W, at constant spacing $y = 1.1$ cm and magnet half-height $H = 1.0$ cm; $x = 0$.

behavior for different values of W with H and y constant. The behavior is reminiscent of that found in Chapter 6 for electric fields.

9.5 Multiple Sources

Equations (9.13), (9.24)–(9.27), (9.30), and (9.31) form a two-dimensional description of the force attracting a magnetizable sphere toward a rectangular magnet. Since the field in space is the vector sum (i.e., linear superposition) of field contributions from whatever sources are present, it is a very simple matter to treat magnetic brushes that have more than one magnet in them. Some magnetic brushes are made of one cylindrically shaped ferrite piece that is magnetized with several magnetic poles about its periphery. The field varies almost sinusoidally with position around the cylinder, so the field equations are particularly simple to treat. When the magnetic sources are physically

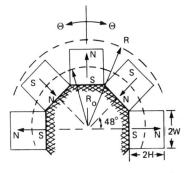

Figure 9.11 Five identical sources with alternating polarity. $R_0 = 2.3$ cm, $R = 3.3$ cm, $2W = 2H = 1.27$ cm. The operating surface of a magnetic brush is at R; this surface is a nonmagnetic, conducting material.

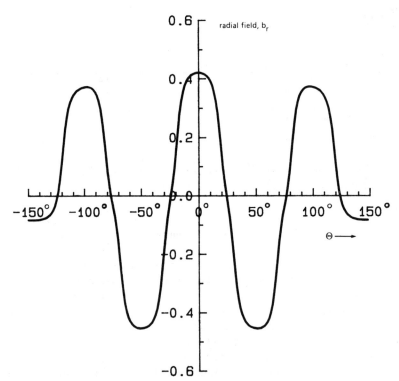

Figure 9.12 Normalized field in the radial direction. See Figure 9.11 for magnetic geometry. $R_0 = 2.3$ cm; $R = 3.3$ cm; $H = W = 0.635$ cm.

192

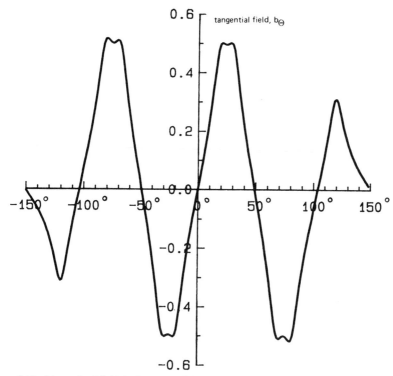

Figure 9.13   Normalized field in the tangential direction. See Figure 9.11 for magnet geometry. $R_0 = 2.3$ cm; $R = 3.3$ cm; $H = W = 0.635$ cm.

identified with separate magnets attached to a soft iron core, the fields of isolated sources are added algebraically, taking correct account of the polarity or direction of the magnetization M in each magnet. After the total field is determined, the gradient is found.

Figures 9.11 through 9.14 show the geometry, composite field components, and normalized radial force f_r for a magnetic brush having five identical sources of alternating polarity. If all magnets had the same polarity (say the North poles were each outward), the magnetic force would drop by roughly a factor of four owing to the loss of field gradient primarily, and to a decrease in field magnitude secondarily. In Figure 9.14, notice the deep valleys in f_r between each of the magnets. These force minima ($f_r = 0.15$) are a strong function of spacing between magnets, and f_r (min) increases rapidly as the distance between magnets decreases. The magnets necessarily require a trapezoidal shape, if they are to be crowded together without interference at the bottom edges. With tapered sides, the equations for magnetic force are modified by $\cos^2 \theta$, where θ is the taper angle at an edge. For an angle of 18° or less, the force equation is within 10% of the untapered value, as $\cos^2(18°) = 0.904$.

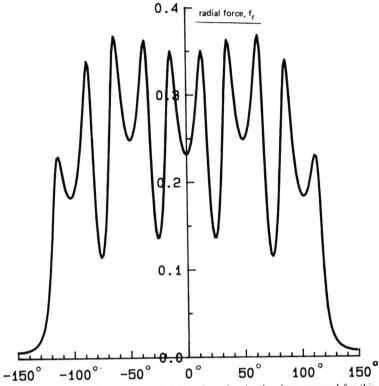

Figure 9.14   Normalized force in the radial direction; the sign has been reversed for this plot. (Attractive is "minus," shown here as "pos.") $R_0 = 2.3$ cm; $R = 3.3$ cm; $H = W = 0.635$ cm.

9.6   Carrier–Carrier Interactions

The force equations derived earlier do not include the local field and gradient arising from the polarized carrier sphere, so the force is underestimated when the distance between carrier and magnet is less than about one carrier diameter. In this section, the local field and gradient in the vicinity of a sphere is treated under the condition that the carrier is immersed in a uniform field. The magnetic field about a magnetized sphere is formally analogous to the electric field case discussed in Chapter 8; the external field is the sum of a dipole field and the original uniform field. The radial and tangential components of the magnetic field are

$$H_r = H_0 \cos \theta \left[1 + 2 \left(\frac{\mu - 2}{\mu + 2} \right) \left(\frac{b}{r} \right)^3 \right] \quad \text{(radial)} \qquad (9.36)$$

$$H_\theta = H_0 \sin \theta \left[1 - \left(\frac{\mu - 1}{\mu + 2} \right) \left(\frac{b}{r} \right)^3 \right] \quad \text{(tangential)} \qquad (9.37)$$

The moment of an induced dipole of an isolated sphere is given by (9.12). If two spheres are brought into proximity, there is a dipole–dipole interaction. The moments are induced by the local external field, so the first sphere is magnetized to a higher value because of the field disturbance of the second sphere, and the second sphere responds in like manner to the influence of the first sphere. Many orders of interaction occur, but the long process of getting an exact result is truncated by counting only the first-order interactions of two identical spheres. In this manner, one obtains a result that can be readily compared with experiment to see if the first-order estimate is close enough to justify its use.

The magnetic moment is in the same direction as the applied field; hence, if two carriers are lined up along the field direction, they will be attracted to each other. If the carriers are lined up with an axis perpendicular to the field direction, they will repel each other. This behavior is the basis for the well-known chaining of magnetic particles; each particle is a magnet in its own right, and unlike poles attract while like poles repel. In (9.36) and (9.37), the field direction is defined by the angle θ; thus, if two spheres are aligned with the applied field, then $\theta = 0$, and the dipole moment is

$$m_t = m_1 + m_{12} = m_2 + m_{21} \quad \text{(emu)} \tag{9.38}$$

where the moment of either sphere without interaction with the other is given by

$$m_1 = m_2 = \left(\frac{\mu - 1}{\mu + 2}\right) b^3 H_0 \tag{9.39}$$

and the first-order interaction between spheres is given by

$$m_{12} = m_{21} = m_1 \left[1 + 2\left(\frac{\mu - 1}{\mu + 2}\right)\left(\frac{b}{r}\right)^3 \right] \tag{9.40}$$

The total magnetostatic energy of this dipole–dipole interaction is approximately

$$W_m \cong -\frac{2m_t^2}{r^3} \cong -8\left(\frac{\mu - 1}{\mu + 2}\right)^2 b^3 H_0^2 \left[\left(\frac{b}{r}\right)^3 + 2\left(\frac{\mu - 1}{\mu + 2}\right)\left(\frac{b}{r}\right)^6 + \left(\frac{\mu - 1}{\mu + 2}\right)^2 \left(\frac{b}{r}\right)^9 \right] \tag{9.41}$$

The distance between sphere centers is r, so the force of attraction is along r and it is found by taking the negative gradient of the energy.

$$F_r = -\frac{\partial W_m}{\partial r} = -24\left(\frac{\mu - 1}{\mu + 2}\right)^2 b^2 H_0^2 \left[\left(\frac{b}{r}\right)^4 + 4\left(\frac{\mu - 1}{\mu + 2}\right)\left(\frac{b}{r}\right)^7 \right.$$

$$\left. + 3\left(\frac{\mu - 1}{\mu + 2}\right)^2 \left(\frac{b}{r}\right)^{10} \right] \tag{9.42}$$

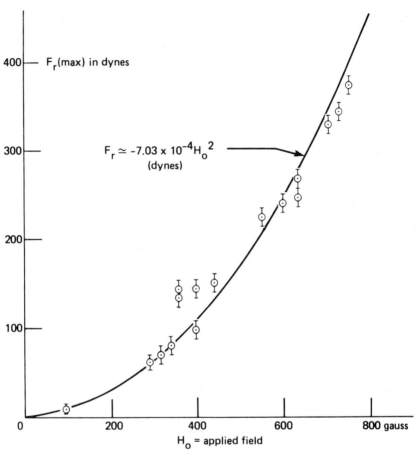

Figure 9.15   Experiment and simple theory for the dipole–dipole force between two steel spheres with $\mu = 40$ and $b = 0019$ cm.

The spheres touch at $r = 2b$, and this is the condition of maximum force between spheres.

$$\mathbf{F}_r(\text{max}) = -24\left(\frac{\mu-1}{\mu+2}\right)^2 b^2 \mathbf{H}_0^2 \left[\left(\frac{1}{2}\right)^4 + 4\left(\frac{\mu-1}{\mu+2}\right)\left(\frac{1}{2}\right)^7 + 3\left(\frac{\mu-1}{\mu+2}\right)^2\left(\frac{1}{2}\right)^{10}\right]$$

$$(9.43)$$

This relation shows that the maximum force goes as H_0^2, and Figure 9.15 shows experimental results with two carrier spheres with a permeability of about 40 and $b = 0.019$ cm. One carrier was glued to a nonmagnetic base, under which was placed a permanent magnet. The applied field H_0 was varied by changing the location of the magnet whose field vs. distance curve was known. The second carrier was attached to a force balance, as described earlier, and the force necessary to separate the two carriers was measured. The calculated curve agrees well with the experimental results, so first-order theory is adequate for describing the interaction between two carrier beads.

9.7   Sphere Chaining

The operating field at the surface of a magnetic brush may be 500 G or more, so the force holding carriers together in a chain would be about 170 dynes for identical spheres with $b = 0.019$ cm. The force attracting the carrier to the

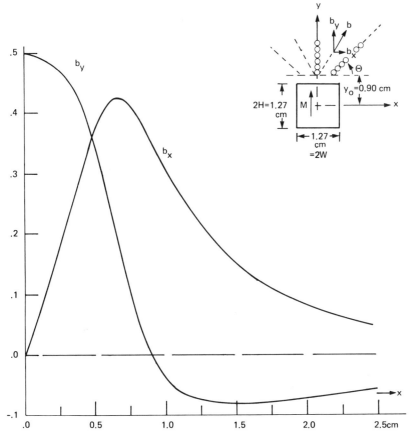

Figure 9.16   Normalized field components at $y_0 = 0.90$ cm for a square cross section magnet, with $2H = 2W = 1.27$ cm. The field angle is given by $\Theta = \tan^{-1} (b_y/b_x)$ (radians).

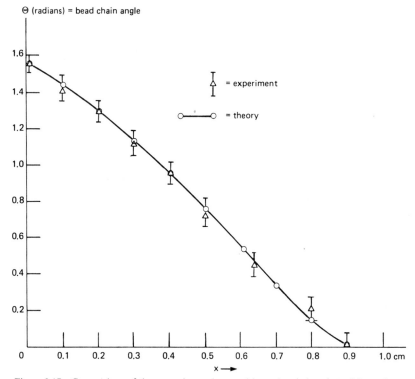

Figure 9.17   Comparison of theory and experiment with carrier chains about 0.3 mm long.

magnetic brush is about 10 dynes, however. The force between beads is, therefore, much greater than the force on a bead, so the bead chain behaves as a
mechanical entity on the surface of the magnetic brush assembly. Chains of
carrier beads whip and cartwheel end over end as they travel on the rotating
cylinder over a fixed array of permanent magnets. Under static conditions,
the angle formed by a short chain is determined by the field components as
given in (9.24) and (9.25). The magnetic "lines of force" (Michael Faraday's
words) or field lines are essentially the mental pictures decorated in the real
world by the chains of carrier beads distributed over the face of a magnet. The
faithfulness of short bead chains in showing the field direction is illustrated in
Figures 9.16 and 9.17. The plots in Figure 9.16 are computed for a magnet of
square cross section at a distance $y_0 = 0.90$ cm above the center of the magnet.
The angle (θ) of the field is given by

$$\theta = \tan^{-1}\left(\frac{b_y}{b_x}\right) \quad \text{(radians)} \tag{9.44}$$

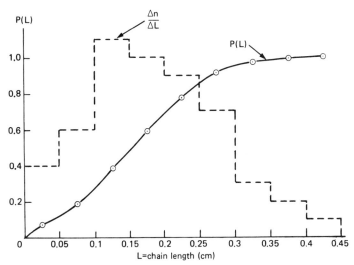

Figure 9.18   The distribution of chain lengths $P(L)$ and the frequency of occurrence $\Delta n/\Delta L$ as a function of chain length L (cm). In the absence of magnetic forces, the beads would collapse into a uniformly packed layer, 0.10 cm thick. The mean diameter of the spheres was 0.025 cm by number.

This relation is plotted in Figure 9.17 along with the measured angles for chains about 0.3 cm long. With multiple sources, chains bridge between north and south poles, and point radially outward when over a pole.

Each bead chain behaves as a small magnet, repelling adjacent chains because of the identical north–south polarity. Close inspection of a chain reveals that the individual carriers prefer to pack closely into a stalagmitic arrangement, having a base with four to five beads across, which is two or three beads thick and tapers off to one bead at the chain tip. Occasionally, one finds a linear chain (a chain whose thickness is constant), but the majority are roughly triangular when viewed from the side.

Chain length is a random variable. Figure 9.18 gives a histogram for relative frequency of occurrence as a function of chain length. The smooth solid curve $P(L)$ is the distribution function or probability of finding a chain of length L, or less. For these data, the unchained beads (no magnetic field) would have formed a pack 0.10 cm thick. The mean diameter of beads was 0.025 cm. Additional experiments with bead chains showed that the chain length at which $P(L) = 0.50$ occurred at $L = 1.5G$, where G is the packed thickness of unchained beads. In practice, G would be the gap distance between the magnetic brush cylinder and the PC surface. When traveling through the developer gap, bead chains are pressed down to form a close-packed array at the nip formed by the roll and the PC drum. Upon emerging from the nip, chains once again are formed in random lengths from the supply of carrier beads.

9.8   Bead Carry-Out

When chains whip over a magnetic pole (see Figure 9.11), at high rotational speeds, very long chains develop a centrifugal force that is sufficient to escape the constraining magnetic force. Impacts between carriers produce decelerations on the order of $10^6 g$, such that toner leaves the carrier denuded; the highly charged carrier is attracted electrically to nonimage regions of the PC. When carrier beads escape from the developer housing, the phenomenon is called "bead carry-out," and the carrier must be removed from the PC surface by an auxiliary device called a "bead scavenger." Since carriers are much larger than toner particles, they interfere with toner transfer if not removed by a bead scavenger. Laser printers create original documents; thus, a major concern is data integrity on the printed page. One carrier bead, $250 \, \mu m$ in diameter, can obliterate information lying within a 0.5-cm range because the "tent" formed by the paper over the bead does not touch the developed image on the PC. Because dispersion forces are large, it is essential to have paper–toner contact along with appropriate electrostatic force to transfer toner. Office copier–duplicator machines work from an original document provided by the user, so the demand for data integrity is often not as great as with laser printers. With small diameter carriers (50–100 μm), data loss becomes less obvious to the unaided human eye, although bead carry-out is much increased, because the magnetic force competes less well with electrical forces. High-gradient magnetic scavengers and monofilament nylon scrapers have been successfully used as bead scavengers; the nylon wires do not disturb the toned image and are effective in removing nonmagnetic debris as well as carrier beads.

9.9   Competition Between Electric and Magnetic Forces

When toner is stripped away from a carrier, the residual carrier charge is more than sufficient to counteract gravitational attraction, and if the volume of magnetic material is small, electrical forces can also overwhelm magnetic forces. The minimum diameter that can be magnetically retained against an electrical force is easily computed using information given earlier in this and other chapters. Because electrical force scales with surface area and magnetic force scales with volume, small charged beads attach to the PC surface and resist magnetic scavenging. The treatment of this problem is idealized for tutorial purposes, and the estimated sphere diameters are only approximately correct. Dispersion force contribution to carrier–PC adhesion is ignored here, but there is sufficient information in Chapter 7 to include it, should one be motivated to do so.

    Assume that a carrier has been stripped of all toner and is left with a total charge Q distributed uniformly over its surface. The bead is stuck to the PC surface with an electric force arising from the polarization of the PC by the field of the carrier and the field of the PC by image exposure variations in surface potential. So, to a first approximation, the electrical force is

$$F_e = QE_{PC} + \frac{Q^2}{4b^2} = 4\pi b^2 \sigma(E_{PC} + \pi\sigma) \quad \text{(dynes)} \tag{9.45}$$

The carrier radius is b (cm); the surface charge density is $\sigma(esu/cm^2)$; E_{PC} is the free-space electric field at a distance $z = b$ above the PC surface. In a large region of constant potential away from the influence of a developer electrode, $E_{PC} = 0$, whereas near the edge of an exposed image, E_{PC} might be roughly $5\,kV/cm = 16.7\,esu/cm^2$.

The magnetic force on an isolated bead depends on the design of the bead scavenger and on the presence or absence of carrier beads at the operating surface of the scavenger. Without the perturbing influence of beads on the scavenger, the magnetic force is written

$$F_{m1} = \left(\frac{\mu - 1}{\mu + 2}\right) b^3 B_0^2 f_r \quad \text{(dynes)} \tag{9.46}$$

and f_r is the normalized force equation which depends on the design of the scavenger and the distance from the isolated bead. When beads chain up, the field and gradient are increased substantially, so an isolated and electrically stuck carrier is attracted with a much greater magnetic force than that given by (9.46). An estimate of the attractive force between two beads just touching is found with (9.43). With a permeability of 40, (9.43) reduces to

$$F_{m2} \cong -2b^2 H_0^2 \quad \text{(dynes)} \tag{9.47}$$

where H_0 is the magnetic field with beads removed. In (9.46), recall that B_0 is the flux density at the center of the permanent magnet scavenger. The smallest bead capable of magnetic scavenging is found by equating the electrical and magnetic forces. Without another bead present, the scavenger itself could attract a sphere whose radius is

$$b_{min} = \frac{4\pi\sigma(E_{PC} + \pi\sigma)}{[(\mu - 1)/(\mu + 2)]B_0^2|f_r|} \quad \text{(cm)} \tag{9.48}$$

In the second case, a bead attracts another bead, so the magnetic force scales with b^2, which is the same power law found with electrical forces; therefore, carrier size is irrelevant. Magnetic scavenging fails with small beads unless the scavenger uses magnetic pole pieces with very sharp edges to obtain high field gradients. Using (9.45) and (9.47), and solving for the minimum field H_0 at which high gradient (bead chain) scavenging occurs, one obtains

$$H_0(min) \cong [2\pi\sigma(E_{PC} + \pi\sigma)]^{1/2} \quad \text{(G)} \tag{9.49}$$

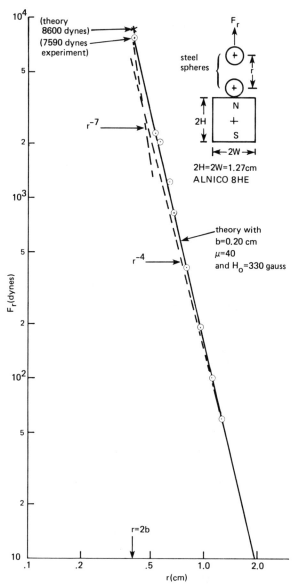

Figure 9.19 Theory and experiment for interaction between two identical spheres—an excess force, from the gradient of the field of the ALNICO magnet, has been suppressed.

. Carrier surface charge density is found with (7.6) with the assumption that charge is conserved and neutralization current does not flow. In this case, the result is

$$\sigma = -\frac{C_t}{C_{t0}}\sigma_0 \quad (\text{esu/cm}^2) \tag{9.50}$$

The reader will recall that C_t is the toner concentration, C_{t0} is defined in (7.9) with carrier radius $b = R_c$, and σ_0 is the toner surface charge density (esu/cm^2) in the limit of very small C_t. In the worst case, all toner has been stripped from a carrier so that $\sigma \cong 30$ esu/cm^2. Under normal development conditions, only about 10% of the toner would be removed from a carrier, so the carrier surface charge density would average about 3 esu/cm^2. For the isolated sphere case, with $E_{PC} = 16.7$ esu/cm^2, $\mu = 40$, $B_0 = 1200$ G, and $f_r = 0.5$, Equation (9.48) yields the minimum radius that can be removed.

$$b_{\min} = 1.5 \times 10^{-3} \text{ cm} = 15 \quad \mu\text{m} \tag{9.51}$$

If the carrier has lost all toner, the surface charge density increases to the average value of about 30 esu/cm^2, and the minimum radius that can be scavenged increases to about 0.06 cm. In other words, magnetic scavenging becomes impossible without high-gradient geometry.

In the sphere–chain case (high gradient), the minimum field required to capture a bead with $\sigma = 30$ esu/cm^2 and $E_{PC} = 16.7$ esu/cm^2 is found directly from (9.49).

$$H_0(\min) = 127 \quad \text{G} \tag{9.52}$$

The magnetic force given by (9.42) diminishes rapidly with distance between spheres; there are terms in r^{-4}, r^{-7}, and r^{-10} with the relative contributions of about 0.66, 0.31, and 0.03, respectively, at closest approach ($r = 2b$). Experimental verification of (9.42) is shown in Figure 9.19, with two steel ball bearings of $b = 0.20$ cm used in the field of a permanent magnet. The excess force arising from the field gradient of the magnet has been suppressed in the plotted results. Magnetic force was measured with an electrobalance connected to the upper sphere, as shown in the inset of Figure 9.19. The dotted lines indicate power laws of r^{-4} and r^{-7}. The term in r^{-10} does not contribute enough force to be worth including in this figure. The solid line is computed from (9.42), with $b = 0.20$ cm, $\mu = 40$, and $H_0 = 330$ G. The simple theory passes through all data points except at $r = 2b$, where the computed force was 8600 dynes and the experimental value was 7590 dynes (about 0.88 that of the theory).

For rough estimates of scavenging force, the term in r^{-4} can be retained while discarding higher-order terms. The practical consequence of a force going as r^{-4} is that the force drops a factor of $2^4 = 16$ over a distance of one bead diameter. This implies that the efficacy of a high-gradient magnetic scavenger depends on a very small spacing between the scavenger and the PC surface.

TEN

TRANSFER OF DEVELOPED IMAGES ONTO PAPER

Particle adhesion and detachment processes were discussed in Chapters 7 and 8 on image development, and much of that work can be applied to this chapter on the physical and engineering aspects of image transfer to plain paper. Experiments with image transfer demonstrate that toner particles deposited on the PC form a loosely packed array—perhaps 50 μm high with line images, and that somewhat less high (on the average) with large area images—and that paper–toner contact is required along with an appropriate electric field to cause the image to be transferred. The necessity for physical contact emphasizes once again the role played by dispersion forces in the adhesive bond between a particle and a substrate. Electrical corona devices are very often used in high-speed copier and printer transfer units to generate the required electric field to attract the charged toner from the PC to the paper. If xerographic paper is quite dry, the electrical resistance will be large, and ions from the corona become trapped in the paper fibers until the field reaches the breakdown level. If, for some reason, the paper does not contact the PC and toner, electrical breakdown may occur across the air gap, with the electrical sparks converting much of their energy into acoustic pulses. Uman et al. (1968) studied very large sparks and concluded that more than half of the input electrical energy is converted to acoustic energy because of the rapidly expanding arc plasma. The bang of a sparking transfer corona is sufficient to shear the dispersion force component of toner–PC adhesion, and the transferred image quality may be seriously degraded. Xerographic machines do not normally operate with a gap between paper and PC, and the transfer corona devices are adjusted to prevent sparking.

Andrus and Hudson (1965) give a qualitative review of electrostatic transfer. Quantitative treatment of the transfer process is apparently limited to one paper by Yang and Hartmann (1976), who give a physical model of electrostatic separation of a layer of charged particles sandwiched between two electrodes at different potentials. Although their electrode geometry does not correspond to that of corona devices, their model does bring out the underlying physics in a straighforward manner. The Yang–Hartmann transfer model is reviewed in this chapter and some of the implications are discussed. Because image quality depends, among other things, upon the quantity of toner transferred to paper, the subject of transfer efficiency and its dependence on paper type is introduced. The electrical behavior of paper is quite interesting, and some speculations on the transport of ions through paper are given. The geometry and electrostatic field of transfer corona devices depart considerably from the parallel-plate model given by Yang and Hartmann; therefore, the total electric field resulting from bias electrodes and space charges of typical corona devices is discussed. Experiments show that the charge of residual toner is altered by the transfer corona device, so this chapter ends with a discussion of ion bombardment of particles.

10.1 The Transfer Model of Yang and Hartmann

If a layer of charged particles is sandwiched between two electrodes at different potentials and the electrodes are separated, the particle layer splits into two portions and each electrode retains a fraction of the original amount of particles. The transfer efficiency, or fraction transferred to a designated electrode, depends on the space charge density of the particle layer, the electric field between electrodes, and the cohesive forces between particles. Yang and Hartmann published a physical model of particle transfer along with supporting experimental results. An abridged treatment of their paper is given here. Particle layer and electrode geometry is shown in Figure 10.1. The layer of charged particles is in a state of stress from mechanical and electrical sources. This stress, $P(z)$, is given by the relation

$$P(z) = \int_0^z \rho(z')E_2(z')dz' + P_m - \varepsilon_3 E_3^2 \quad \text{(newton/m}^2) \qquad (10.1)$$

where ρ is the space charge density (C/m^3) of the particle layer, E_2 is the electric field (V/m) within the layer, P_m is the mechanical stress (N/m^2), and the last term is the compressive stress resulting from the electrostatic attraction of the two electrodes. The cohesive strength $C(z)$ (N/m^2) of the particle layer has its origins in particle–particle interactions and particle–electrode adhesion arising from electrostatic, dispersion, or chemical forces.

Consider the boundary between layers 2 and 3: when the mechanical stress is tensile, the particle layer separates where $P(z)$, the sum of electrostatic

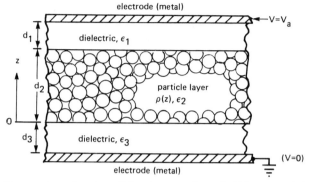

Figure 10.1   Three regions of various dielectric properties and thickness, sandwiched between two electrodes at different potentials. The particle layer is charged with density $\rho = \rho(z)$, where z is a variable $(0 \leq z \leq d_2)$ within the particle layer.

stresses, and P_m first exceed the cohesive strength $C(z)$. The location of layer separation is $z = z_s$, and this locus is found by solving for the minimum extremum in total stress $P(z) - C(z)$. The condition existing at z_s is, therefore, given by the relations

$$\frac{d}{dz}[P(z) - C(z)] = 0 \tag{10.2a}$$

and

$$P(z) - C(z) = 0 \tag{10.2b}$$

The fraction F of material attached to layer 1 is defined as the "transfer efficiency."

$$F = 1 - \frac{z_s}{d_2} \tag{10.3}$$

If the cohesive strength within the particle layer is constant, then the condition given by (10.2a) and (10.1) reduces to

$$\rho(z_s)E_2(z_s) = 0 \tag{10.4}$$

Equation (10.4) has the trivial solution $\rho(z_s) = 0$, and the useful result $E_2(z = z_s) = 0$. The field within the particle layer (E_2) is found by solving Poisson's Equation and setting $z = z_s$.

$$E_2(z) = \frac{1}{\varepsilon_2}\int_0^z \rho(z')dz' + E_0 = 0, \text{ at } z_s \tag{10.5}$$

The constant field E_0 is found by using Gauss's Law, according to the conditions that must exist at the boundary between region 1 and 2, and at the boundary between 2 and 3.

$$E_1 = \frac{\varepsilon_2}{\varepsilon_1} E_2(d_2) \tag{10.6}$$

$$E_3 = \frac{\varepsilon_2}{\varepsilon_3} E_2(0) \tag{10.7}$$

The applied voltage V_a is equal to the sum of the potentials across each layer. These potentials are obtained from the fields and distances across which these fields exist.

$$V_a = -E_1 d_1 - \int_0^{d_2} E_2(z)dz - E_3 d_3. \tag{10.8}$$

The unknown field E_0 is obtained from (10.5) through (10.8).

$$E_0 = -\frac{V_a}{\varepsilon_2 D} - \frac{D_1}{\varepsilon_2 D} \int_0^{d_2} \rho(z)dz - \frac{1}{\varepsilon_2^2 D} \int_0^{d_2} \int_0^{z} \rho(z')dz'\, dz \tag{10.9}$$

where

$$D_i = \frac{d_i}{\varepsilon_i} \quad (i = 1, 2, 3) \tag{10.10}$$

and

$$D = \sum_{i=1}^{3} D_i \tag{10.11}$$

Since $E_2(z_s) = 0$, with (10.5) one obtains the relation

$$\int_0^{z_s} \rho(z)dz = -\varepsilon_2 E_0 = \frac{V_a}{D} + \frac{D_1}{D} \int_0^{d_2} \rho(z)dz + \frac{1}{\varepsilon_2 D} \int_0^{d_2} \int_0^{z} \rho(z')dz'\, dz \tag{10.12}$$

Yang and Hartmann solved this equation for three cases:

$$\rho = \rho_0 \tag{10.13a}$$

$$\rho = \rho_0 e^{-\gamma z} \tag{10.13b}$$

$$\rho = \rho_1 e^{-\gamma z} - \rho_2 e^{-\gamma(d_2 - z)} \tag{10.13c}$$

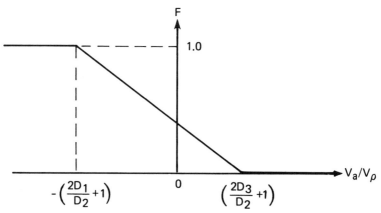

Figure 10.2   Transfer efficiency F vs. normalized applied potential for $\rho(z) = \rho_0$. From Yang and Hartmann, *IEEE Trans. Elec. Dev.*, **ED-23**, 308 (1976). Copyright 1976, IEEE.

Insulating particles would most likely have a constant charge density (10.13a); semiconducting particles might follow a spatially nonuniform density like that given in (10.13b). The third case shows two exponentials, and this might be found in photoactive particle electrophotography. With the constant charge density case, (10.12) is solved for the transfer efficiency F by finding the distance z_s at which each layer separates. There are three regimes for F.

$$F = 1.0 \quad \text{for } \frac{V_a}{V_\rho} \leq -\left(\frac{2D_1}{D_2} + 1\right) \tag{10.14a}$$

$$F = 1 - \frac{2D_1 + D_2 + D_2(V_a/V_\rho)}{2D} \quad \text{for } -\left(\frac{2D_1}{D_2} + 1\right) < \frac{V_a}{V_\rho} < \left(\frac{2D_3}{D_2} + 1\right) \tag{10.14b}$$

$$F = 0 \quad \text{for } \frac{V_a}{V_\rho} \geq \frac{2D_3}{D_2} + 1 \tag{10.14c}$$

where $V_\rho = \rho_0 d_2^2/(2\varepsilon_2)$ = the space charge potential across layer 2.

A plot of F vs. V_a/V_ρ is given in Figure 10.2. Yang and Hartmann verified this model by experiments with electrophoretically deposited particles on an aluminum substrate; particle space charge density was controlled with a DC corotron unit. Particles were transferred to a polyethylene terephthalate sheet placed over the layer of particles. At $V_a = 0$, (10.14b) predicts the efficiency $F = 1 - (2D_1 + D_2)/(2D)$, a result verified in the experiments.

10.2   Implications of the Model for Organic and Layered Photoconductors

It is instructive at this juncture to apply the Yang–Hartmann model to a set of conditions that could exist in a xerographic machine. One of the dielectrics is plain paper and the other is either OPC or LPC structures, which are discussed in Chapter 2. The space charge density of the sandwiched layer of toner is determined with (8.17).

$$\rho_0 = \left(\frac{q}{m}\right)pd_t = 3\sigma\frac{p}{R} \quad \text{(esu/cm}^3\text{)} \tag{10.15}$$

Recall that σ is the surface charge density (C/cm^2 or esu/cm^2), and p is the particle packing fraction; $p = \pi/6$ for cubic packing of spheres and $p = \sqrt{2}\,\pi/6$ for close-packed spheres; R is toner radius. With most toner, p is roughly equal to 0.5 experimentally. At $R = 5 \times 10^{-4}$ cm and $\sigma = -15$ esu/cm^2, the space charge density is -4.5×10^4 esu/cm$^3 = -1.5 \times 10^{-5}$ C/cm^3. A reasonable layer thickness would be $d_2 = 2.5 \times 10^{-3}$ cm for a large area developed image, and $\varepsilon_2 \cong 2.5\,\varepsilon_0$. These values yield a space charge potential difference across the toner layer $V_\rho = -121$ V. From (10.10), the dielectric thickness is $D_2 = 2.5 \times 10^{-3}$ cm/$(2.6\,\varepsilon_0)$. With LPC, the dielectric thickness of this PC is $D_3 = 1.5 \times 10^{-3}$ cm/$(3.0\,\varepsilon_0)$. Layer 1 is composed of a medium weight paper (about 20-lb paper), which gives $D_1 = 10^{-2}$ cm/$(2.5\,\varepsilon_0)$, approximately. The total dielectric thickness is found with (10.11): $D = D_1 + D_2 + D_3 = 5.38 \times 10^{-3}$ cm/ε_0. From (10.14b), transfer begins at a threshold value of applied voltage

$$V_a = V_\rho\left(\frac{2D_3}{D_2} + 1\right) \tag{10.16}$$

For OPC and the parameters given above, this threshold voltage is $1.76V_\rho = -373$ V. With $V_a = 0$, transfer efficiency $F = 0.16$. The voltage at which complete transfer occurs $(F = 1.0)$ is determined from (10.14b), using the upper limit.

$$V_a = -V_\rho\left(\frac{2D_1}{D_2} + 1\right) \tag{10.17}$$

With 20-lb paper and OPC dielectrics, $V_a = -9.0V_\rho = +1908$ V.

Layered PCs have slightly different thicknesses and dielectric constants, so the transfer efficiency F will have different limits on V_a/V_ρ. The limits and values are:

$$F = 0 \text{ at } V_a = 2.0V_\rho = -424 \text{ V,}$$
$$F = 1 \text{ at } V_a = -9.0V_\rho = +1908 \text{ V,}$$
$$F = 0.18 \text{ at } V_a = 0.$$

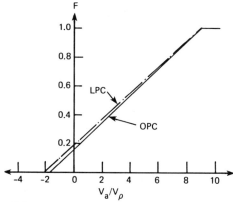

Figure 10.3   Transfer efficiency F vs. normalized voltage V_a/V_ρ for OPC and LPC films (layer 3), computed with a 25 μm thick particle layer (2).

This model predicts a transfer efficiency for OPC that is always less than for LPC, because the latter has a greater dielectric thickness. This is shown in Figure 10.3. In some unpublished experiments, R. S. Colby of IBM Corporation verified this prediction; his data are plotted in Figure 10.4. All else remaining equal, the model also predicts that thicker paper (layer 1) should decrease F, but this runs in opposition to the facts. If the model is basically sound — and it seems that this is so — then other variables must be invoked to reconcile experiment with theory. Because corona transfer is used in most high-speed machines, the electric field is due in part to the space charge of gaseous ions, and the Yang–Hartmann model does not directly apply to this situation. Paper is not a simple insulating dielectric, so the electrical properties of plain paper in an ionized gas have some influence on toner transfer. These subjects are examined in the following sections.

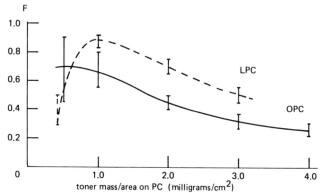

Figure 10.4   Transfer efficiency F vs. toner mass/area on a PC. Experimental results, using a modified 3800 printer, are from R. Colby (IBM Corporation).

10.3   Transfer Efficiency and Paper Type

Experiments with a variety of paper types, manufacturers, and thicknesses (i.e., weights) have established that heavier papers yield improvement in transfer efficiency. This is shown in Figure 10.5; the unpublished data are from P. Sündstrom of IBM Corporation. Sündstrom also studied the dependence of F upon the permeability of gases through different papers, as shown in Figure 10.6. Paper with high permeability has high porosity, so the flow time (in seconds) for a fixed volume of gas will be short. These paper types do not transfer toner as efficiently as papers with low permeability (low porosity). Variation in gas permeability between different paper types is due to the overall thickness, degree of filling with clays, sizings, and other paper treatments. Why transfer efficiency (with corona devices) depends on gas permeability might be explained in the following manner.

Because toner particles adhere with electrostatic and dispersion forces, transfer (like development) depends on intimate contact between toner and the deposition surface, and on the magnitude and direction of the transfer electric field provided by the corona device. Figure 4.1 shows a cross-sectional view of a transfer device. Part of the transfer field is due to DC potentials at the corona wire and the bias cylinder, and part is the result of the space charge of ions flowing from the corona wire down to the paper, through it, and onto the PC surface. Experiments show that paper is permeable to gas ions as well as to neutral molecules, and as ions drift through it, an electrostatic pressure is generated between the paper and the underlying PC. This pressure depends on the quantity of charge flowing along the fibers of the paper and the trapping behavior of the fibers and clay fillers. A sheet that is perfectly insulating, for example, is essentially impermeable to ions and gases; thus, all corona ions become immobilized at the surface, and the electrostatically derived pressure

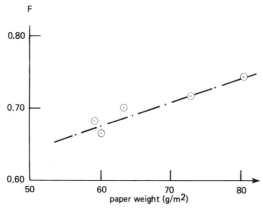

Figure 10.5   Transfer efficiency vs. paper weight. Experiments were on a 3800 printer. Data from P. Sundström, IBM Corporation.

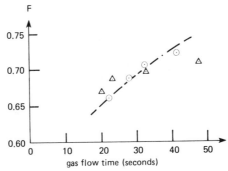

Figure 10.6   Transfer efficiency vs. gas flow time of a fixed volume of air through a paper sample. Very porous paper has low flow time, or high gas permeability. Data from P. Sundström, IBM Corporation.

between substrate and insulating sheet can be so great that the sheet is peeled away only with great difficulty. In the spirit of conjecture, polyethylene tereph-thalate (PET) films would exhibit excellent transfer efficiency, as is the case, and this would result from the intimacy of contact between toner and PET caused by the electrostatic pressure.

Adequate physical contact between toner and plain paper is achieved with most xerographic quality papers by injecting gaseous ions into the paper and letting the electrostatic forces deform the paper to obtain good compliance with the developed PC. Occasionally, paper is improperly stored and excess moisture distorts the fibers, leaving the paper with wrinkles that will not flatten; toner does not transfer to wrinkles whose depths exceed the thickness of the toned image. As with bead carry-out (discussed in Chapter 9), data integrity is jeopardized by such transfer failures; hence, data losses are minimized by properly specifying paper and storage conditions in addition to designing the machine to accept a reasonable variety of paper types.

Transfer pressure caused by electrostatic charge can be estimated from the information given in Chapter 4 on corona devices. Assume that paper travels at 80 cm/sec past a transfer corona with a 0.64-cm aperture, through which a total current of 120 μA flows. If the paper is 38 cm wide, each square centimeter receives about 8×10^{-8} C of charge as it passes through the transfer zone. Transit time for 0.64 cm is 8 msec at 80 cm/sec, so there is ample time for ions to drift through the paper and onto the PC surface. The drifting ions impact paper fibers and generate a force between paper, toner, and PC. Static (i.e., trapped) charge represents the maximum transmission of electrostatic force, so if all ions are trapped, the pressure is

$$P_{\max} \cong \frac{\sigma^2}{2\varepsilon} = 1.4 \times 10^4 \quad \text{N/m}^2 \tag{10.18}$$

or about 2.0 lb/in.^{2}. Corson and Lorrain (1972) discuss the conditions applying to (10.18). Pressure decreases as gas permeability increases, so a thin unfilled sheet is expected to conform less well with a developed image; therefore, the transfer efficiency is reduced. The pressure estimated in (10.18) was measured by L. Kuhn (formerly of IBM Corporation) and the experimental result verifies the essential correctness of the physical mechanism. With narrow line images, the electric field at the PC surface usually exceeds 10^4 V/cm. Without toner on the image, paper adheres so strongly to the PC that computer printout (fan-fold) paper tears apart at the perforations and wraps around the PC drum. (Several commercially available x-y plotters use electrostatic forces to hold down the graph paper, although the electric fields are produced by arrays of conductors buried under a thin dielectric film, so the pressures involved would be less than the estimate given above.) Adhesion of paper is much reduced if the PC image is developed, because the toner charge partially neutralizes the electric field of the image, and the physical height of the toner (about 50 μm for line images) prevents intimate contact with the PC in the image region.

10.4   The Electrical Behavior of Paper

Many specialized instruments exist for measuring various properties of paper; however, it is sometimes difficult to establish a clear relationship between the quantity measured and the ultimate function of the paper. This seems particularly true of the electrical behavior of paper in xerographic processes. Figure 10.7 shows the surface resistance vs. moisture content for several paper types. As the moisture content increases from about 3 to 10% by weight, the surface resistance decreases nearly six orders of magnitude. Dry paper has very good insulating behavior, so it stores electrostatic charge rather well. Figure 10.8 gives the moisture content vs. relative humidity for paper stored in the environment long enough to reach equilibrium. These unpublished data are from R. Cutts of IBM Corporation.

Current density flowing through paper is plotted as a function of potential difference across the paper thickness in Figure 10.9; the electrodes were nickel plated. At low potentials the $J - V$ characteristic is linear in V (Ohm's Law regime), but with increasing voltage the current density becomes quadratic in V. Mott and Gurney (1964, p. 172) derive an expression for the current density flowing through an insulator in contact with a metal. In the regime where space charge is important, they show that J follows the relation

$$J = \frac{kV^2}{L^3} \quad (\text{A/cm}^2) \tag{10.19}$$

where k is a constant of proportionality, V is the potential across the insulator, and L is its thickness. It is interesting to speculate on the conduction process of gaseous ions through paper and to apply the approach of Mott and Gurney

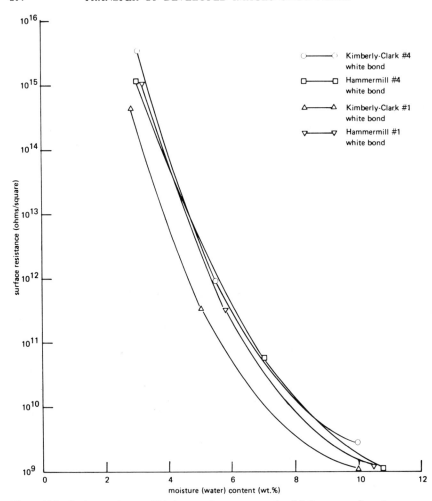

Figure 10.7   Surface resistance (Ω/sq) vs. moisture content (wt. %) for papers from two manufacturers. Data from R. Cutts, IBM Corporation.

to this problem. If one assumes a drift mobility μ for gas ion conduction, then the current density is

$$\mathbf{J} = \rho\mathbf{v} = \rho\mu\mathbf{E} \tag{10.20}$$

where ρ is the space charge density (C/cm^3), $\mathbf{v}$ is the drift velocity (cm/sec), and $\mathbf{E}$ is the electric field (V/cm). Poisson's Equation becomes

$$\mathbf{V} \cdot \mathbf{E} = -\frac{\rho}{\varepsilon} = -\frac{\mathbf{J}}{\mu\varepsilon\mathbf{E}} \tag{10.21}$$

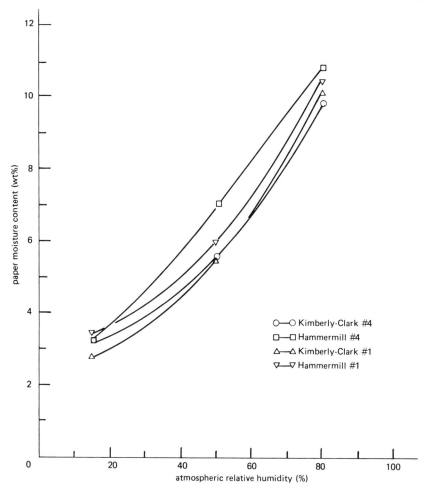

Figure 10.8   Moisture content (by weight %) vs. relative humidity of the atmosphere for papers from two manufacturers. Data from R. Cutts, IBM Corporation.

For current flow along the z-direction (say), the solutions

$$|\mathbf{J}| = \frac{\mathbf{E}^2}{2\mu\varepsilon z} \tag{10.22}$$

and since $E = -dV/dz$, then (10.22) is easily solved for $\mathbf{E}$. The potential is therefore

$$V = \int_0^L E\,dz = \int_0^L \left(\frac{2Jz}{\mu\varepsilon}\right)^{1/2} dz = \frac{2}{3}\left(\frac{2J}{\mu\varepsilon}\right)^{1/2} L^{3/2} \tag{10.23}$$

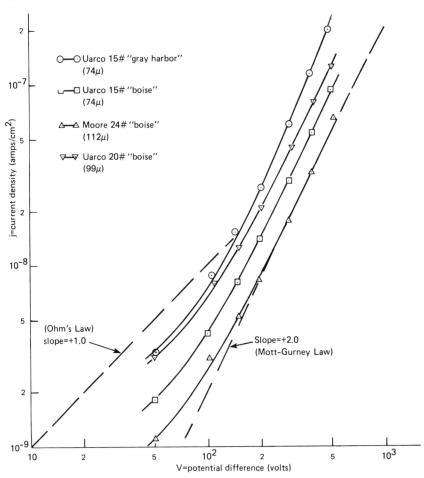

Figure 10.9 Current density vs. voltage for various paper samples. Conduction through the paper is ohmic at low voltages and becomes "space charge limited" at higher voltages. (Ambient: 21°C; 45% RH). Paper thickness L is given in the inset.

This relation is solved for the current density J.

$$J = \frac{9}{8}\mu\varepsilon \frac{V^2}{L^3} \tag{10.24}$$

Applying this "Mott–Gurney Law" to the data of Figure 10.9 gives a drift mobility of about $1 \times 10^{-6} \ \text{cm}^2/(\text{V-sec})$ for the 20-lb UARCO "Boise" sample at $V = 200\,\text{V}$, assuming that the paper dielectric constant $\varepsilon/\varepsilon_0 = 2.5$. The experimental results of Figure 10.9 were obtained with paper sandwiched between the nickel-plated electrodes of a volume resistivity instrument. In additional experiments in which two, three, and four layers of paper were used, the dependence of J on L conformed with the Mott–Gurney relation. The metal electrodes of the instrument most likely formed ohmic contacts with the paper (tests were at 45% relative humidity or about 6% moisture content) and injected electrons into the paper network. Lampert and Mark (1970) should be consulted for the analysis of current injection in solids. Keiss (1975) discusses models for charge carrier transport in dielectrics.

Experiments with positive and negative corona current injection into paper show that both polarities of ions flow readily over the surface of paper and through it to an underlying surface, either PC or metallic plane. Measurements of PC surface voltage before and after image transfer reveal that nearly all (99%) of the transfer current passes through paper and adsorbs to the PC surface, thereby shifting the surface potential accordingly. If the paper is very dry (less than about 4% moisture by weight), some of the transfer charge is trapped in the paper; this residual charge causes unwanted electrostatic fields which, in conjunction with mechanical forces, leads to movement or migration of toner away from the transferred image. L. L. Williams of IBM Corporation is acknowledged for supplying this information on toner migration. The conduction process for large ions through paper may also follow the Mott–Gurney Law; however, this subject has received little attention in the technical literature. Rothgordt (1974) discusses the influence of contact impedance between paper and the back electrode in electrostatic recording. Brodie, Dahlquist, and Sher (1968) describe techniques for measuring electrical relaxation of dielectric coated paper, and Schramm and Witter (1973) studied the gas discharge in the air gap between a dielectric sheet and an electrode. The American Paper Institute (1974) and the Institute of Paper Chemistry (1975) compile information on paper products and related technical studies. The Society of Electrophotography of Japan publishes *Denshi Shashin* (*Electrophotography*) in Japanese, with some papers occasionally in English; N. Kutsuwada published a series of papers, *Studies on Transfer of Electrophotographic Powder Image* (Nos. 1–9; Vols. 9–16; 1970–1978), in Japanese.

10.5 Electric Field of a Transfer Corona

A corotron used for image transfer is shown in Figure 4.1. Devices similar to this are used in high-speed copiers and printers; the polarity of the corona potential opposes that of the toner charge such that the transfer electric force attracts toner to the paper. A nominal set of operating conditions — 6 kV at the wire and 1.5 kV at the outer cylinder — establishes a current of perhaps 120 μA flowing through the paper. The configuration given in Figure 4.1 shows the corona wire mounted eccentrically, but parallel with the axis of the biased cylinder, and the device is placed a distance H above the PC, as shown in Figure 10.10. The exact electric field of such a device is not readily computed with simple closed-form equations, as the space charge of the corona current has a

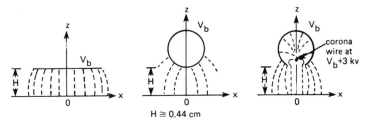

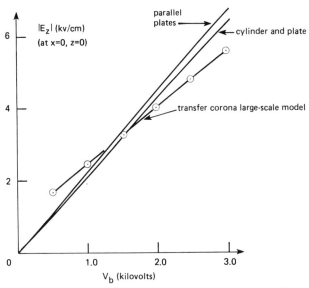

Figure 10.10   Comparison of electric field caused by a bias voltage for three electrode geometries. The transfer corona (without space charge) vertical field is within 10% of the cylinder and plate, and within 16% of the parallel plate cases.

complicated distribution and the wire eccentricity further complicates analysis. A large scale two-dimensional model of the transfer corona was drawn with conductive paint on resistance paper (Teledeltos paper) and equipotentials were found with a voltmeter. The graphical results showed that the device in Figure 4.1 could be reasonably approximated by a simple cylinder without any slot cut out. A graphical summary of the results is given in Figure 10.10 and, for comparison, the electric field of parallel plates and a cylinder are also shown. The vertical component of the electric field is given because it alone directs toner particles toward the paper. The electrostatic aspect of the transfer corona is greatly simplified by replacing the slotted cylinder, corona wire, and PC plane with a circular cylinder above a flat plane. The vertical field is then approximated by by (4.25).

. The total electric field must include space charge effects of the corona ions. Near the corona wire, the space charge density is high, but outside the cylinder the ions spread and the density becomes more uniform. As a first approximation, the current density is assumed constant in the region outside the slotted cylinder. A distribution that varies inversely with distance from the wire results in more complicated equations, but with little effect on the electric field at the PC surface. From (10.20), (10.21), and (10.22), the field arising from the space charge is

$$E_1 = \left(\frac{2JH}{\varepsilon\mu}\right)^{1/2} \tag{10.25}$$

and the electrostatic contribution arising from the difference in potentials of the biased cylinder and the PC is approximately

$$E_2 = \frac{V_{PC} - V_b}{H} \tag{10.26}$$

The total electric field of the transfer device is the sum of these contributions.

$$E_t = E_1 + E_2 = \left(\frac{2JH}{\varepsilon\mu}\right)^{1/2} + \left(\frac{V_{PC} - V_b}{H}\right) \quad (V/cm \tag{10.27}$$

With constant current power supply (yielding $J = 5 \times 10^{-6}$ A/cm^2) and fixed potentials V_{PC} and V_b, the total field behavior with spacing H is shown in Figure 10.11. The potentials given are appropriate for negatively charged toner. The transfer field rapidly becomes more negative (better) for small spacing, and has very little sensitivity to variations in spacing at $H = 0.5$ cm. Since a large transfer field is desirable, transfer efficiency is improved for smaller values of spacing. At $H = 0.2$ cm, the space charge contribution is about one-third of the total, so the transfer field is in the electrostatic regime. At $H = 0.8$ cm, about one-quarter of the total field is electrostatic, so one has entered the space charge regime, and transfer efficiency is more sensitive to variations in J or μ. Using (10.27), the total transfer field at $H = 0.5$ cm, $J = 5 \times 10^{-6}$ A/cm^2, $V_{PC} = -800$ V, $V_b = 1500$ V, $\varepsilon = \varepsilon_0$ and, $\mu = 1.0$ cm^2/V-sec is estimated at approximately -12 kV/cm, which is sufficient to overcome the PC field attracting toner away from the paper. Transfer efficiency can be improved by flooding the PC with light to reduce the field just prior to image transfer. That is, ignoring dispersion forces, the electrostatic force at transfer is

$$\mathbf{F}_{toner} \cong q(\mathbf{E}_t + \mathbf{E}_{PC}) \tag{10.28}$$

With the coordinate system adopted earlier, toner is deposited where $\mathbf{E}_{PC}$ is positive and normal to the PC plane, so transfer toward paper occurs when $\mathbf{E}_t$ is negative and greater in magnitude than $\mathbf{E}_{PC}$.

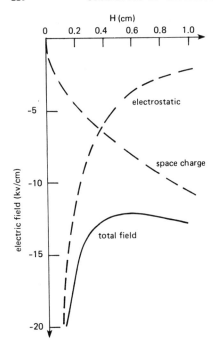

Figure 10.11 Hypothetical electric field of the transfer unit corotron. The total transfer field is composed of space charge and electrostatic components. Curves computed for $\varepsilon = \varepsilon_0$, $\mu = 1.0$, $V_{PC} = -800$ V, $V_b = +1500$ V, and $j = 5 \times 10^{-6}$ A/cm^2.

10.6   Additional Transfer Considerations

Transfer efficiency per se is an important measure of system effectiveness, but perhaps more revealing are the data showing M_t, the absolute mass/cm^2 transferred vs. absolute mass/cm^2 developed, M_{PC}. R. Colby of IBM Corporation showed empirically that this relation follows an exponential of the form

$$M_t = K(1 - e^{(B - M_{PC}/C)}) \qquad (10.29)$$

where K, B, and C are constants (all in mass/cm^2) that depend on the PC used. Table 10.1 gives these constants for OPC and LPC. Figure 10.12 shows the smoothed data of Colby, according to (10.29).

Table 10.1   Transfer Constants (mg/cm^2)

Constant	OPC	LPC
K	1.00	1.60
B	0.15	0.35
C	0.80	0.80

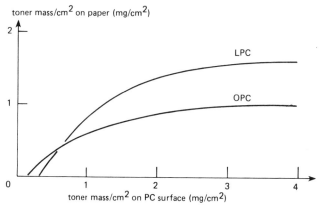

Figure 10.12   Absolute toner mass/cm^2 of image transferred to paper vs. absolute mass/cm^2 deposited on the PC. Curves are smoothed from the experiments of R. Colby, IBM Corporation.

The Yang–Hartmann model predicts qualitatively that K should be greater for LPC, as is the case, but their model says nothing directly about B or C. When performing the experiments, Colby controlled M_{PC} by changing the toner concentration C_t (see Chapter 7). At high C_t, toner charge of both polarities exists and both polarities develop, with a portion going to the image region and the opposite sign depositing onto background regions. The polarity of the transfer field attracts only toner in image regions and repels background toner (which is removed by the cleaning unit). The measurement of transfer efficiency used by Colby did not distinguish between positive and negative toner, so at high M_{PC}, a good portion of the toner on the PC (untransferred) could have been background toner. This speculation might explain the saturation phenomenon given in (10.29), but it does not explain the shifting parameter B or the slope C at small M_{PC}.

DePalma (1982) measured the size of residual toner after transfer of the image and found that the small diameters are preferentially left on the PC. This phenomenon was noted by many workers in xerography, who found that larger sized particles are always are the first to go from one surface to another whenever three-body contact is involved. DePalma also observed that residual toner charge was reversed in polarity by the transfer corona. This phenomenon is discussed in the next section.

10.7   Toner Charging by Ion Bombardment

Electrostatic precipitators charge aerosols by ion bombardment, and some of the principles of this technology are applicable to xerographic processes. A microscopic model of corona ion trajectories around toner particles at a PC latent image would be most useful in clarifying the physics of image transfer;

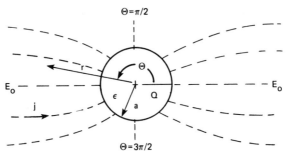

Figure 10.13   Geometry for computing the total field at the surface of a charged sphere Q, immersed in an external field that polarizes the sphere. Ions (j) follow field lines.

however, xerographic science, as revealed in the published literature, has not progressed to this level of sophistication.

Consider a uniformly charged semiconducting sphere that is polarized by an external electric field E_0. Mobile corona ions flow along field lines and impinge on the sphere until the radial component of the electric field is zero at the surface of the sphere. When the radial field just reaches zero, the sphere has received the maximum charge possible by ion bombardment. Analytically, this charging process is treated directly. The total radial field is composed of the original polarizing field, the induced dipole field arising from the polarized sphere, and a monopole term caused by the charge of the particle.

$$E_r = E_0 \cos\theta \left[1 + 2\left(\frac{k-1}{k+2}\right)\left(\frac{a}{r}\right)^3 \right] + \frac{Q}{4\pi r^2 \varepsilon_0} \qquad (10.30)$$

where k = dielectric constant.

The geometry for this situation is given in Figure 10.13; ions flow from left to right, which is shown by $\mathbf{J}$, the current density vector. Over the left hemisphere, the average radial electric field at $r = a$ is

$$\bar{E}_r = \frac{\int_{\pi/2}^{3\pi/2} E_r \, d\theta}{\int_{\pi/2}^{3\pi/2} d\theta} = \frac{[1 + 2(k-1)/(k+2)]E_0(\sin\frac{3}{2}\pi - \sin\frac{1}{2}\pi) + Q\pi/4\pi a^2 \varepsilon_0}{\pi} \qquad (10.31)$$

$$= -\frac{2}{\pi}\left[1 + 2\left(\frac{k-1}{k+2}\right)\right]E_0 + \frac{Q}{4\pi a^2 \varepsilon_0}$$

Charging stops when $\bar{E}_r = 0$, and the total charge becomes

$$Q_m = 8a^2 \varepsilon_0 \left[1 + 2\left(\frac{k-1}{k+2}\right)\right]E_0. \qquad (10.32)$$

The estimated value of Q_m is based on the assumption that impinging ions move along the surface of the sphere and reach a uniform distribution such that the external field caused by the charged sphere is always dipolar. Approximate values for (10.32) might be $E_0 = 12 \, kV/cm$, $a = 5 \times 10^{-4} \, cm$, and $k = 2.5$ (k is the dielectric constant of the sphere), which yields $Q_m = 3.5 \, esu/cm^2$. This is roughly one-eighth of the initial surface charge density achieved (opposite polarity) by contact electrification. Charging time is estimated from the average current density over the left hemisphere.

$$\frac{dQ}{dt} = \bar{I} = 2\pi a^2 \bar{J} = -2\pi a^2 \rho \mu \bar{E}_r = 4a^2 \rho \mu \left[1 + 2\left(\frac{k-1}{k+2}\right) \right] E_0 - \frac{\rho \mu}{2\varepsilon_0} Q$$

(10.33)

This current is integrated to find the charge as a function of time.

$$Q(t) = Q_m(1 - e^{-(\rho\mu/2\varepsilon_0)t}) + Q_0 e^{-(\rho\mu/2\varepsilon_0)t}$$ (10.34)

Q_m is defined in (10.32) and Q_0 is the initial charge of the particle. If Q_0 is the same polarity as the corona ions, the initial radial field may be repellant, but this situation can be checked with (10.30). The charging time constant τ (sec) is estimated from $J = 5 \times 10^{-6} \, A/cm^2$ and $E_0 = 12 \, kV/cm$, which yields $\rho = 4.2 \times 10^{-10} \, C/cm^3$ with a drift mobility $\mu = 1.0 \, cm^2/(V\text{-sec})$, thus

$$\tau = \frac{2\varepsilon_0}{\rho\mu} \cong 4.2 \times 10^{-4} \quad (sec)$$ (10.35)

For negative exponential charging, the particle reaches $0.98Q_m$ within four time constants, or roughly 1.7 msec. At 80 cm/sec, the PC travels past a 0.64 cm transfer zone in 8 msec, so there is ample time to charge untransferred toner to an opposite polarity.

Studies of transferred toner show that the charge is not greatly altered by charging from the transfer corona; that is, the charge to mass spectrum of toner on paper is quite similar to that of the developed toner, unless the corona space charge is very high and leads to sparking. With sparking, some of the transferred toner is dislodged from the paper, recharged to opposite polarity by ion bombardment, and redeposited onto the PC.

10.8 Non-electrostatic Image Transfer

Zimon (1969, p. 330), Andrus and Hudson (1965), and Schaffert (1975) discuss adhesive transfer of images, which requires paper specially coated with a pressure sensitive adhesive. Transfer of fine detail and continuous tone images are possible with this technique. This method does not transfer thick dense multi-layers of toner, however, as it depends on two-body contact and does not electrostatically attract the underlying toner layers. Chester Carlson, the inventor of modern xerography, used moistened paper to transfer images. Transfer efficiency was fairly good, even with small particles. Andrus and Hudson mention the use of strip-film transfer, where the image is covered with a layer of strip-film lacquer that rapidly dries. After drying for 5 sec or more, the lacquer is covered with white pressure sensitive tape and the image is stripped away from the underlying PC. They point out that this process not only transfers the image, but also completely cleans the PC and fixes the image permanently to the white tape; thus, strip-film transfer takes the place of three processing steps.

ELEVEN

PHOTOCONDUCTOR CLEANING AND RESTORATION

Under normal usage, a PC, such as LPC, might be expected to produce over 10^5 images in a given region before the image quality degrades below acceptable standards. This expectation is based on a rigid control of all process steps, including PC cleaning and restoration. Image transfer to plain paper is usually 80–90% efficient, as determined by measurements of toner mass/cm^2 before and after the transfer step. The residual toner must be removed from the PC, otherwise the toner particles interfere with corona charging and image exposure. In addition, any remaining toner will transfer to paper on the next process cycle and produce an undesirable ghost image. Most often, a PC reaches its end-of-life when the surface accumulates a layer of toner permanently fused onto areas correlated with background toner that has been developed and transferred to paper. That is, failure occurs when the PC is not completely cleaned, and when microscopic sites of toner particles are pressure bonded to the PC surface. These sites then function as nucleation centers for additional growth of a toner film, which eventually covers significant areas of the PC. Because toner is highly absorbent to visible light, the exposing beam is absorbed by the toner layer instead of the photogeneration layer of the PC. Thus, the surface potential does not decay in proportion to the exposure energy/cm^2 where toner intervenes, and the electrostatic field of the intended image is seriously damaged.

Photoconductors can be cleaned of residual toner in several ways. Schaffert (1975) mentions cleaning by rotating brush, solvents, wiping with disposable fiber webs, sonic air blasts, rubber scraping blades, and cascading granular (oppositely charged relative to toner) material over the dirty PC surface. In high-speed xerographic copiers and printers, it is most common to find vacuum-assisted rotating brushes and blade scrapers. These techniques are discussed along with particle detachment forces, aerodynamic forces on detached particles, and particle deposition by impaction on surfaces.

11.1 Particle Detachment Forces

Deryagin, Krotova, and Smilga (1978 p. 322) studied the adhesion of charged particles to a selenium surface, found that the detachment force scaled roughly with the square of particle radius, and concluded that adhesion was dominated by electrostatic forces. The instrument used for these studies was a gas fired bullet which impacted the rear side of a particle-laden substrate, and the accelerations achieved were between 10^3 and $10^6 g$. Mastrangelo (1982) and Nebenzahl et al. (1980) studied particle detachment with an ultracentrifuge capable of over $10^5 g$, and concluded that adhesion was dominated by dispersion forces (van der Waals–London forces). In their experiments, the adhesion depended slightly on the particle charge. Donald (1969), in a much earlier study, concluded that adhesion was dominated by electrostatic forces. He used a centrifuge capable of about $10^4 g$ acceleration. In a study with Xerox Type 364 toner, Kottler, Krupp, and Rabenhorst (1968) concluded that adhesion depended on particle charge, the van der Waals–dispersion force, hardness of adherents, and the length of time particles resided on the substrate before detachment. Hays (1978) finds the detachment force exceeds that caused by the electrostatic force alone. The adhesion between metal particles and metal substrates was studied by St. John (1969), who used a centrifuge in which the angle between the detaching force and the normal to the plane substrate could be varied. He concluded that particles must be treated as plastic bodies whose adhesion is controlled by the tangential component of the applied force. The combination of centrifugation with an applied electric field shows that the conductive particles are charged in proportion to the field, thereby receiving an additional force that scales with the particle area and the square of the applied electric field. St John and Montgomery (1971) showed that the removal force is affected by the substrate hardness. Cho (1964) analyzed induction charging of conducting particles in intense electric fields and measured the charge to mass with a quadrupole mass spectrometer.

All of these studies emphasize the importance of experimental technique and the roles played by dispersion and electrostatic forces in adhesion. Mastrangelo (1982) showed that the *threshold* force for toner removal is nearly proportional to the square of particle surface charge density; however, the force required to remove 50 % or more of the particles is only partially influenced by particle charge. Only 6–24 % of the particles were detached in the experiments of Donald (1969); thus, the low end of the distribution in adhesive force was sampled and Donald concluded that the electrostatic forces dominated.

Deryagin (Derjaguin) et al. (1978) dusted charged particles onto their gas-powered adhesiometer substrate; since the elastic wave created by the impacting bullet traveled from the back of the substrate to the front, the particles first received an acceleration that increased the pressure at the particle–substrate interface; then, as the elastic was reflected from the front of the substrate, a portion of the charged particles detached. This technique is capable of very high accelerations, but it alters the initial charge of the particles by forcing intimate contact between particle and substrate just prior to detachment. The experimental technique therefore introduces excess surface charge and biases the results toward adhesion which could be dominated by electrostatic forces. Indeed, Deryagin et al. (1978, pp. 423–443) discuss this aspect. They analyze elastic deformation of a particle on a rigid substrate and conclude that the increase in dispersion force adhesion (from the increased contact area) is balanced by the elastic recovery force, but the particle receives charge ". . . under the influence of the pulse in which the particle is pressed onto the substrate, this layer formed all over the pressed-on area of attachment. When detachment takes place under the influence of inertial forces, the attractive forces between the electrical double-layer plates are considerably greater than the molecular sticking forces, so that we find the sticking force to be proportional to the square of the ball radius. This conclusion has been confirmed by quantitative measurements of the density of the charge carried away by the detached particles." If particles suffer plastic deformation at the real areas of contact, there is no question of elastic recovery; thus, the work of deformation is dissipated as heat and the van der Waals dispersion force of adhesion could dominate electrostatic forces. Mastrangelo's work (1982) with toner particles on polymer substrates (LPC and OPC) showed that adhesion depended on the hardness of the substrates.

Krupp (1967, p. 194) discusses van der Waals adhesion vs. hardness. In the absence of elastic recovery, and ignoring electrostatic forces, the total contact area A_c between a particle and a substrate is determined by the adhesive force F and the hardness H (in dynes/cm^2) of the softer material (assuming one material is much harder). That is,

$$A_c = \frac{F}{H} \quad (\text{cm}^2) \tag{11.1}$$

and the force/cm^2 caused by the dispersion or van der Waals interactions (see Chapter 7) is given by the relation

$$f = \frac{A}{6\pi D^3} \quad (\text{dynes/cm}^2) \tag{11.2}$$

(where A is the Hamaker constant and D is the minimum distance of approach), so the total force between a sphere of radius R and a plane is

$$F_t = \frac{AR}{6D^2} \left(1 + \frac{A}{6\pi D^3 H}\right) \quad (\text{dynes}) \tag{11.3}$$

Krupp observes that H may be a function of time; thus, the region of true contact would depend on the residence time of the particle.

The implications of these ideas for cleaning a PC are clear. Hard substrates and hard particles have reduced contact area and are relatively easier to detach when compared to a system having soft particles, soft substrate, or both. If a particle is plastically deformed when initially deposited on the PC, it will be more difficult to remove, because the dispersion force increases as a result of the increased contact area. Contact electrification may also play a role; the particle charge can increase or decrease depending on initial change and the difference in effective work functions between toner and PC. In any event, squashing a toner particle onto a PC surface is a leading cause of permanent adhesion, so avoiding high pressures at the developer and transfer devices assists cleaning procedures. As discussed in previous chapters, it is necessary to have intimate contact between toner and PC for good image development, and image transfer requires pressure between paper, toner, and PC; thus, a successful xerographic process requires rather good control of contact pressures at each step. If a developer unit, for example, generates excessive pressure on the PC, a film of toner grows rapidly (a few thousand process cycles) on the PC surface and on the magnetic brush surface as well.

Experiments with illumination of the PC before cleaning show that the adhesive force is reduced with illumination. Deryagin et al. (1978) experimented with polystyrene particles on illuminated selenium and showed about 26% reduction in adhesion for particles with a diameter of 10 μm and about 36% reduction for those with 20 μm diameters. The measurements were performed with their bullet adhesiometer, which enhanced the electrostatic component of adhesion. Jewett (1977) discusses the use of illumination to assist in PC cleaning. In the Kodak EKTAPRINT copier, the PC ground plane is transparent and allows effective use of backlighting to eliminate residual electric fields of images. Studies by Nebenzahl et al. (1980) include the effect of corona charge and erase lamp illumination on PC cleaning. Cleaning efficacy depended in a complicated manner on the preclean corona current, lamp intensity, and on the age of the carrier beads. Old carrier beads are partially covered by a layer of fused-on toner; thus, the average charge/cm^2 of a toner sample is reduced (see Chapter 7, Section 7.5). As the studies of DePalma (1982) showed, untransferred toner charge polarity is altered by the transfer corona. With the IBM 3800 printer discussed by DePalma, developed toner is negatively charged on the average, and the positive transfer corona reverses the charge polarity of untransferred toner. Ion bombardment of toner is discussed in Chapter 10. Nebenzahl and colleagues DePalma and Mastrangelo found that residual toner cleaning was assisted by the preclean corona (positive ions) only over a limited range of current. At low positive current, cleaning failure occurred, leaving toner particles attached to the latent image regions on the PC. At high preclean corona current, failure was evidenced by streaks of toner in nonimage regions. Apparently, the toner was removed first and then redeposited by the rotating brush-cleaner. Under the conditions of the tests, the PC voltage, prior to the erase lamp and preclean corona, was of negative polarity. As a consequence, cleaning was achieved by a combination of lamp intensity and corona current that brought the surface potential of the PC close to zero.

In summary, electrostatic and dispersion forces are important in the adhesion of toner to a PC. All the experiments show the importance of electrostatic forces, but only some claim that dispersion forces dominate adhesion. An experiment that presses particles onto the substrate before detaching them may create additional charge by contact electrification such that adhesion is indeed controlled by electrostatic forces, provided that the particles and substrate elastically recover. With plastic deformation, the contact area can remain high and adhesion is controlled by dispersion forces. With photogenerator–photoconductor substrates, illumination can reduce electrostatic adhesion under some conditions, although shadowing of the PC by opaque toner particles could create rather high electric fields at the edges of shadows, so it is not clear that illumination would assist particle cleaning under all circumstances. Neutralizing the PC surface charge with a preclean corona assists in cleaning, although the optimal corona current depends in a complicated way on the illumination intensity and the charge of the residual toner.

11.2 Particle Detachment by Rotating Brush

DePalma (1982) discusses toner removal with a vacuum-assisted rotating brush. His studies show that the removal process consists of two steps. First, the toner is separated from the substrate and becomes airborne. In the second step, the airborne toner is collected and deposited in a location where it cannot break loose and redeposit onto the PC at a later time. DePalma associated a probability (P_s) with separating the toner from the substrate and another probability (P_t) with trapping that particle in the airstream. When a rotating brush is pressed down onto the moving PC, the number of brush fibers (n) touching or colliding with the particle represents a collision frequency or attempt frequency at removing a particle. Fiber lengths in a brush are statistically distributed about a mean value, and the angle between a fiber and the number of fibers impacting the PC surface depends on the brush–PC engagement, brush rpm, and PC velocity. Assuming that the collision events are statistically independent of each other, DePalma used the binomial distribution to calculate the probability (P_c) of cleaning a toner particle.

$$P_c = 1 - (1 - P_s P_t)^n \qquad (11.4)$$

DePalma studied various combinations of brush density (measured in fiber weight per square yard of uncut rug used in the brush), speed (in rpm), and PC–brush engagement (measured as the distance by which the brush axis is moved toward the PC after the longest fibers just touch the PC surface.) Both Table 11.1 and Figure 11.1 were adapted from DePalma's results. These data

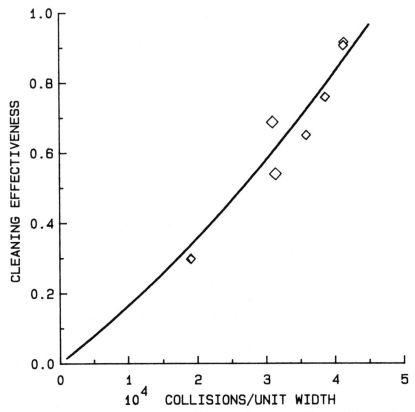

Figure 11.1   Cleaning effectiveness vs. collisions/cm. Data adapted from DePalma (1982).

show that cleaning ability with a rotating brush depends primarily on the number of fibers that collide with the particle-laden PC. The first two entries in Table 11.1, for example, show that the reduction in brush RPM is compensated for by an increase in the brush–PC engagement, because more of the shorter fibers are allowed to impact the PC surface. The mass of a fiber is much greater than a toner particle, so the brush momentum is essentially unaltered by collisions with toner particles. DePalma's microscopic cleaning model takes the change in velocity of an impacted toner as the mean value between a purely elastic $[V_t = 2(V_b + V_{PC})]$ and a purely inelastic collision $(V_t = V_b + V_{PC})$. That is, the velocity change at collision is

$$V_t = 1.5 \, (V_b + V_{PC})$$

Table 11.1   Cleaning Test Results for Rotating Brush

Brush Density (oz/yd^2)	Brush Speed (rpm)	Brush–PC Engagement (mm)	Collisions per Unit Width (10^4/cm)	Cleaning Effectiveness (maximum = 1.0)
15	1450	1.9	4.2	0.93
15	1200	2.5	4.2	0.93
15	1300	1.9	3.8	0.74
15	1000	2.5	3.6	0.64
15	880	2.5	3.2	0.59
7	1450	4.3	3.2	0.68
4.5	1300	4.3	1.9	0.30

where V_b is the linear velocity of the brush fiber moving across the PC surface and V_{PC} is the surface velocity of the PC. Because the brush rotates against the PC rotation, the velocity of approach is $V = V_b + V_{PC}$. In the IBM 3800 laser printer, V_b is approximately 500 cm/sec at 1200 rpm and V_{PC} is 80 cm/sec. Collision force is estimated by taking the change in toner velocity and dividing by the estimated impact duration. Timoshenko and Goodier (1970, p. 421) derived the equations for impacting spheres; their results can be adapted for a small toner particle and a large brush fiber by allowing the fiber radius of curvature to approach that of a nearly flat plane. With this approximation, the duration of the collision is

$$\Delta t \cong \frac{\alpha_1}{V} \int_0^1 \frac{dx}{\sqrt{1 - x^{5/2}}} = 2.94 \frac{\alpha_1}{V} \tag{11.5}$$

where $x = \alpha/\alpha_1$, is the distance of approach, α_1 is the approach distance at the instant of maximum compression between toner and fiber, given by the expression

$$\alpha_1 = \left(\frac{5V^2}{4nn_1} \right)^{2/5} \tag{11.6}$$

with

$$n = \frac{4R_t^{1/2}}{3\pi(k_1 + k_2)} \tag{11.7}$$

and

$$n_1 = \frac{m_t + m_b}{m_t m_b} \cong \frac{1}{m_t} \tag{11.8}$$

The elastic behavior of brush and particle is described by k_1 and k_2 where

$$k_i = \frac{1 - v_i^2}{\pi E_i} \tag{11.9}$$

Poisson's ratio (v) for polymers is about 0.2 and Young's Modulus (E) is about 4.5×10^{10} dynes/cm^2. The collision force is evaluated as the time rate change of the particle momentum.

$$F_{coll} = m_t \frac{\Delta V_t}{\Delta t} \quad \text{(dynes)} \tag{11.10}$$

At $V = 600$ cm/sec, the collision force exceeds 10 dynes for $R_t = 5$ μm. This force greatly exceeds even the largest experimentally determined adhesive forces between toner and PC.

Because brush fiber length is distributed, increased engagement between the PC and the brush increases the number of fibers colliding with toner particles. This is not without a penalty, however, as the long fibers suffer an increased normal component to the collision force; thus, toner can be deformed plastically and pressure fused to the PC surface. An optimal engagement distance therefore exists, such that fiber collision frequency must be traded off against the tendency

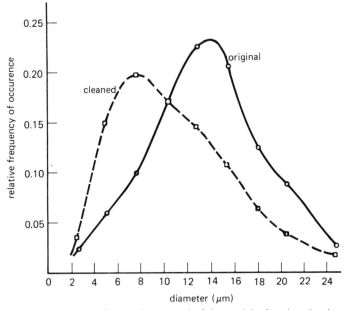

Figure 11.2   Size distribution of original toner and of the particles found at the cleaner. From DePalma (1982).

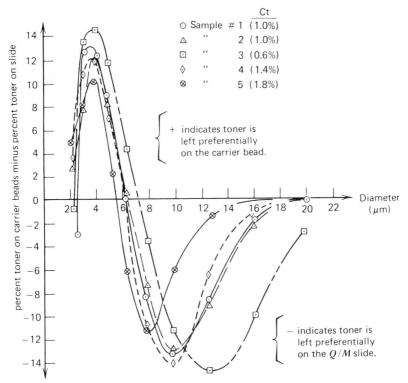

Figure 11.3   Percent toner on carrier beads less the percent toner deposited on the image. Values for C_t: ⊙ (sample 1) = 1.0%; △ (sample 2) = 1.0%; □ (sample 3) = 0.6%; ◇(sample 4) = 1.4%; ⊗ (sample 5) = 1.8 %.

to create fused-on toner. Toner particles fused to the PC show evidence of flattening and smearing out, most likely because of the heat and pressure generated by the rotating brush.

Selective removal of the larger particles from a distribution of sizes seem to be a general rule. Figure 11.2 shows the size distribution of toner from a fresh supply package of IBM type 760 and toner that was removed by a rotating cleaner brush. The original median diameter is 14 μm (by mass); that in the cleaner is about 11 μm (by mass). Figure 11.3 shows the equivalent information for toner developed onto an image and toner that remained on the carrier beads; in this figure, the difference in percent (by number) of particles on the carrier and on the image is plotted as a function of the equivalent spherical diameter. As in other experiments, the large particles were preferentially removed from the host surface. DePalma showed in his experiments that smaller particles are more difficult to remove when the basis of comparison is the mass of toner; however, when the comparison is by number of particles at a given diameter, small particles are much more prevalent, and the cleaning system may be overwhelmed merely by the absolute number of small particles (having almost a negligible mass) relative to the brush fiber collision frequency.

11.3 Particle Detachment by Elastometric Blade

Particles can be effectively removed by a sharp blade that conforms precisely to the surface topography of the PC. Harvapat (1977) analyzed the mechanics of the zerographic blade, Abowitz (1974) discussed deformation of elastomeric materials and cleaning performance, and McMullen and Salamida (1974) investigated lubricants used to assist blade cleaning. In a NASA publication (1982), the care and handling of magnetic recording tapes is discussed, and many of the cleaning problems associated with small particles are addressed with blade scrapers. In this publication, Whysong (1982, p. 71) analyzes and evaluates tape cleaning with blade scrapers.

As common sense would demand, the blade should create shear forces at the particle–substrate junctions. Since the particles are distributed with diameters down to perhaps 1–2 μm, the blade must conform very closely to the microscopic topography of the PC surface, and over widths of 30–40 cm, surface irregularities would disallow the use of rigid blades with PCs mounted on rigid substrates. Elastomeric blades can be used with PC drums, and the blade is loaded with a controlled compressive force to provide good conformation between blade edge and PC surface. If the blade suffers a transient stress from a small asperity, the edge may not reseat rapidly enough to scrape away a toner particle adjacent to the asperity; thus, the particle goes under the blade and becomes pressure fused to the PC. At 80 cm/sec PC velocity, a blade reseating time of 1 msec could allow 0.08 cm pathlength to escape the cleaning edge. Blade edges eventually become grooved and must be replaced.

McMullen and Salamida (1974) and Schaffert (1975, p. 58) discuss the use of dry lubricants to assist in particle cleaning. Metal salts of fatty acids (zinc stearate, for example) and silica have been mixed in with the toner particles. A film of the lubricant grows on the PC and reduces the adhesive force largely by reducing the true area of contact at the adhesive junctions. This occurs because the film of dry lubricant is mostly discontinuous in nature. In their studies of film growth, however, McMullen and Salamida treated the measurements as though the film was thin but continuous. The equivalent thickness over which acceptable cleaning was achieved depended on the type of lubricant, but the optimal thickness, according to McMullen and Salamida, was about 1–2 monolayers. The films undergo a continuous process of formation and removal; formation occurs at the development step, whereas removal of the dry lubricant can occur at the development, transfer, and cleaning steps. Without silica added to the toner, the metal stearate film would continue to grow on the selenium PC drum and excessive film thickness would result. Silica (e.g., Aerosil) is known to be abrasive, and adding a small amount to the toner

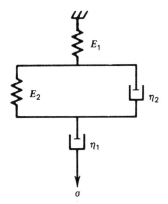

Figure 11.4   Four-element viscoelastic model of an elasto-meric cleaning blade. From Abowitz (1974).

results in reduction of the steady-state thickness of the metal stearate film. The behavior of lubricant film growth shares many features with the adsorption and desorbtion kinetics of thin film theory [see, for example, Neugebauer in Maissel and Glang (1970)].

Cleaning blades have the advantage of being mechanically quite simple and direct in their shearing action on toner particles. Blades cannot be used on PCs that are seamed or that have a gap in the rotating drum, and blades are rather prone to exhibit stick-slip motion (chatter). Abowitz (1974) analyzed the four-element viscoelastic model shown in Figure 11.4; this model is the simplest one exhibiting the three major deformation modes common to the viscoelastic materials. Abowitz describes these modes as:

1. Instantaneous elastic response (from the spring E_1 in Figure 11.4).
2. Viscous flow (from dashpot η_1).
3. Delayed elastic response (caused by E_2 and η_2, the Voigt element).

The creep compliance (J) is defined as the ratio of strain to stress:

$$J = \frac{\varepsilon}{\sigma} \tag{11.11}$$

Abowitz solves the four-element system for a step input of stress; the time–domain response is

$$J(t) = \frac{t}{\eta_1} + \frac{(E_1 + E_2)}{E_1 E_2}(1 - e^{-t/\tau}) + \frac{1}{E_1}e^{-t/\tau} \tag{11.12}$$

where

$$\tau = \frac{\eta_2}{E_2} \quad (\text{sec}) \tag{11.13}$$

The viscosity (η) is in g/cm-sec (or poise) and the modulus of elasticity (E) is in dynes/cm^2. For a blade of cast unfilled urethane, Abowitz gives the following viscoelastic properties: $E_1 = 7.2 \times 10^7$ dynes/cm^2, $E_2 = 4.5 \times 10^7$ dynes/cm^2, $\eta_1 = 1.3 \times 10^5$ poise, $\eta_2 = 1.4 \times 10^4$ poise. This four-element model can be reduced to three elements with little inaccuracy, since η_1 is much greater than η_2. The transient response to a half-sine asperity stress is given by Abowitz, and his figure is sketched in Figure 11.5. The dotted line is the asperity profile and the solid line shows the blade strain, which has a reseating time of about 1 msec ($\tau = 0.31$ msec and at $t = 1$ msec, the exponential has died away for most practical purposes).

Unlike the high speed rotating brush, which imparts substantial momentum to a toner particle, a scraping blade builds up a pile of toner (in bulldozer fashion) at the blade edge, unless the debris is removed by auxiliary forces. Successful, long-term cleaning requires that toner (and other material such as paper chads and carrier beads) must be transported away from the interface between the cleaning device and the PC surface. Vacuum-assisted air flow is a very effective technique for collecting debris from the cleaning device and, in the next section, some of the dynamics of aerosols are discussed.

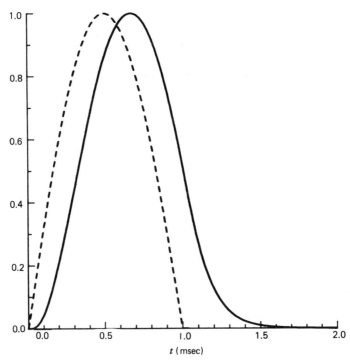

Figure 11.5   Time response of viscoelastic blade to a half-sine stress input. (— — —) Stress input; (——) response $J(t)$. From Abowitz (1974).

11.4 Aerodynamic Entrainment and Particle Saltation

Bagnold (1941) studied the motion of sand dunes driven by the action of winds, and "saltation" is the term he used to describe the bouncing, rolling, and jumping action of sand particles in migrating dunes. Corn (1966), Hidy and Brock (1970), and Fuchs (1964) each discuss the experimental and theoretical attempts at understanding the dispersement of particles from surfaces by aerodynamic forces. A theory that predicts the air velocity for particle detachment from a flat surface would necessarily require detailed specification of particle adhesion forces and contact geometry. In experimentation, such knowledge seldom exists, and in the work reviewed by Corn, Hidy and Brock, and Fuchs, there is general agreement that more study is required to understand adhesive and cohesive forces of particles. In Chapter 7, the studies with charged aerosols showed that the drag force was due to gas pressure differences on the leading and trailing surfaces of particles; thus, the drag force is proportional to the square of the gas velocity. This observation is to be contrasted with the assumption of the validity of Stokes's Law for particles, in which the Reynold's number (Re) is small (less than 1.0). The drag force on a particle is given by the relation

$$F_D = \frac{C_D A_p \rho_g V^2}{2} \quad \text{(dyne)} \tag{11.14}$$

where C_D is the drag coefficient (dimensionless), A_p is the particle cross section (cm^2), ρ_g is the gas density (g/cm^3), and V is the gas velocity (cm/sec). The particle Reynolds number is

$$\text{Re} = \frac{2R\rho_g V}{\eta} \quad \text{(dimensionless)} \tag{11.15}$$

where η is the gas viscosity (g/cm-sec or poise) and R is the particle radius (cm). For a perfectly smooth sphere with Re less than 1.0, classical theory gives the drag coefficient for streamline flow (laminar flow) as

$$C_D = \frac{24}{\text{Re}} \quad \text{(dimensionless)} \tag{11.16}$$

In this case, $A_p = \pi R^2$ and the drag force, found with (11.14) and (11.16), becomes

$$F_D = 6\pi\eta R V \quad \text{(dyne)} \tag{11.17}$$

This relation is of course better known as Stokes's Law.

When the Reynold's number is greater than unity and less than about 1000, gas flow—in the classical view—undergoes a transition from laminar to turbulent flow. In this transition region, Corn (1966, p. 384) gives the drag coefficient as

$$C_D = \frac{18.5}{\text{Re}^{0.6}} \qquad (11.18)$$

As turbulence becomes well-developed, the drag coefficient is nearly independent of Re. The experiments of Chapter 7 showed that the drag coefficient for small particles at high velocity was approximately

$$C_D = \frac{R}{L_0} \quad \text{with } L_0 = 9 \times 10^{-6} \text{ cm.} \qquad (11.19)$$

The particles used in the experiments were rough toner particles size classified into three narrow fractions with mean diameters of about 6, 12, and 20 μm, and the velocities relative to the air flow were on the order of 100 cm/sec. With $\rho_g = 1.2 \times 10^{-3}$ g/cm^3 and $\eta = 1.8 \times 10^{-4}$ g/cm-sec, one obtains particle Reynold's numbers in the range of 0.4–1.3; therefore, it is normal to apply Stokes' Law to find the drag force, although there appears to be sufficient evidence in the literature to seriously question the applicability of Stokes' Law to small rough particles in normal air. Whitby and Liu (1966, p. 68), for example, apply this law to electrically charged particles to compute the electrical mobility, and they find disagreement between theory and experiment. Most of their experimental work can be reconciled with a theory in which pressure drag is predominant. Use of Stokes' Law for particle impaction theory also suffers with serious flaws. Hidy and Brock (1970, p. 74) review the literature and conclude that viscous flow theory is in disagreement with experiment. There is neither space nor justification to pursue these interesting questions in this book, although it appears that much of the literature on aerosol science has ignored the existence of internal modes for energy absorption in the transporting gas, and much effort has been expended on attempts at reconciliation between experiment and theories that view the gas as a fluid with very low viscosity.

With very small particles, the detachment force depends on electrostatic and dispersion adhesive forces. If this force is supplied by an air current, the particle must experience a torque and begin rolling about a contact fulcrum. In this manner, a horizontal force caused by Stokes drag acting on a particle of radius R would be given by (11.17), and according to (11.14) and (11.19), for pressure drag. This force must exceed the adhesive force. If adhesion is dominated by intermolecular (dispersion) forces with contact radius R_c much smaller than the particle dimension, then the adhesion can be written as

$$F_{ad} = \frac{AR_c}{6D^2} \quad \text{(dyne)} \qquad (11.20)$$

where $A \sim 10^{-12}$ erg is the Hamaker Constant (see Chapter 7) and D is the minimum distance of approach of particle and substrate (about 3×10^{-8} cm).

A rough estimate of threshold velocity for particle detachment is found by equating the horizontal drag force acting about a contact fulcrum with the opposing adhesive force. For viscous (Stokes) drag, the threshold velocity would be

$$V_t = \frac{AR_c}{6D^2 6\pi\eta R} \quad \text{(cm/sec)} \tag{11.21}$$

In air with $R_c = 10^{-5}$ cm, $R = 5 \times 10^{-4}$ cm, according to this reasoning, V_t would be roughly 1×10^3 cm/sec. For pressure drag,

$$V_t = \left(\frac{AR_c 2L_0}{6D^2 \pi R^3 \rho_g}\right)^{1/2} \quad \text{(cm/sec)} \tag{11.22}$$

and with $L_0 = 9 \times 10^{-6}$ cm, V_t is about 250 cm/sec. Fuchs (1964) cites experiments giving the critical velocity as between 20 and 50 cm/sec for corundum particles with radii between 25 and 30 μm. Using $R = 2.5 \times 10^{-3}$ in (11.22) yields $V_t = 22$ cm/sec. Even with such crude estimates as these, experimental results with aerodynamic detachment are in better agreement with pressure drag.

Rotating brushes and blade scrapers overcome the adhesion of toner particles rather directly. Air flow suffers from boundary layer difficulties, because the air velocity is very low at a substrate; Schlichting (1960) should be consulted for methods of determining the air velocity in the laminar sublayer in the vicinity of a surface. Hidy and Brock (1970, p. 155) discuss momentum transfer to a particle in the slip flow regime, and they emphasize the theoretical difficulties in treating air flow very near the surfaces.

With rotating brush and blade scrapers, air flow is most important to transport detached toner particles and it is necessary to control the flow pattern so that gross turbulence does not deposit particles by inertial impaction on the walls of the cleaner housing. Nebenzahl et al. (1980) measured the air flow velocity in the IBM 3800 cleaner and found velocities between 200 and 400 cm/sec; these values were less than the linear velocity of the brush fibers. Toner is transported adequately by these velocities, although deposits build up wherever gross air turbulence occurs. Cyclone precipitators are used to collect toner.

11.5 Inertial Deposition of Toner Particles

Davies (1966), Hidy and Brock (1970), and Fuchs (1964) discuss particle deposition from moving aerosols. Davies characterizes particle inertia with the stopping distance

$$d_s = V_0 \tau_s \quad \text{(cm)} \tag{11.23}$$

This is the distance traveled by a particle with initial velocity V_0 when projected into still air. The characteristic time constant τ_s (sec) is given for particles following Stokes's Law:

$$\tau_s = \frac{m}{6\pi\eta R} = \frac{2R^2\rho_p}{9\eta} \quad (\text{sec}) \tag{11.24}$$

With pressure drag (see Chapter 7), the equation of motion for gravitational acceleration is

$$m\frac{dv}{dt} = mg - \frac{C_D\pi R^2\rho_g v^2}{2} \quad (\text{dyne}) \tag{11.25}$$

for which the solution is

$$v(t) = K \tanh(KBt) \quad (\text{cm/sec}) \tag{11.26}$$

where

$$K = \left(\frac{2mg}{C_D\pi R^2\rho_g}\right)^{0.5} \quad (\text{cm/sec})$$

and

$$B = \left(\frac{C_D\pi R^2\rho_g}{2m}\right)^{0.5} \quad (\text{cm}^{-1})$$

The relaxation time constant is

$$\tau_p = (KB)^{-1} = \left(\frac{8\rho_p L_0}{3\rho_g g}\right)^{0.5} \quad (\text{sec}) \tag{11.27}$$

for the drag coefficient $C_D = R/L_0$. Note that the pressure drag relaxation time is independent of particle size according to this treatment. In (11.24) and (11.27), particle density is ρ_p (g/cm^3). With air at standard temperature and pressure ($\rho_g = 1.2 \times 10^{-3}$ g/cm^3), $g = 980$ cm/sec^2, $\rho_p = 1.2$ g/cm^3, and $L_0 = 9 \times 10^{-6}$ cm, the estimated relaxation time is a little less than 5 msec. This is to be compared with the Stokes relaxation (11.24) for a particle with $R = 5 \times 10^{-4}$ cm in air ($\eta = 1.8 \times 10^{-4}$ g/cm-sec) where $\tau_s = 370$ μsec. Viscous and pressure effects are always present in air, so the equation of motion can be written to include both kinds of drag forces

$$\frac{dm}{dt} = a + bv + cv^2 \tag{11.28}$$

The general solution to this differential equation is

$$v = \frac{2a(1 - e^{-t/\tau})}{(b + \sqrt{b^2 - 4ac})e^{-t/\tau} - b + \sqrt{b^2 - 4ac}} \tag{11.29}$$

with

$$\tau = \frac{m}{\sqrt{b^2 - 4ac}} \qquad (b < 0, c < 0)$$

If $c = 0$, (11.29) reduces to the well-known relation for viscous drag

$$v = \frac{a}{b}(e^{-t/\tau} - 1) \tag{11.30}$$

where the sign of b is negative, since the drag opposes the driving force [a in (11.28) is positive with this sign convention]. If viscous drag is negligible (b is small relative to c), then (11.29) can be written as

$$v = \frac{2a}{\sqrt{-4ac}} \left(\frac{e^{t/2\tau} - e^{-t/2\tau}}{e^{t/2\tau} + e^{-t/2\tau}}\right)$$

$$= \sqrt{\frac{-a}{c}} \tanh\left(\frac{t}{2\tau}\right) \tag{11.31}$$

which is precisely the form given in (11.26).

In the general solution for particle velocity (11.29) with $a = mg, b = -6\pi\eta R$, and $c = -C_D \pi R^2 \rho_g/2$, the relaxation time becomes

$$\tau = \frac{m}{[(6\pi\eta R)^2 + 4mgC_D \pi R^2 \rho_g/2]^{0.5}} \tag{11.32}$$

where $m = (4/3)\pi R^3 \rho_p$ (g). A particle with $R = 5 \times 10^{-4}$ cm in air at STP would have a calculated relaxation time of 366 μsec according to (11.32), whereas the value found with (11.24) is 370 μsec. Figure 11.6 shows a comparison between relaxation times computed with viscous drag only [Equation (11.24)], and with pressure and viscous terms according to (11.32) with $C_D = R/L_0$. Over the range of interest in xerography (about 1–50 μm diameter), it would be difficult to tell the difference between the mechanisms, except with a sensitive instrument (such as a charge spectrometer); the two curves are nearly equal for $R < 10^{-3}$ cm, but the line for Stokes drag always exceeds the curve drawn

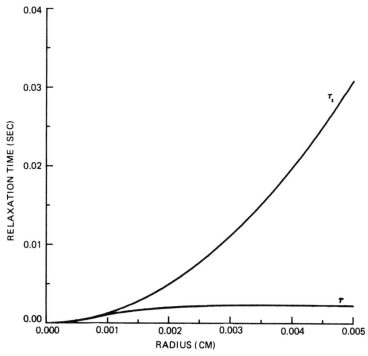

Figure 11.6   Comparison of relaxation times for viscous drag (τ_s) and pressure plus viscous drag (τ).

according to (11.32). Equation (11.32) can be rewritten in terms of the previous quantities τ_s and τ_p:

$$\tau = \left[\left(\frac{1}{\tau_s}\right)^2 + \left(\frac{1}{\tau_p/2}\right)^2\right]^{-1/2} \tag{11.33}$$

The relaxation time is less than expected according to the Stokes regime; thus, particle deposition by inertial impaction on plates, walls, or obstacles occur with greater efficiency than predicted by viscous flow theory. This conclusion is in accord with the literature; Liu and Agarwal (1974) discuss aerosol deposition in turbulent flow and conclude that viscous theory alone cannot explain results at large theoretical relaxation times. Hidy and Brock (1970 p. 74) compare theory and experiment for inertial deposition on a flat plate and find unsatisfactory agreement. Figure 11.7 depicts a narrow air jet from a slit impinging on a plate. The slot width is $2h$ (cm) and the distance between plate and slot is d (cm). Inertial deposition is characterized by the Stokes Number

$$\text{Stk} = \frac{d_s}{2h} \quad \text{(dimensionless)} \tag{11.34}$$

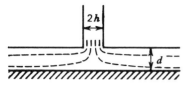

Figure 11.7 Air jet impingement on a flat plate.

where d_s, given by (11.23), is the inertial path length of the particle according to Stokes' Law. A theoretical value of the critical Stokes Number (Stk_{cr}), below which deposition will not occur, is given by Levin (1953) as $Stk_{cr} = 2/\pi$. Experimental values lie between 0.2 and 0.3, or roughly from one-third to one-half of the theoretical value.

Fuchs (1964, ch. 4) discusses an incomplete theory of cyclone precipitators and states that design has been almost totally empirical. Air enters the cyclone and forms a turbulent spiraling pathway that forces particles to the cylindrical wall of the container. Particles then fall to the bottom where they are collected in a chamber, and the relatively clean air leaves through the top of the device; Figure 11.8 shows a typical cross section. A simplified treatment of air flow yields a relation for the minimum radius particle that can be centrifugally collected in a cyclone. Letting V_i = air velocity at the input port, R_2 = radius of the outer cylinder, and S = number of turns of the outer spiral of air, Fuchs (1964) gives the approximate minimum collected particle radius as

$$R_{min} = \frac{3}{2}\left(\frac{\eta R_2}{\pi V_i S \rho_p}\right)^{1/2} \quad \text{(cm)} \tag{11.35}$$

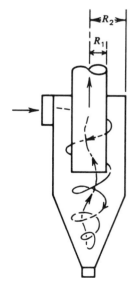

Figure 11.8 A cyclone precipitator.

With $V_i = 4000$ cm/sec, $R_2 = 5$ cm, $S = 3$ (the value usually assumed), $\eta = 1.8 \times 10^{-4}$ g/cm-sec, and $\rho_p = 1.2$ g/cm^3, one obtains $R_{\min} = 2 \times 10^{-4}$ cm, approximately. Fuchs states that cyclones 5–15 cm in outer diameter work much better than those with very large (several meters) diameters, but that with increasing V_i, operation improves at first and with further increase in velocity, turbulence degrades performance. For this reason, (11.35) must be regarded as a very rough approximation for evaluating cyclone performance. Particles smaller than $R_{\min}$ are aerodynamically entrained in the exhaust air, so these very small aerosols must be trapped in a fiber filter. Yeh and Liu (1974) can be consulted for a theoretical discussion of aerosol filtration by fibrous filters.

TWELVE

XEROGRAPHIC IMAGE FUSING

Xerographic images are composed of numerous toner particles transported and deposited on paper by the control of adhesive forces. When toner is first transferred from the PC to paper, it adheres to the paper fibers because of electrostatic and dispersion forces, although the real area of contact is limited to a few small asperities. In this condition, the xerographic image is easily rubbed off by the slightest contact with another surface, so the image must be fixed permanently to the paper substrate. Several techniques are used, and all vastly increase the area of real contact between toner and paper fibers by causing the toner to flow, join together, spread, wet, and penetrate somewhat into the paper. In other words, the image is fused to the paper.

In this chapter, the physics and technology of thermal and pressure fusing are discussed, and several literature sources are cited. Toner rheology and the kinetics of sintering, spreading, wetting, and penetration are introduced and some of the advantages and disadvantages of radiant, pressure, and temperature–pressure fusing are discussed.

12.1 Thermal, Mechanical, and Rheological Properties of Toner

Toner is made from thermoplastic materials. O'Reilly and Erhardt (1973) review some of the physical properties of toners used in xerographic processes and Prime (1983) discusses the relationship between toner properties and fusing behavior. The thermal behavior of toner is characterized by the glass transition temperature, T_g, which divides the hard, brittle regime from the soft, liquid or flowing regime. O'Reilly and Erhardt denote T_g as the temperature where the viscosity is about 10^{13} poise, and Prime states that T_g is typically 60–70°C for toners used in pressure–temperature fusers. At temperatures below T_g, the elastic modulus (Young's Modulus) E for most toners is about 10^{10} dynes/cm² ; with increasing temperature, E drops about 4 orders of magnitude and reaches a rubbery plateau. At even higher temperatures, E drops further, and the material is said to be in the steady state flow regime. The change with temperature from elastic solid to viscoelastic to rubber to fluid is a remarkable property of amorphous materials; with high molecular weight toners, the rubbery plateau is broader than with low molecular weights. Prime (1983) characterizes toners used in the IBM 3800 laser printer and plots the creep compliance $J(t)$ cm²/dyne (the reciprocal of E) as a function of time under a condition of constant stress.

$$J(t) = \frac{\text{shear strain}}{\text{shear stress}} = J_g + \sum J_i(1 - e^{-t/\tau_i}) + \frac{t}{\eta} \qquad (12.1)$$

Here, J_g is the glassy compliance for the material which, in general, may have a

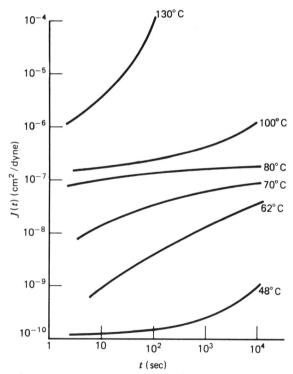

Figure 12.1 Creep compliance for IBM # 790 toner at a constant stress of 2.4×10^5 dynes/cm². From Prime (1983).

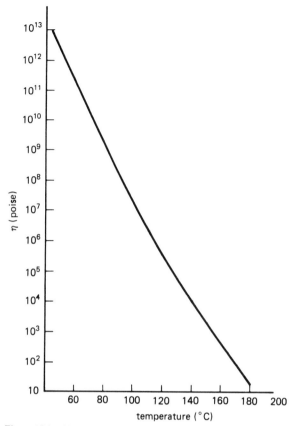

Figure 12.2   Shear viscosity (Newtonian) for a hypothetical toner.

distribution J_i of compliances, each with a relaxation time τ_i (sec). The viscosity, η (poise), is a strong function of temperature.

$$\eta(T) \cong \eta_0 \exp\left(\frac{E_a}{kT}\right) \quad \text{(poise)} \tag{12.2}$$

where E_a (erg) is the activation energy for viscosity, k is Boltzmann's constant, and T is the absolute temperature (kelvins). Figure 12.1 shows creep compliance results and Figure 12.2 shows viscosity vs. temperature for a hypothetical toner.

Many toners, with styrenes as the primary constituent, are essentially co-polymers. Carbon black is added for pigmentation, but this also increases the viscosity and can alter the flow behavior from a simple linear stress–strain (Newtonian) relation to non-Newtonian (thixotropic) behavior. Table 12.1 lists some of the physical properties of polystyrene (see Kirk and Othmer,

Table 12.1 Properties of Polystyrene

Density	1.05 g/cm^3
Modulus of elasticity	$2.8-4.1 \times 10^{10} \text{ dynes/cm}^2$
Compressive strength	$7.9-11 \times 10^8 \text{ dyne/cm}^2$
Tensile strength	$3.4-6.2 \times 10^8 \text{ dynes/cm}^2$
Thermal conductivity	$2.4-3.3 \times 10^{-4} \text{ cal/cm-sec-}°\text{C}$
Specific heat	$0.32 \text{ cal/g-}°\text{C}$
Thermal expansion	$60-80 \times 10^{-6} \text{ parts/}°\text{C}$

1954, Vol. 13, p. 158.) O'Reilly and Erhardt (1973) discuss surface energies of polymers and give values for typical toners as ranging between 28 and 38 ergs/cm². Lee (1975) experimented with a styrene–acrylate copolymer containing 5% carbon black and gives the surface energy as 32 ergs/cm² at 20°C for the base polymer.

12.2 Physical Properties of Paper

Xerographic quality bond paper is a complex material based on wood cellulose free of lignin. Hunter (1978), in his history of papermaking, observes that spruce is preferred for its light color and strong fiber. Natural cellulose is a well-crystallized organic polymer which has a fiber about 0.3 cm long and 30 μm thick in conifers. Paper is made by lifting macerated cellulose fibers out of a soaking vat onto a sieve-like mould made of wire cloth. Water is pressed out and the fiber matrix is heat-dried and then mechanically smoothed. Gelatinous sizing and fillers are added to bond the fibers, improve mechanical strength, and lower the surface energy (about 45 ergs/cm² for xerographic papers). Table 12.2 is a compilation of properties from various sources. K. Loeffler of IBM

Table 12.2 Physical Properties of Paper

Modulus of elasticity	$3 \times 10^{10} \text{ dynes/cm}^2$
Compressive strength	$1.5 \times 10^9 \text{ dynes/m}^2$
Thermal conductivity	$4 \times 10^{-4} \text{ cal/cm-sec-}°\text{C}$
Specific heat (dry spruce)	$0.27 \text{ cal/g-}°\text{C}$

Corporation has supplied some of the information and Skar (1972) may be consulted for additional information; values are approximate. At 50% RH, bond paper may contain about 5–8% moisture; Figure 10.8 gives the moisture content for several typical xerographic papers. The specific heat of water is about 1.0 cal/g-°C, so the presence of moisture in paper significantly increases the total heat capacity.

Loeffler (private communication) states that bond paper suffers compression damage (permanent compression deformation) at a pressure P_0 of about 7×10^8 dynes/cm^2 (10^4 psi); that is, the compressive strength given in Table 12.2 is about twice the value at which yielding is just noticeable. The dependence of P_0 on process velocity V_p is rather weak. According to Loeffler, the experimental results give the dependence as

$$P_0 = K(V_p)^{0.16} \qquad (12.3)$$

Paper fibers can be damaged by tensile forces normal to the surface. With hot roll pressure fusers, molten toner adheres to paper fibers and to the hot roll, and at high shear or release rates, toner can "pick" fibers from the paper. "Picking" starts at toner viscosities in the neighborhood of 400 poise for $V_p = 80$ cm/sec. Schirmer and Albrecht (1961) studied printing ink rheology and film splitting, and their data suggest that a critical viscosity for fiber picking is

$$\eta_c(\text{poise}) = 3 \times 10^4 V_p^{-1.0} \qquad (12.4)$$

where the process velocity V_p is in (cm/sec). Squeeze film theory can be applied to this problem to derive a relation between critical viscosity and process velocity. See Moore (1972, p. 116) for a review of squeeze films. With circular toner drops of diameter D (cm), thickness h (cm), and a footprint width $2x_0$ (cm) between paper and pressure roll of radius R (cm), a straightforward derivation yields

$$\eta_c = \frac{F_p h^3 R}{(3\pi/32)D^4 x_0 V_p} \quad \text{(poise) or (g/cm-sec)} \qquad (12.5)$$

Here, F_p is the force (dyne) required to pick out a fiber, so it depends on paper quality, sizing, and fiber strength. Upon dividing F_p by the drop area, one obtains a stress of about 2×10^{10} dynes/cm^2, which is somewhat less than the modulus of elasticity.

12.3   Thermal Fusing

When heat is applied to unfused toner and paper, the temperature of the system increases, sharp edges of toner particles become rounded, particles sinter together, the coalesced mass spreads along paper fibers, and the molten mass penetrates into the fiber network. After cooling down, toner resolidifies and becomes brittle, and the image is said to be fused to the paper. Lee (1975) analyzes thermal fusing according to this sintering, spreading, penetrating sequence and much of the following is adapted from his work.

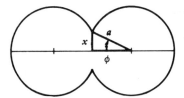

Figure 12.3   Contact geometry for two spheres in the sintering process of Frenkel. From Lee (1975).

The physics of particle sintering has been analyzed by Frenkel (1945), and Strella (1970) adapted Frenkel's model to styrene–acrylate copolymer. Surface tension (surface free energy) is the driving force behind particle sintering, and the forces of shear viscosity from the flowing material retard the speed of coalescence. Frenkel's approximate relation for two spheres in contact is

$$\frac{x^2}{a} = \left(\frac{3}{2}\right)\left(\frac{\gamma}{\eta}\right)t \tag{12.6}$$

The geometry is given in Figure 12.3; the surface energy is γ ergs/cm^2 or dynes/cm, and the viscosity is η g/cm-sec or poise. More precise relations have been developed by Van Oene (1973):

$$\frac{du}{dt} = 1.9\left(\frac{\gamma}{\eta a_0}\right)\left[\frac{(1-u)}{(2-u)}\right]^{4/3} \tag{12.7}$$

where $u = 1 - a/a_0$ and a_0 is the original radius of the identical spheres. In either case, the analyses show that sintering proceeds rapidly with low viscosity and high surface energy. The dependence of toner viscosity on temperature, as depicted in Figure 12.2 or by Equation (12.2), therefore plays a fundamental role in the kinetics.

Drop spreading and wetting involves a reduction in surface energy of one surface of relatively high energy by another material of lower surface energy. Adamson (1967) may be used as a general reference on the physics and chemistry of surfaces. Toner surface energy is about 32 ergs/cm^2 at room temperature, and at a fusing temperature of 130°C, the surface energy would reduce to perhaps 25 ergs/cm^2. Since xerographic papers are bonded with sizing, a surface energy of 45 ergs/cm^2 is favorable for wetting by molten toner, and the equilibrium contact angle will be approximately zero. Van Oene, Chang, and Newman (1969) give the normalized drop spreading velocity as

$$(R_0)^{-1}\frac{dr}{dt} = K(\theta)\frac{\gamma\cos\theta_f}{R_0\eta}\left[1 - \left(\frac{\cos\theta}{\cos\theta_f}\right)\right]\left(\frac{r}{R_0}\right)\left(\frac{h}{R_0}\right)^2 \tag{12.8}$$

where R_0 is the initial drop radius, $K(\theta)$ is a constant that depends on the contact angle θ, r is the instantaneous drop radius, θ_f is the equilibrium contact angle,

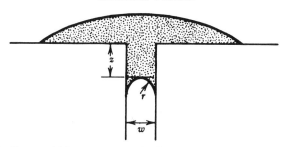

Figure 12.4 Capillary model for toner penetration into spaces between paper fibers ($r = w/2$).

and h is the cap height of the spherical segment. The result is physically plausible; spreading velocity will be high for small drops (the driving pressure scales with γ/R_0), and while the drop spreads, the velocity reduces as the equilibrium contact angle is approached. As in sintering, low viscosity hastens spreading.

Lee (1975) distinguishes three types of capillaries into which toner fluid can penetrate. The parallel slit, the V-shaped groove, and the round cylindrical tube can be used to model capillaries formed by paper fibers; Lee considered the parallel slit and V-shaped groove in his study. Figure 12.4 shows a toner drop sitting above a capillary formed by parallel fibers. The radius of curvature of the drop above the slit is large in comparison to the width (w) of the slit; thus, the capillary pressure will be approximately

$$\Delta p = \frac{2\gamma \cos \theta}{w} \quad \text{(dynes/cm}^2\text{)} \tag{12.9}$$

Since the pressure drops from the edge of the slit to the advancing meniscus of toner, the gradient in pressure is

$$\frac{dp}{dz} = \frac{2\gamma \cos \theta}{wz} \tag{12.10}$$

The average velocity of laminar flow in a parallel slit is found by integrating the parabolic velocity profile over the slit width (w); Landau and Lifshitz (1959) or Batchelor (1967) are general references for problems in fluid dynamics. The average flow velocity is

$$\bar{v} = \frac{dz}{dt} = \frac{w^2}{12\eta} \frac{dp}{dz} = \frac{\gamma \cos \theta w}{6\eta z} \tag{12.11}$$

Upon integrating this relation, one obtains the final equation for depth of penetration as a function of time (with $\cos \theta = 1.0$):

$$z = \left(\frac{\gamma wt}{3\eta}\right)^{0.5} \tag{12.12}$$

For the V-shaped groove, Lee (1975) gives the relation (with $\cos \theta = 1$)

$$z = \left(\frac{\gamma w t}{8.4\eta}\right)^{0.5} \tag{12.13}$$

and for the semicylindrical groove, Williams and Wang (1982) give the result

$$z = \left(\frac{\gamma w t}{2\eta}\right)^{0.5} \tag{12.14}$$

In (12.12), (12.13), and (12.14), w represents the width of the slit, the depth of the groove, and the radius of the semicylinder, respectively. These equations may be inverted to find the penetration time for a given depth of penetration; for high-speed fusing, the time allowed for penetration could be more important than the depth. At a fusing temperature of 130°C, for example, toner viscosity would be in the range of 500 poise and surface energy $= 25$ ergs/cm^2; so for a capillary slit $w = 20 \times 10^{-4}$ cm and a penetration depth of 10^{-3} cm (10 μm), penetration time, according to (12.12), is roughly 30 msec.

In summary, thermal fusing depends on increasing the real area of contact between toner and paper fibers. Toners are chosen for their thermoplastic and rheological behavior over a range of fusing temperatures; thus, melt viscosity emerges as a fundamental parameter which determines flow velocity. Surface energy of paper and toner and capillary size determine the driving pressure; if this pressure is small, the penetration time may be long, the penetration depth could be rather shallow, or both conditions could prevail.

12.4   Radiant Heating

Andrus and Hudson (1965) discuss various principles of image fixation to paper. In the visible wavelengths, toner absorbs about 97% of the radiation and paper reflects 70–80%; as the wavelength increases to the infrared, Andrus and Hudson show that paper absorption increases significantly. They tabulate values of absorptance ($A = 1 -$ reflectance) obtained from the International

Table 12.3   Toner Absorptance (A)

Wavelength (μm)	A
0.60	0.97
0.95	0.97
4.40	0.97
8.80	0.96

Table 12.4   Paper
Absorptance (A)

Wavelength (μm)	A
0.40	0.34
0.50	0.26
0.60	0.19
0.70	0.11
0.75	0.10
0.80	0.11
0.90	0.20
1.00	0.27
4.40	0.82
8.80	0.95

Critical Tables. Table 12.3 gives absorptance for toner at wavelengths from the visible up to the far infrared. The behavior of paper absorptance is much more complicated, as there is a large variety of paper types and the moisture content can be significant because of the absorption peaks of water. Table 12.4 gives approximate values of white bond paper absorptance for very dry conditions.

Two sources of radiant energy are successfully used in xerographic fusers: the xenon flash tube emission spectrum is shown in Figure 5.2 and the spectrum of a tungsten–halogen quartz lamp is shown in Figure 12.5. The hot filament

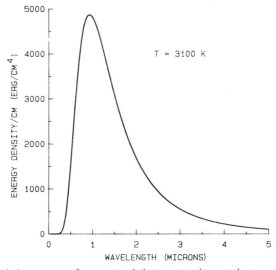

Figure 12.5   Emission spectrum for tungsten–halogen quartz lamp; color temperature = 3100°K.

may have a color temperature of about 3100°K or greater and the shape of the spectrum is given by Planck's radiation law.

$$\frac{d\varepsilon}{d\lambda} = \frac{8\pi hc}{\lambda^5} \frac{1}{e^{hc/\lambda kT} - 1} \quad (\text{erg-cm}^{-4}) \qquad (12.15)$$

The wavelength λ_m at which the emission spectrum is maximum is given by Wien's displacement law.

$$\lambda_m = \frac{5hc}{8\pi kT} = \frac{0.2898 \text{ cm-deg}}{T(°K)} \qquad (12.16)$$

where h = Planck's Constant, c = speed of light in vacuo, k = Boltzmann's Constant, and T is the color temperature of the grey body. At $T = 3100°K$, $\lambda = 0.9348 \ \mu m$.

The spectrum of the xenon arc plasma consists of discrete lines superimposed on a continuous background of black body radiation. The color temperature of the spectrum shown in Figure 5.2 is about 6500°K. Flash duration is typically from 0.1 msec to several msec, and the efficiency of conversion from electrical energy to radiant energy may be 50%. For design purposes, a question arises regarding the energy required per flash or, in the case of the tungsten lamp, the power input required to heat toner and paper to the necessary temperature. This question can be answered by considering the heat capacity and the heat of vaporization of water.

12.5   Energy Requirements for Fusing

The specific heat of toner (see Table 12.1) is about 0.32 cal/g-°C) or 1.3 J/g-°C and the density is nearly 1.1 g/cm³. Paper is a more complicated material, having a specific heat of 0.27 cal/g-°C when dry; however, moisture collects in paper and, under some extreme storage conditions, about 10% (by weight) of the paper can be water. The specific heat of water is 1.0 cal/g-°C and the heat of vaporization is 540 cal/g at 100°C (2260 J/g). Because the fusing temperature of toner exceeds the boiling point of water, all moisture in paper must be vaporized to reach the required fusing temperature (which depends on the time allowed for sintering, spreading, and wetting). The following estimate helps to clarify the importance of water in the fusing process.

Let the fusing temperature $T_f = 200°C$, process velocity = V_p (cm/sec), paper width = W (cm), and thickness = h (cm). The density of paper is about 0.5 g/cm³; including 10% water, the specific heat is about 0.37 cal/g-°C or 1.55 J/g-°C. Let the ambient temperature = 25°C, so the change in temperature is 175°C. Ignoring the heat of vaporization of water, the heat per unit volume of paper and toner processed is

$$\frac{Q}{\text{vol}} = (1.55 \text{ J/g-}°\text{C})(175°\text{C})(0.5 \text{ g/cm}^3) = 135 \text{ J/cm}^3$$

At 10% moisture content, the heat of vaporization per unit volume of paper processed is

$$\frac{Q_v}{\text{vol}} = (2260 \text{ J/g})(0.1 \text{ g/cm}^3) = 226 \text{ J/cm}^3$$

so the total heat required to raise paper and toner to 200°C is

$$\frac{Q_t}{\text{vol}} = \frac{Q + Q_v}{\text{vol}} \cong 360 \text{ J/cm}^3$$

The mass of toner is insignificant compared to the paper, and the heat required to boil away water is about 63% of the total, so one can ignore the energy required by toner to raise its temperature. Heat flow rate (J/sec or W) is

$$\dot{Q} = \frac{dQ}{dt} = \left(\frac{Q_t}{\text{vol}}\right) W h V_p \quad \text{(W)} \tag{12.17}$$

Various weights of paper are used in xerography; the approximate thickness of 15, 20, and 24-lb paper are 75, 100, and 155 μm, respectively. As a numerical example, the power required to fuse 14-in, 24-lb paper with 10% moisture at a process velocity of 80 cm/sec would be approximately 12 kW. In 1 hr, nearly 12 liters of water would be released as steam. Paper does not usually contain 10% water, so this example represents an approximate upper bound for engineering design. It is useful to normalize the heat flow rate by the paper width (W) and the process velocity (V_p) to obtain a design rule for thermal fusing on paper about 100 μm thick:

$$\frac{\dot{Q}}{W V_p} = \left(\frac{Q_t}{\text{vol}}\right) h \cong 3.6 \text{ W-sec/cm}^2 \tag{12.18}$$

12.6 Pressure and Temperature Fusing

The energy requirements for pressure and temperature fusing are quite similar to those estimated for radiant fusing. The advantages of radiant fusers, such as quick warm-up period ("instant" start-up) and noncontact with the fused image, must be contrasted with the problems of fire hazard (should there be a paper jam at the fusing device) and the relatively high cost of power supply and flash tube hardware. Hot-roll (pressure-temperature) fusers do not pose a safety hazard, because the operating temperature is less than the flash point of paper; hardware costs are lower than flash tube fusers, but more than tungsten lamps, and the warm-up time is quite long (5–10 min from cold start). Usually, hot-roll fusers are designed to maintain a stand-by temperature; thus, power is wasted when the xerographic machine is idle. For high-speed applications, the hot-roll fuser yields good fuse quality and handles a wide variety of paper types and weights; therefore, these devices are found in many copier–duplicators and laser printers. The hot-roll surface is subject to damage and build-up of contaminations from paper resins, and if the temperature becomes too high, a phenomenon called "hot offset" occurs, in which molten toner fails to release from the roll. Therefore, hot-roll temperature must be controlled within upper and lower limits; fusing is incomplete if the temperature is low, and molten toner splits from the image and sticks to the roll at higher temperatures. Release agents (such as silicon oil) are used by most hot-roll devices; release liquids have low surface tension (20 dynes/cm) and viscosity (0.65 poise). According to Loeffler (private communication), silicone oil wets paper and a layer about 0.3 μm thick is carried away; thus, the original oil film on the roll may be 0.6 μm thick. This release agent probably acts as a hydrodynamic squeeze film lubricant and requires continuous replenishment by a wicking device across the width of the hot roll.

Hot rolls are conventionally made from an aluminum cylinder covered with a thin elastomer layer, and the hot roll runs against a back-up roll covered with a thicker elastomer. The pressure between rolls may be in the range of 100–200 psi at the maximum level in the nip formed by deformation of the elastomers. The residence time (T_r) of a toned image depends on the nip width and process velocity (V_p). Pressure distribution in the nip can be approximated by a half-sine, parabolic, or elliptic curve. For the parabolic distribution, the nip width (s) depends on the thickness (h) and the modulus of elasticity (E) of elastomers, the diameter (D) of the rolls (assumed equal here), and the load per unit length (F/L).

$$s = \left(\frac{3hDF}{4EL}\right)^{1/3} \quad \text{(cm)} \qquad (12.19)$$

As a numerical example, let $h = 0.3$ cm, $D = 10$ cm, $F = 2 \times 10^8$ dynes (450 lbf), $E = 2 \times 10^7$ dynes/cm^2 (290 psi), and $L = 35$ cm. Assume the hot-roll elastomer is much thinner than the back-up elastomer. For this case, $s = 0.80$ cm, approximately. The residence time is

$$T_r = \frac{s}{V_p} \quad \text{(sec)} \qquad (12.20)$$

The maximum pressure P_0 in the nip is approximately

$$P_0 = \frac{3F}{2Ls} = \left(\frac{9F^2E}{2L^2hD}\right)^{1/3} \quad (\text{dynes/cm}^2) \tag{12.21}$$

For the values given above, $P_0 = 1.07 \times 10^7$ dynes/cm^2 (155 psi). The maximum pressure from the nip may be compared to the capillary pressure given by (12.9) with $\gamma = 25$ dynes/cm, $\cos\theta = 1.0$, and $w = 20 \times 10^{-4}$ cm; $\Delta p = 2.5 \times 10^4$ dynes/cm^2 or a factor of 400 less than P_0. Therefore, without the assistance of P_0, the penetration of toner into paper could be slight.

The hot roll is heated from within by a tungsten quartz lamp, so the heat energy flows through the aluminum cylinder and the thin elastomer covering into the toner–paper combination. Carslaw and Jaeger (1959) analyze the conduction of heat through solids and, for the geometry of two rolls with toner and paper between, the temperature can be approximated by the relation

$$T(z, t) = T_0 + (T_s - T_0)\text{erfc}\left[\frac{z}{2(\alpha t)^{0.5}}\right] \tag{12.22}$$

where $z =$ distance from the hot roll into the toner–paper combination, $t =$ time, $T_0 =$ temperature of toner–paper at the entrance to the nip, $T_s =$ surface temperature of the hot roll, $\alpha = k/c\rho$ (cm^2/sec) is the heat diffusivity, $k =$ thermal conductivity (J/cm-sec-°C) of the toner–paper combination, c (J/g) is the specific heat, and ρ (g/cm^3) is the density. In this simplified approach, toner is not distinguished from paper, so the combination of paper and toner is treated as a homogeneous solid with $\alpha \cong 9.4 \times 10^{-3}$ cm^2/sec. The function erfc$(x) = 1 - $ erf(x) is the complimentary error function. At a process velocity $V_p = 80$ cm/sec and a nip width $s = 0.80$ cm, the residence time $t = T_r = 0.010$ sec, so $2(\alpha T_r)^{0.5} \cong 0.02$ cm. At a depth $z = 10^{-3}$ cm, the temperature $T(z, T_r) = T_0 + (T_s - T_0)0.944 = 0.056T_0 + 0.944T_s$. At a depth $z = 10^{-2}$ cm (the bottom of the paper), $T(z, T_r) = 0.52T_0 + 0.48T_s$.

Hot-roll life is a strong function of the surface temperature T_s, so in practice, it is common to reduce T_s to a level yielding acceptable life and to raise T_0 from room ambient by the use of a preheat platen. In the IBM 3800 laser printer, T_s is about 150°C and T_0 is 110°C, so at $z = 10^{-3}$ cm, paper is approximately at $T = 157$°C. At this temperature, the viscosity of IBM 790 toner is about 10^4 poise and toner readily penetrates into the paper. Brooms (1978) discusses the design of a hot-roll fusing system for the IBM 3800 printer.

12.7 Pressure Fixing

Pressure fixing is remarkably simple, requires no warm-up, and consumes no stand-by power; however, the mechanical properties of toner must be such that plastic deformation and flow readily occur. This aspect of pressure (only) fixing may cause problems, as toner films readily grow on the PC or the magnetic brush developer roll surface. Paper of xerographic quality suffers compressive damage at approximately 7×10^8 dynes/cm^2; therefore, pressure fixing quite often calenders the paper fibers and yields a glossy appearance to the final document.

Pressure is achieved with hardened steel rollers perhaps 5 cm or so in diameter. The axes of the rollers are crossed at an angle of nearly 1° to compensate for bending, and the surface finish and run-out of the rollers must be very good. The rollers are loaded against each other by compression springs; the load per unit width might be 2.5×10^7 dynes/cm (140 lb/in). The torque required to elastically deform the rollers is about 3.5×10^7 dyne-cm (30 cm wide) without paper inserted. With 20-lb paper (thickness = 100 μm before pressure deformation), the drive torque can increase by nearly a factor of two. Loeffler (private communication) suggests that paper contains about 35 % air space which must be squeezed out to achieve intimate contact between paper, toner, and rollers. Andrus and Hudson (1965) observe that room temperature pressure fixing occurs with Xerox 914 toner at 6000 psi (4.1×10^8 dynes/cm^2); however, the fused image has impaired abrasion resistance and the paper suffers some compression damage (changes in dimensions and loss of strength). At a drive torque of 7×10^7 dyne-cm (half rotates the rollers against forces of elastic deformation and half deforms paper and toner plastically), the power used to deform paper and toner by adiabatic compression would be

$$\text{Power} = 3.5 \times 10^7 \, \frac{V_p}{R} \quad \text{(ergs/sec)} \qquad (12.23)$$

where R is the radius of a roller and V_p (cm/sec) is the process velocity. At 80 cm/sec and $R = 2.5$ cm, the power expended on deformation is approximately 112 W; that is, the work per unit velocity and per unit width is roughly 0.05 W-sec/cm^2, which is to be contrasted with 3.6 W-sec/cm^2 [see Equation (12.18)] for thermal fusing. The temperature rise, and subsequent softening of toner, should be quite modest in pressure fusing; therefore, fixing most likely occurs as a result of cold flow at pressures beyond the compressive yield strength of the toner. Brittle toner materials would not produce images of high fixing quality in pressure (only) fusers; hence, materials that are softer and that yield gradually (e.g., polyethelyne based polymers) are preferred. The surface of the pressure rollers requires wiping with a felt pad to keep it free of toner and paper debris, and the paper must be split away from the rollers with stripping fingers.

12.8   Quality of the Fixed Image

In 1977, the ASTM issued a standard ($\#$D-3458-75) for determining the quality of a fused xerographic image. The test can assess the ability of a fused image to resist abrasion by well-controlled abrasive wheels, and quality is ranked according to the loss of fused toner as a function of the number of abrasion cycles in the testing equipment (Taber Abraser, Teledyne Inc.) Prime (1983) discusses fusing quality and shows that resistance to abrasion depends on the product of pressure and time for hot-roll fusers; this dependency is analyzed and is shown to be consistent with the amount of viscous flow of toner into and around paper fibers in a well-coalesced mass. If paper is not heated, there is a tendency for toner to sinter together, but not penetrate into the paper; thus, images that are flash fused may be judged as less resistant to abrasion when compared to hot-roll fused images. Glossy images on glossy paper are hard to read under some illumination conditions; hence, pressure (only) fusing may be judged as too glossy, especially if the paper is highly calendered by the rollers.

The quality of a fixed image can be determined by criteria other than visual. When xerographic documents are stored for long periods. toner flows and sticks to the adjacent sheet of paper in a stack, so there is some question regarding the wisdom of archival storage at elevated temperatures. The amount of sticking depends on the type of toner, the pressure between adjacent sheets, the temperature, and the time allowed for toner flow, so the phenomenon is attributable to viscous flow, albeit at a much reduced rate.

APPENDIXES

Appendix A: Derivation of Potential and Field for a Charged Strip

The potential of a charged strip above a ground plane is given by

$$V(x, z) = \int_{-\infty}^{\infty} \int_{-W}^{W} \frac{\sigma_0}{4\pi\varepsilon} \left[\frac{1}{r_1} - \frac{1}{r_2} \right] dx'\, dy'$$

where

$$r_1 = [(x - x')^2 + (y - y')^2 + (z - z')^2]^{1/2}$$

and

$$r_2 = [(x - x')^2 + (y - y')^2 + (z + z')^2]^{1/2}$$

The integration along y' yields

$$V(x, z) = \int_{-W}^{W} \frac{\sigma_0}{2\pi\varepsilon} \left[\log_e\sqrt{(x - x')^2 + (z - z')^2} \right.$$

$$\left. - \log_e\sqrt{(x - x')^2 + (z + z')^2} \right] dx'$$

261

and integrating along x' yields the desired result.

$$V(x, z) = \frac{\sigma_0}{4\pi\varepsilon}\left[(x - W)\log_e[(x - W)^2 + (z - z')^2] + 2(z - z')\tan^{-1}\left(\frac{x - W}{z - z'}\right)\right.$$

$$-(x + W)\log_e[(x + W)^2 + (z - z')^2] - 2(z - z')\tan^{-1}\left(\frac{x + W}{z - z'}\right)$$

$$-(x - W)\log_e[(x - W)^2 + (z + z')^2] - 2(z + z')\tan^{-1}\left(\frac{x - W}{z + z'}\right)$$

$$\left.+ (x + W)\log_e[(x + W)^2 + (z + z')^2] + 2(z + z')\tan^{-1}\left(\frac{x + W}{z + z'}\right)\right]$$

The field components are:

$$E_x = -\frac{\partial V}{\partial x} = \frac{\sigma_0}{4\pi\varepsilon}\log_e\left[\frac{[(x + W)^2 + (z - z')^2][(x - W)^2 + (z + z')^2]}{[(x - W)^2 + (z - z')^2][(x + W)^2 + (z + z')^2]}\right]$$

$$E_z = -\frac{\partial V}{\partial z} = \frac{\sigma_0}{2\pi\varepsilon}\left[\tan^{-1}\left(\frac{x + w}{z - z'}\right) - \tan^{-1}\left(\frac{x - W}{z - z'}\right)\right.$$

$$\left.+ \tan^{-1}\left(\frac{x - W}{z + z'}\right) - \tan^{-1}\left(\frac{x + W}{z + z'}\right)\right]$$

where the relations

$$\log\frac{AB}{CD} = \log A + \log B - \log C - \log D$$

and

$$\tan^{-1}\frac{A}{B} = \frac{\pi}{2} - \tan^{-1}\frac{B}{A}$$

were used.

Appendix B: Derivation of Potential and Field For Arctangent Transitions

The potential on the boundary is specified as

$$V(\bar{x}, 0) = V_d + \frac{V_c}{\pi}\left[\tan^{-1}\left(\frac{\bar{x} + W}{a}\right) - \tan^{-1}\left(\frac{\bar{x} - W}{a}\right)\right]$$

The potential everywhere can be found by using the Green's function for the upper half space. That is,

$$V(x, z) = \frac{1}{\pi} \int_{-\infty}^{\infty} V(\bar{x}, 0) \frac{dG}{dz} d\bar{x}$$

where

$$G = \log\sqrt{(x - \bar{x})^2 + (z - \bar{z})^2}$$

is the Green's function; $(x, \bar{y})$ is a field point, and $(\bar{x}, \bar{z})$ is a source point

$$\frac{dG}{dz}\bigg|_{\bar{z} = 0} = \frac{z}{(x - \bar{x})^2 + z^2}$$

The potential everywhere becomes

$$V(x, z) = \frac{1}{\pi} \int_{-\infty}^{\infty} \left\{ V_d + \frac{V_c}{\pi} \left[\tan^{-1}\left(\frac{\bar{x} + W}{a}\right) - \tan^{-1}\left(\frac{\bar{x} - W}{a}\right) \right] \right\} \frac{z \, d\bar{x}}{(x - \bar{x})^2 + z^2}$$

Each term of the integral will be integrated separately.

$$I_1 = \frac{1}{\pi} \int_{-\infty}^{\infty} \frac{V_d y \, d\bar{x}}{(x - \bar{x})^2 + z^2} = \frac{V_d}{\pi} \left[-\tan^{-1}\left(\frac{x - \bar{x}}{z}\right) \right]\bigg|_{-H}^{H} = \frac{V_d}{\pi} [\pi] = V_d$$

The next term can be integrated by using the identity

$$\tan^{-1} z = \frac{i}{2} \log\left(\frac{i + z}{i - z}\right) = \frac{i}{2} [\log(i + z) - \log(i - z)]$$

where $i = \sqrt{-1}$, and by transforming to the variable

$$\eta = \frac{x - \bar{x}}{z} \quad \text{with } d\eta = -\frac{d\bar{x}}{z}$$

The second integral becomes

$$I_2 = \frac{V_c}{\pi^2} \int_{-\infty}^{\infty} \frac{\dfrac{i}{2} \left[\log\left(i + \dfrac{x + W - z\eta}{a}\right) - \log\left(i - \dfrac{x + W - z\eta}{a}\right) \right]}{(\eta + i)(\eta - i)} \, d\eta$$

The two terms of this integral are evaluated using the Cauchy Integral Formula and residue theory. The branch point for

$$\log\left(i + \frac{x + W - z\eta}{a}\right) \quad \text{is} \quad \eta = \frac{ai + x + W}{z}$$

which is in the upper half space, so the contour of integration will be in the lower half space.

$$\frac{I_{2a}}{(V_c/\pi^2)} = -2\pi i(\text{sum of residues in } \textit{lower} \text{ half space})$$

$$\text{Residue} = \lim_{\eta \to -i} \frac{(\eta + i)(i/2)\log[i + (x + W - z\eta)/a]}{(\eta + i)(\eta - i)}$$

$$= -\frac{1}{4}\log\left(i + \frac{x + W + zi}{a}\right)$$

and

$$I_{2a} = \frac{\pi i}{2}\log\left[i\left(1 + \frac{z}{a}\right) + \left(\frac{x + W}{a}\right)\right]$$

The second logarithmic term is evaluated similarly, recognizing that the branch point for

$$\log\left(i - \frac{x + W - z\eta}{a}\right) \quad \text{is} \quad \eta = -\frac{ia - x - W}{z}$$

so the contour of integration is in the upper half space.

$$I_{2b} = -\frac{\pi i}{2}\log\left[i\left(1 + \frac{z}{a}\right) - \left(\frac{x + W}{a}\right)\right]$$

The normalized integral then becomes

$$I_{2a} + I_{2b} = \frac{\pi i}{2}\left\{\log\left[i\left(1 + \frac{z}{a}\right) + \left(\frac{x + W}{a}\right)\right] - \log\left[i\left(1 + \frac{z}{a}\right) - \left(\frac{x + W}{a}\right)\right]\right\}$$

$$= \frac{\pi i}{2}\log\frac{i(z + a) + (x + W)}{i(z + a) - (x + W)}$$

Converting the logarithmic form back to the arctangent form yields the desired result, and the final relation is

$$\frac{V_c}{\pi^2} I_2 = \frac{V_c}{\pi} \tan^{-1}\left(\frac{x + W}{z + a}\right)$$

The third term is integrated in precisely the same manner as the second, except that $(x - W)$ replaces $(x + W)$. The final result for the potential everywhere is

$$V(x, z) = I_1 + I_2 + I_3 = V_d + \frac{V_c}{\pi}\left[\tan^{-1}\left(\frac{x + W}{z + a}\right) - \tan^{-1}\left(\frac{x - W}{z + a}\right)\right]$$

Field components are obtained by taking the negative gradient of the potential. Recall that

$$\frac{d}{dz}\tan^{-1}\left(\frac{z}{a}\right) = \frac{a}{z^2 + a^2} \quad \text{and} \quad \tan^{-1}\left(\frac{a}{z}\right) = \frac{\pi}{2} - \tan^{-1}\left(\frac{z}{a}\right)$$

Appendix C: Electric Field of an Infinite Series of Lines

The total electric field for a series of arctangent transition lines with constant spacing L between line centers is:

$$E = \sum_{-N}^{N} E_z(x + nL, z)$$

$$= \frac{V_c}{\pi L} \sum_{-N}^{N} \frac{\left(\frac{x + W}{L}\right) + n}{\left(\frac{x + W}{L} + n\right)^2 + \left(\frac{z + a}{L}\right)^2}$$

$$- \frac{\left(\frac{x - W}{L}\right) + n}{\left(\frac{x - W}{L} + n\right)^2 + \left(\frac{z + a}{L}\right)^2}$$

For an infinite series of lines, the sum can be evaluated using the calculus of residues, with the sum replaced by a contour integral. This requires a function that has simples poles at $q = n$ and is bounded at infinity. (See Morse and Feshbach, *Methods of Theoretical Physics*, Vol. I, Chapter 4.) One function that meets these requirements is $\pi \cot(\pi q)$. Following the guidance of Morse and Feshbach, the sum is:

$$\sum_{-\infty}^{\infty} E(n) = -\sum \text{residues of } \pi E(q)\cot(\pi q) \text{ at the poles of } E(q).$$

Normalizing $E(q)$ for the moment, the z-component of E becomes

$$E(q) = \frac{1}{L}\left[\frac{(q + W)/L}{[(q + W)/L]^2 + (a/L)^2} - \frac{(q - W)/L}{[(q - W)/L]^2 + (a/L)^2}\right]$$

It is seen that $E(q)$ has four poles:

$$q_1 = -\frac{(W + ia)}{L}, \quad q_2 = -\frac{(W - ia)}{L}$$

$$q_3 = \frac{(W - ia)}{L}, \quad \text{and} \quad q_4 = \frac{(W + ia)}{L}$$

The residues are:

$$R_1 = \frac{\pi}{2L}\cot\left[-\frac{\pi}{L}(W + ia)\right]$$

$$R_2 = \frac{\pi}{2L}\cot\left[-\frac{\pi}{L}(W - ia)\right]$$

$$R_3 = -\frac{\pi}{2L}\cot\left[\frac{\pi}{L}(W - ia)\right]$$

$$R_4 = -\frac{\pi}{2L}\cot\left[\frac{\pi}{L}(W + ia)\right]$$

The negative sum of these residues is the required result.

$$E = \sum_{-\infty}^{\infty} E(n) = -\frac{1}{\pi}\sum_i^4 R_i = \frac{V_c}{L}\left\{\cot\left[\frac{\pi}{L}(W + ia)\right] + \cot\left[\frac{\pi}{L}(W - ia)\right]\right\}$$

The cotangent with imaginary argument can be rewritten through the use of standard trigonometric identities. The final result is

$$E = \frac{2V_c}{L}\frac{\sin(2\pi W/L)}{[\cosh(2\pi a/L) - \cos(2\pi W/L)]}$$

It is easily shown that the expression given above for E reduces to that for the isolated line when L becomes very large.

Appendix D: Photoconductor Field With a Bias Electrode

Let the PC lie in the x-y plane and the z-axis be perpendicular to this plane. A ground plane is at $z = 0$, the PC has a thickness $z = t$, and at $z = G$ there is an electrode set to a bias potential. The space between $z = t$ and $z = G$ has a dielectric constant that differs from that of the PC. The potential at the PC surface is

$$V(x, t) = V_d + \Delta V(1 + \cos kx)$$

where $k = 2(\pi/\lambda)$. The potential between the PC and the bias electrode is found by solving Laplace's equation. The solution for this problem is:

$$V(x, z) = B_0 + B_1 z + (B_2 e^{kz} + B_3 e^{-kz})\cos kx$$

The coefficients are found by applying the boundary conditions to the solution. That is, for the potential at $z = t$

$$V = V_d + \Delta V(1 + \cos kx) = B_0 + B_1 t + (B_2 e^{kt} + B_3 e^{-kt})\cos kx$$

At $z = G$,

$$V = V_b = B_0 + B_1 G + (B_2 e^{kG} + B_3 e^{-kG})\cos kx$$

Because the bias electrode is a conductor, it cannot have a tangential field (the gradient of V with respect to x will be zero.) This yields

$$B_2 = -B_3 e^{-2kG}$$

These equations are solved for each of the coefficients.

$$B_0 = V_b - \left[\frac{V_b - V_d - \Delta V}{G - t}\right]G$$

$$B_1 = \frac{V_b - V_d - \Delta V}{G - t}$$

$$B_3 = \frac{\Delta V}{e^{-kt} - e^{k(t - 2G)}}$$

The potential then becomes

$$V(x, z) = V_b + \frac{(V_b - V_d - \Delta V)}{G - t}(z - G) + \Delta V \frac{e^{-kz} - e^{k(z - 2G)}}{e^{-kt} - e^{k(t - 2G)}} \cos kx$$

Field components are obtained from the negative gradient of $V(x, z)$. The perpendicular component is important for toner development.

$$E_z = -\frac{\partial V}{\partial z} = \frac{V_d + \Delta V - V_b}{G - t} + k\Delta V \frac{e^{-kz} + e^{k(z - 2G)}}{e^{-kt} - e^{k(t - 2G)}} \cos kx$$

The developing field is thus composed of a constant term and a periodic term whose amplitude depends on distance above the PC plane. As the gap distance (G) becomes very large, the influence of the DC field becomes negligible.

BIBLIOGRAPHY

Abowitz, G. (1974). *IEEE-IAS Ann. Conf. Proc.*, **153**.

Abramowitz, M. and Stegun, I. A. (1968). *Handbook of Mathematical Functions.* NBS Applied Math Series-55, U.S. Department of Commerce, Washington, D.C.

Adamson, A. W. (1967). *Physical Chemistry of Surfaces*, Interscience, New York.

Ahuja, S. K. (1976). *J. Appl. Phys.*, **47**, 4706.

Alston, L. L. (1968). *High Voltage Technology*, Oxford/Harwell Press, London.

American Paper Institute (1974). *Subject Index and Listing of American Paper Institute Instrumentation Reports and Studies*, 260 Madison Ave., New York, N.Y. 10016.

Andrus, P. G. and Hudson, F. W. (1965). Chapter 14 in Dessauser, J. H. and Clark, H. E. (1965), op. cit.

Attwood, S. S. (1967). *Electric and Magnetic Fields*, Dover Publications, New York, 141ff.

Bagnold, R. A. (1941). *Physics of Blown Sand and Desert Dunes*, Metheun, London. Also see *Proc. R. Soc. London Ser. A*, **157**, 594 (1936); **163**, 250 (1937); **167**, 282 (1938).

Banks, W., IBM Corp., San Jose, Calif., private communication.

Batchelor, G. K. (1967). *An Introduction to Fluid Dynamics*, Chapter 5, Cambridge University Press, Cambridge.

Beard, K. V. and Pruppacher, H. R. (1969). *J. Atmos. Sci.*, **26**, 1066.

Benda, J. A. and Wnek, W. J. (1981). *IEEE Trans. Ind. Appl.*, **IA-17**, 610.

Berg, T. G. O. and Gaukler, T. A. (1969). *Am. J. Phys.*, **37**, 1013.

Berg, W. F. and Hauffe, K. (Eds.) (1972). *Current Problems in Electrophotography*, Walter de Gruyter and Co., Berlin.

Biberman, L. M. (ed.) (1973). *Perception of Displayed Information*, Plenum Press, New York.

Bickmore, J. T., Gunther, K. W., Knapp, J. F., and Sullivan, W. A. (1970). *Phot. Sci. Eng.*, **14**, 42.

Born, M. and Wolf, E. (1975). *Principles of Optics*, Chapter 12, 5th ed., Pergamon Press, New York.

Bowden, F. P. and Tabor, D. (1964). *The Friction and Lubrication of Solids*, Parts 1 and 2, Oxford University Press, London.

Bozorth, R. M. (1968). *Ferromagnetism*, D. van Nostrand Company, Princeton.

Brodie, I., Dahlquist, J. A., and Sher, A. (1968). *J. Appl. Phys.*, **39**, 1618.

Brooms, K. D. (1978). *IBM J. Res. Dev.*, **22**, 26.

Bube, R. H. (1960). *Photoconductivity in Solids*, John Wiley & Sons, New York.

Buettner, A. V. and May, W. (1982). *Phot. Sci. Eng.*, **26**, 80.

Burkinshaw, L. D. and Caird, D. W. (1975). "Polycarbonates," in *The Science and Technology of Polymer Films*, Vol. 2, Sweeting, O. J. (Ed.), Wiley-Interscience, New York, 479 ff.

Carlson, C. F. (1965). Chapter 1 in Dessauer and Clark, op. cit.

Carslaw, H. S. and Jaeger, J. C. (1959). *Conduction of Heat in Solids*, 2nd ed., Oxford at Clarendon Press, Oxford.

Casimir, H. B. G. and Polder, D. (1948). *Phys. Rev.*, **73**, 360.

Cassiers, P. M. and van Engeland, J. (1965). *Phot. Sci. Eng.*, **9**, 273.

Castellan, G. W. (1971). *Physical Chemistry*, Addison-Wesley Publishing Co., Reading.

Chapman, S. and Cowling, T. G. (1970). *The Mathematical Theory of Non-uniform Gases*, 3rd ed., Cambridge University Press, Cambridge.

Chen, I. (1974). *J. Appl. Phys.*, **45**, 4852.

Chen, I. (1978). *IEEE-IAS Ann. Conf. Proc.*, 230.

Chen, I. (1982). *Phot. Sci. Eng.*, **26**, 153.

Cheng, Y. C. and Hartmann, G. C. (1980). *J. Appl. Phys.*, **51**, 2332.

Cho, A. Y. H. (1964). *J. Appl. Phys.*, **35**, 2561.

Cobine, J. D. (1958). *Gaseous Conductors*, Dover Publications, New York.

Coehn, A. (1898). *Wied. Ann. (Ann. der Phys.)*, **64**, 217.

Colby, R., IBM Corp., San Jose, CA, unpublished results.

Collins, L. F. (1977). *J. Appl. Phys.*, **48**, 4569.

Coquin et al. (1971). *J. Appl. Phys.*, **42**, 2162.

Corbett, R. P. and Bassett, J. D. (1971). *Stat. Elec. Conf.*, *Ser. 11*, 307, The Institute of Physics, London.

Corn, M. (1966). *Aerosol Science*, Chapter 11, Davies, C. N. (Ed.), Academic Press, New York.

Corson, D. R. and Lorrain, P. (1962). *Introduction to Electromagnetic Fields and Waves*, W. H. Freeman Company, San Francisco.

Cottrell, G. A., Lowell, J., and Rose-Innes, A. C. (1979). *J. Appl. Phys.*, **50**, 374.

Cottrell, G. A., Lowell, J., and Rose-Innes, A. C. (1980). *J. Appl. Phys.*, **51**, 1250.

Cutts, R., IBM Corp., San Jose, CA, private communication.

Davidson, R. C. (1978). *IEEE-IAS Ann. Conf. Proc.*, 148.

Davies, C. N. (1966). *Aerosol Science*, Academic Press, London and New York.

Davis, T. G. (1977). *IEEE-IAS Ann. Conf. Proc.*, 587.

DePalma, V. M. (1982). *Phot. Sci. Eng.*, **26**, 198.

Derjaguin, B. V., Aleinikova, I. N., and Toporov, Yu. P. (1968/1969). *Powder Tech.*, **2**, 154.

Deryagin, B. V., Krotova, N. A., and Smilga, V. P. (1978). *Adhesion of Solids*, Consultants Bureau, New York and London.

Dessauer, J. H. and Clark, H. E. (1965). *Xerography and Related Processes*, Focal Press, New York.

Donald, D. K. (1969). *J. Appl. Phys.*, **40**, 3013.

Donald, D. K. and Watson, P. K. (1970). *Phot. Sci. Eng.*, **14**, 36.

Dorris, G. M. and Gray, D. G. (1979). *J. Colloid Interface Sci.*, **71**, 93.

Duke, C. D. and Fabish, T. J. (1978). *J. Appl. Phys.*, **49**, 315.

Dwight, H. B. (1961). *Tables of Integrals and Other Mathematical Data*, 4th ed., MacMillan Publishing, New York.

Fabish, T. J. and Duke, C. B. (1980). *J. Appl. Phys.*, **51**, 1247.

Faraday, M. (1843). "Experimental Researches in Electricity," *Trans. Roy. Soc.*, 18th Series, para. 2141.

Fenstor, A., Plewes, D., and Johns, H. E. (1974). *Med. Phys.*, **1**, 1.

Fleischer, J. M., Latta, M. R., and Rabedeau, M. E. (1977). *IBM J. Res. Dev.*, 479.

Frank, C. W., et al. (1974). *2nd Int. Conf. Electrophot.*, 52, SPSE, Washington D.C.

Frenkel, J. (1945). *J. Phys. USSR*, **9**, 385.

Fridkin, V. M. (1972). *The Physics of the Electrophotographic Process*, Focal Press, New York.

Fuchs, N. A. (1964). *Mechanics of Aerosols*, Pergamon Press, New York.

Gallo, C. F. et al. (1967). *Phot. Sci. Eng.*, **11**, 11.

Gallo, C. F. et al. (1969). *Appl. Opt. Suppl. #3, Electrophot.*, 111.

Gallo, C. F. (1975). *IEEE Trans. Ind. Appl.*, **IA-11**, 739.

Gallo, C. F. and Hammond, T. J. (1976). *IEEE Trans. Ind. Appl.*, **IA-12**, 199.

Gallo, C. F. and Lama, W. L. (1971). *IEEE Trans. Ind. Gen. Appl.*, **IGA-7**, 420.

Gardiner, P. S. and Craggs, J. D. (1978). *IEEE-IAS Ann. Conf. Proc.*, 148.

Gill, W. D. (1972). *J. Appl. Phys.*, **43**, 5033.

Gillespie, T. and Langstroth, G. O. (1952). *Can. J. Chem.*, **30**, 1056.

Goldstein, S. (1929). *Proc. R. Soc. London*, **A123**, 225.

Goodman, J. W. (1968). *Introduction to Fourier Optics*, McGraw-Hill, San Francisco.

Gradshteyn, I. S. and Ryzhik, I. W. (1965). *Tables of Integrals, Series and Products*, Academic Press, New York.

Harper, W. R. (1967). *Contact and Frictional Electrification*, Oxford at Clarendon Press, London.

Harvapat, G. (1975). *IEEE-IAS Ann. Conf. Proc.*, 145.

Harvapat, G. (1977). *IEEE-IAS Ann. Conf. Proc.*, 569.

Hastings, N. A. J. and Peacock, J. B. (1974). *Statistical Distributions*, John Wiley & Sons (Halstead Press), New York, 68ff.

Hays, D. A. (1977). *J. Appl. Phys.*, **48**, 4430.

Hays, D. A. (1978). *Phot. Sci. Eng.*, **19**, 232.

Hecht, D. L. (1977). *IEEE Trans. Son. Ultrason.*, **SU-24**, 7.

Henderson, M. C. (1963). *Sound*, **2**, 28.

Henderson, M. C. and Herzfeld, K. F. (1965). *J. Acoust. Soc. Am.*, **37**, 986.

Hendricks, C. D. and Yeung, K. F. (1976). *IEEE Trans. Ind. Appl.*, **IA-12**, 56.

Herbert, N., Donald, D. K., and Collins, L. F. (1975). *IEEE IAS Ann. Conf. Proc.*, 135.

Herzfeld, K. F. and Litovitz, T. A. (1959). *Absorption and Dispersion of Ultrasonic Waves*, Academic Press, New York.

Hewlett-Packard Journal (1982). **33**, No. 6 and 7.

Hidy, G. M. and Brock, J. R. (1970). *The Dynamics of Aerocolloidal Systems*, Vol. 1 of International Review in Aerosol Physics and Chemistry, Pergamon Press, New York.

Holmes, R. D., IBM Corp., San Jose, CA, unpublished results.

Hughes, R. C. (1976). "Charge Transport in Disordered Molecular Systems," in *Photoconductivity in Polymers: An Interdisciplinary Approach*, A. V. Patsis and D. A. Seanor, (Eds.), Technomic Publishing Co., Westport, 178 ff.

Huntsberger, J. R. (1964). "The Relationship Between Wetting and Adhesion," in *Contact Angle, Wettability and Adhesion*, Advances in Chemistry Series #43, American Chemical Society, Washington, D.C.

Hunter, D. (1978). *Papermaking: The History and Technique of an Ancient Craft*, Dover Publications, New York.

Inculet, I. I. (1973). *Electrostatics and Its Applications*, Chapter 5, A. D. Moore, (Ed.), Wiley-Interscience, New York.

Institute of Paper Chemistry (1975). *Annotated Bibliographies*, P.O. Box 1048, Appleton, Wisconsin 54911.

Ingard, U. (1969). *J. Acoust. Soc. Am.*, **45**, 1038.

ISOMET Corporation, Application Note # AN772A, "All About Bragg Angle Errors in Acousto-Optic Modulators and Deflectors," P.O. Box 1634, 5263 Port Royal Road, Springfield, VA 22151.

Israelachvili, J. N. (1972). *Proc. R. Soc. London*, **A331**, 39.

Israelachvili, J. N. (1973). *J. Chem. Soc. Faraday Trans. II*, **69**, 1729.

Israelachvili, J. N. (1974). *Comtemp. Phys.*, **15**, 159.

Israelachvili, J. N. and Tabor, D. (1972). *Proc. R. Soc. London*, **A331**, 19.

Jackson, J. D. (1962). *Classical Electrodynamics*, John Wiley and Sons, New York.

Jahnke, E. and Emde, F. (1945). *Tables of Functions*, Dover Publications, New York, 24ff.

Jeans, J. (1940). *An Introduction to the Kinetic Theory of Gases*, Cambridge University Press, Cambridge, 233ff.

Jewett, W. S. (1977). *IEEE-IAS Ann. Conf. Proc.*, 557.

Keifer, J. E., Parsegian, V. A., and Weiss, G. H. (1978). *J. Colloid Interface Sci.*, **67**, 140.

Keiss, H. (1975). *RCA Rev.*, **36**, 667.

Keiss, H. (1978). *RCA Rev.*, **40**, 59.

Kirk, R. E. and Othmer, D. F. (Eds.) (1954). *Encyclopedia of Chemical Technology*, Vol. 13, p. 158.

Kittel, C. (1956). *Introduction to Solid State Physics*, John Wiley and Sons, New York.

Klein, M. V. (1970). *Optics*, John Wiley & Sons, New York.

Kneser, H. O. (1933). *J. Acoust. Soc. Am.*, **5**, 122.

Kneser, H. O. (1954). *Proc. R. Soc. London*, **A226**, 40.

Kneser, H. O. (1961). "Schallabsorption und dispersion in Gasen," in *Handbuch der Physik*, Vol. XI/1, S. Flugge, (Ed.), Springer Verlag, Berlin.

Knudsen, V. O. (1931). *J. Acoust. Soc. Am.*, **3**, 126.

Knudsen, V. O. (1933). *J. Acoust. Soc. Am.*, **5**, 112.

Knudsen, V. O. (1935). *J. Acoust. Soc. Am.*, **6**, 199.

Kottler, W., Krupp, H., and Rabenhorst, H. (1968). *Z. Angew. Phys.*, **24**, 219.

Kraemer, H. F. and Johnstone, H. I. (1955). *Ind. Eng. Chem.*, **47**, 2426.

Krupp, H. (1967). *Adv. Colloid Interface Sci.*, **1**, 111.

Krupp, H., Schnabel, W., and Walter, G. (1972). *J. Colloid Interface Sci.*, **39**, 421.

Kuhn, L., formerly with IBM Corp., Tucson, AR, unpublished results.

Kunkel, W. B. (1950). *J. Appl. Phys.*, **21**, 820.

Kutsuwada, N. (1970–1978). *Denshi Shashin* (*Electrophotography*), Vols. 1–9, in Japanese.

Lampert, M. A. and Mark, P. (1970). *Current Injection in Solids*, Academic Press, New York.

Landau, L. D. and Lifshitz, E. M. (1959). *Fluid Mechanics*, Pergamon Press, London, 66ff.

Landau, L. D. and Lifshitz, E. M. (1960). *Electrodynamics of Continuous Media*, Pergamon Press, London and New York, 368ff.

Langbein, D. (1969). *J. Adhesion*, **1**, 237.

Langbein, D. (1971). *J. Phys. Chem. Solids*, **32**, 1657.

Laukaitis, J. F. (1978). *IEEE-IAS Ann. Conf. Proc.*, 208.

Larson, W., IBM Corp, San Jose, CA, unpublished results.

Le Clair, B. P., Hamielec, A. E., and Pruppacher, H. R. (1970). *J. Atmos. Sci.*, **27**, 308.

Lee, L. H. (1975). "Thermal Fixing of Electrophotographic Images," in *Adhesion Science and Technology*, L. H. Lee (Ed.), Plenum Press, New York.

Lengyel, B. A. (1966). *Introduction to Laser Physics*, 217, John Wiley & Sons, New York.

Levin, L. (1953). *Dokl. Akad. Nauk. SSSR*, **91**, 1329.

Lewis, R. B., Conners, E. W., and Koehler, R. F. (1981). *4th Int. Conf. Electrophotgr.*, paper #33, SPSE, Washington, D.C.

Lewis, T. J. (1978). "The Movement of Electrical Charge Along Polymer Surfaces, *Polymer Surfaces*, Chapter 4, D. Clark and W. Feast (Eds.), John Wiley & Sons, New York.

Liu, B. Y. H. and Agarwal, J. K. (1974). "Experimental Observation of Aerosol Deposition in Turbulent Flow," *Aerosol Science*, **5**, 145. Pergamon Press, Great Britain.

Loeb, L. B. (1958). *Static Electricity*, Springer-Verlag, Berlin.

Loeb, L. B. (1961). *The Kinetic Theory of Gases*, 500, Dover Publications, New York.

Loeb, L. B. (1965). *Electrical Coronas*, University of California Press, Berkeley.

Loeb, L. B. and Meek, J. M. (1941). *The Mechanism of the Electric Spark*, Stanford University Press, Stanford, CA.

Loeffler, K. H. IBM Corp., San Jose, CA, unpublished results.

J. Lowell and A. C. Rose-Innes (1980), Adv. Physics, 29, 947.

Mahanty, J. and Ninham, B. W. (1976). *Dispersion Forces*, Academic Press, New York.

Markushevich, A. I. (1977). *Theory of Functions of a Complex Variable*, Vol. 2, Chelsea Publishing Co., New York.

Mastrangelo, C. J. (1982). *Phot. Sci. Eng.*, **26**, 194.

Maxwell, J. C. (1954). *A Treatise on Electricity and Magnetism*, Dover Publications reprint of the 1891 3rd ed., New York.

Maxworthy, T. (1965). *J. Fluid Mech.*, **23**, 369.

McCraig, M. (1977). *Permanent Magnets in Theory and Practice*, Pentech Press, London and Plymouth.

McMullen, T. B. and Salamida, D. P. (1974). *IEEE-IAS Ann. Conf. Proc.*, 161.

Mees, C. E. K. and James, T. H. (1966). *The Theory of the Photographic Process*, 3rd ed., MacMillan, New York.

Meier, H. (1974). *Organic Semiconductors*, Vol. 2 of Monographs in Modern Chemistry, Verlag Chemie, Weinheim.

Melz, P. J., Champ, R. B., Chang, L. S., Chiou, C., Keller, G. S., Liclican, Newman, R. R., Shattuck, M. D., and Weiche, W. J. (1977). *Phot. Sci. Eng.*, **21**, 73.

Millikan, R. A. (1917). *The Electron*, University of Chicago Press, Phoenix Science Series reprint 1963, Chicago and London.

Minor, J. C. (1975). *IEEE-IAS Ann. Conf. Proc.*, 150.

Montgomery, D. J. (1959). *Solid State Phys.*, **9**, 139.

Moore, A. D. (Ed.) (1973). *Electrostatics and Its Applications*, Chapter 9, John Wiley & Sons, New York.

Moore, D. F. (1972). *The Friction and Lubrication of Elastomers*, Chapter 6, Pergamon Press, Oxford.

Morse, P. M. and Feshbach, H. (1953). *Methods of Theoretical Physics*, part 1, 813, McGraw-Hill, New York.

Morse, P. M. and Ingard, K. U. (1968). *Theoretical Acoustics*, McGraw-Hill, New York, 270ff.

Mort, J. and Pai, D. M. (1976). *Photoconductivity and Related Phenomena*, Elsevier Scientific Publishing, New York.

Mott, N. F. and Gurney, R. W. (1964). *Electronic Processes in Ionic Crystals*, 245f, Dover Publications, New York.

Nebenzahl, L., Borgioli, J., DePalma, V., Gong, K., Mastrangelo, C., and Pourroy, F. (1980). *Phot. Sci. Eng.*, **24**, 293.

Neugebauer, C. A. (1970). Chapter 8 in *Handbook of Thin Film Technology*, Maissel, L. I. and Glang, R. (Eds.), McGraw-Hill Book Co., New York.

Neugebauer, H. E. J. (1964). *Appl. Opt.*, **3**, 385.

Neugebauer, H. E. J. (1965). *Appl. Opt.*, **4**, 453.

Neugebauer, H. E. J. (1967). *Appl. Opt.*, **5**, 943.

Ogelsby, Jr., S and Nichols, G. B. (undated). *A Manual of Electrostatic Precipitator Technology, Part 1: Fundamentals*, Report No. PB-196-380, U.S. Department of Commerce, NTIS, Springfield, VA 22161.

O'Reilly, J. M. and Erhardt, P. F. (1974). *2nd Int. Conf. Electrophotgr.*, 97, SPSE, Washington, D.C.

Osborn, J. A. (1945). *Phys. Rev.*, **67**, 351.

Oseen, C. (1927). *Neure Methoden und Ergebnisse in der Hydrodynamik*, Akademische Verlag, Leipzig.

Parsegian, V. A. and Ninham, B. W. (1971). *J. Colloid Interface Sci.*, **37**, 332.

Paschen, F. (1889). *Wied. Ann. (Ann. der Phys.)*, **37**, 69.

Patrick, R. L. (Ed.) (1967). *Treatise on Adhesion and Adhesives*, Vol. 1, Marcel Dekker, New York.

Patsis, A. V. and Seanor, D. A. (1976). *Photoconductivity in Polymers, An Interdisclipinary Approach*, Technomic Publications, Connecticut.

Peek, F. W., Jr. (1929). *Dielectric Phenomena in High Voltage Engineering*, 66, McGraw-Hill, New York.

Peterson, J. W. (1954). *J. Appl. Phys.*, **25**, 907.

Plewes, D. and Johns, H. E. (1975). *Med. Phys.*, **2**, 61.

Potter, R. I. (1970). *J. Appl. Phys.*, **41**, 1647.

Prime, R. B. (1983). *Phot. Sci. Eng.*, **27**, 19.

Pruppacher, H. R. and Steinberger, E. H. (1968). *J. Appl. Phys.*, **39**, 4129.

Rabedeau, M. (1978). IBM Corp., San Jose, CA, private communication.

Rasmussen, C. E., formerly with IBM Corp., San Jose, CA, unpublished work.

Richards, H. K. (1923). *Phys. Rev.*, **22**, 122.

Richmond, P. and Ninham, B. W. (1972). *J. Colloid Interface Sci.*, **40**, 406.

Röbing, G. and Porstendörfer, J. (1979). *J. Colloid Interface Sci.*, **69**, 183.

Robinson, E. and Robbins, R. C. (1968). "Sources, Abundance and Fate of Gaseous Atmospheric Pollutants," Standford Research Institute, SRI Project PR-6755, Feb., 1968, Huntsville, Alabama.

Robinson, M. (1973). Chapter 9 in Moore, A. D. (Ed.), op cit.

Rothgordt, U. (1974). *Philips Res. Rep.*, **29**, 139.

Ruch, T. C. and Patton, H. D. (1965). *Physiology and Biophysics*, 19th ed., 416, W. B. Saunders, Philadelphia and London.

Ruckdeschel, F. R. and Hunter, L. P. (1975). *J. Appl. Phys.*, **46**, 4416.

Sanford, F. (1919). *The Electrical Charges of Atoms and Ions*, Leland Stanford Junior University Publications, University Series, Stanford University, Stanford, CA, 115ff.

Schade Sr., O. (1973). *Perception of Displayed Information*, Biberman, L. M. (Ed.), Plenum Press, New York, 233 ff.

Schaffert, R. M. (1971) *IBM J. Res. Dev.*, 75, January.

Schaffert, R. M. (1975). *Electrophotography*, Halstead Press (John Wiley & Sons), New York.

Schaffert, R. M. (1978). *Phot. Sci. Eng.*, **22**, 149.

Schechtmann, B. H. (1980). unpublished communication.

Schein, L. B. (1975). *IEEE-IAS Ann. Conf. Proc.*, 140.

Schein, L. B. and Cranch, J. (1975). *J. Appl. Phys.*, **46**, 5140.

Schirmer, K. H. and Albrecht, J. (1961). *Adv. Print. Sci. Tech.*, **1**, 233.

Schlichting, H. (1960). *Boundary Layer Theory*, 4th ed., McGraw-Hill, New York.

Schmidlin, F. W. (1976). *Photoconductivity and Related Phenomena*, Chapter 11. Mort, J. and Pai, D. M. (Eds.), Elsevier Publishing, New York.

Schramm, J. and Witter, K. (1973). *Appl. Phys.*, **1**, 331.

Seanor, D. A. (1972). "Triboelectrification of Polymers," in *Electrical Properties of Polymers*, 37, Frisch, K. C. and Patsis, A. V. (Eds.), Technomic Publishing, Connecticut.

Shahin, M. M. (1966). *J. Chem. Phys.*, **45**, 2600.

Shahin, M. M. (1969). *Appl. Opt. Supp. #3 Electrophotgr.*, 106.

Shaw, P. E. (1930). *Phil. Mag., S-7*, **9**, 577.

Skar, C. (1972). *Water in Wood*, Syracuse University Press, Syracuse.

Smith, H. M. (1969). *Principles of Holography*, Wiley-Interscience, New York.

Smythe, W. R. (1968). *Static and Dynamic Electricity*, 3rd ed., McGraw-Hill, New York.

Springett, B. E., Tesche, F. M., Davies, A. R., and Thompson, J. (1977). *3rd Int. Conf. Electrophotogr.*, 63, SPSE, Wash., D.C.

St. John, D. (1969). "Adhesion of Small Metal Spheres to Plane Metal Substrates," Ph.D Thesis, Michigan State University.

St. John, D. F. and Montgomery, D. J. (1971). *J. Appl. Phys.*, **42**, 663.

Stoner, E. C. (1945). *Phil. Mag., S-7*, **36**, 803.

Stover, R. W. and Schoonover, P. C. (1969). *Proc. Ann. Conf. Phot. Sci. Eng.*, 156, SPSE, Washington, D.C.

Strella, S. (1970). *J. Appl. Phys.*, **41**, 4242.

Sündstrom, P., IBM Corp., Järfalla, Sweden, unpublished results.

Suzuki, S. and Tomura, M. (1962). *Denshi Shashin (Electrophotogr.)*, **4**, 20, Japan.

Szaynok, A. T. (1971). *Proc. 3rd. Conf. Stat. Elec.*, {7, The Institute of Physics, London and Bristol.

Takahashi, T., Hosono, N., Kanbe, J., and Toyono, T. (1982). *Phot. Sci. Eng.*, **26**, 254.

Tareev, B. (1975). *Physics of Dielectric Materials*, 177, MIR Publishers, Moscow.

Tateishi, K. and Hoshino, Y. (1981). *IEEE Trans. Ind. Appl.*, **IA-17**, 606.

Theodorovich, E. V. (1978). *Proc. R. Soc. London*, **A362**, 71.

Thompson, J. J. and Thompson, G. P. (1969). *Conduction of Electricity Through Gases*, Vols. 1 and 2, Dover Publications, New York.

Thourson, T. L. (1972). *IEEE Trans. Elec. Dev.*, **ED-19**, 495.

Timoshenko, S. and Goodier, J. N. (1970). *Theory of Elasticity*, 3rd ed., McGraw-Hill, New York, p. 420ff.

Townsend, J. S. (1915). *Electricity in Gases*, Oxford University Press, New York.

Uchida, N. and Ohmachi, Y. (1969). *J. Appl. Phys.*, **40**, 4692.

Uman, M. A., Orville, R. E., Sletten, A. M., and Krider, E. P. (1968). *J. Appl. Phys.*, **39**, 5162.

Vahtra, U. (1982). *Phot. Sci. Eng.*, **26**, 292.

Vahtra, U. and Wolter, R. F. (1978). *IBM J. Res. Dev.*, **22**, 34.

Van Engeland, J. (1979). *Phot. Sci. Eng.*, **23**, 86.

Van Oene, H. (1973). *Recent Advances in Adhesion*, Lee, L. H. (Ed.), Gordon and Breach, New York, 233ff.

Van Oene, H., Chang, Y. F., and Newman, S. (1969). *J. Adhes.*, **1**, 54.

von Engel, A. (1965). *Ionized Gases*, Oxford at Clarendon Press, London.

Vyverberg, R. G. (1958). U.S. Patent No. 2,836,725, May, 1958.

Wagner, P. E. (1956). *J. Appl. Phys.*, **27**, 1300.

Weber, E. (1965). *Electromagnetic Theory*, Dover Publications, New York.

Weigl, J. W. (1977). *Angew. Chem. Int. Ed. Engl.*, **16**, 374.

Whetten, N. R. (1974). *J. Vac. Sci. Technol.*, **11**, 515.

Whitby, K. T. and Liu, B. Y. H. (1966). *Aerosol Science*, Chapter 3. Davies, C. N. (Ed.), Academic Press, London and New York.

White, H. J. (1963). *Industrial Elestrostatic Precipitation*, Addison-Wesley Publishing Co., Palo Alto.

Whysong, D. C. (1982). "Mechanical Removal of Particles Adhered to a Magnetic Tape Surface, *Magnetic Tape Recording for the Eighties*, Chapter 6. Kalil, F. (Ed.), NASA Ref. Publ. 1075, Apr., 1982.

Williams, E. M. (1978). *IEEE-IAS Ann. Conf. Proc.*, 215.

Williams, E. M. (1982). *Phot. Sci. Eng.*, **26**, 88.

Williams, L. L., IBM Corp., San Jones, CA, private communication.

Williams, R. and Wang, C. C. (1982). *RCA Rev.*, **43**, 224.

Winkleman, D. (1977–1978). *J. Electrostat.*, **4**, 193.

Winkleman, D. (1978). *J. Appl. Phot. Eng.*, **4**, Fall.

Wuerker, R. F., Shelton, H., and Langmuir, R. U. (1959). *J. Appl. Phys.*, **30**, 343.

Yang, C. C. and Hartmann, G. C. (1976). *IEEE Trans. Elec. Dev.*, **ED-23**, 308.

Yeh, H.-C. and Liu, B. Y. H. (1974). "Aerosol Filtration by Fibrous Filters," *Aerosol Science*, Vol. 5, Pergamon Press, Great Britain, p. 191.

Zhigarev, A. (1975). *Electron Optics and Electron Beam Devices*, MIR Publishers, Moscow, pp. 133ff.

Zimon, A. D. (1969). *Adhesion of Dust and Powder*, Plenum Press, New York.

AUTHOR INDEX

SUBJECT INDEX